ASTÉRISQUE 264

RINGS OF SEPARATED POWER SERIES AND QUASI-AFFINOID GEOMETRY

Leonard Lipshitz
Zachary Robinson

Société Mathématique de France 2000
Publié avec le concours du Centre National de la Recherche Scientifique

L. Lipshitz

Department of Mathematics, Purdue University, West Lafayette, IN 47907-1395 USA.

E-mail : lipshitz@math.purdue.edu

Z. Robinson

Department of Mathematics, East Carolina University, Greenville, NC 27858-4353 USA.

E-mail : robinson@math.ecu.edu

1991 *Mathematics Subject Classification.* — 32P05, 32B05, 32B20, 32C35, 26E30, 12J25, 03C10, 13J05, 13B40.

***Key words and phrases.* —** Rigid analytic geometry, Non–Archimedean analysis, Subanalytic sets, Quantifier elimination, Model Completeness, Artin approximation, Acyclicity.

Supported in part by the NSF.

RINGS OF SEPARATED POWER SERIES AND QUASI-AFFINOID GEOMETRY

Leonard Lipshitz, Zachary Robinson

Abstract. — The papers in this volume present a theory of rigid analytic geometry over an ultrametric field K that generalizes the classical, affinoid, theory to the setting of relative rigid analytic geometry over an "open" polydisc. The theory is based on the commutative algebra of power series rings $S_{m,n}$ that is developed in the first paper in this volume, *Rings of Separated Power Series*. Quasi–affinoid algebras (quotients $S_{m,n}/I$) share many properties with affinoid algebras (quotients T_m/I of a ring of strictly convergent power series.) Among the principal results are the Nullstellensatz for quasi–affinoid algebras A and the Universal Property for a broad class of open subdomains of Max A, the R–subdomains. The second paper, *Model Completeness and Subanalytic Sets*, obtains a structure theory for images of analytic maps based on any subcollection of $S = \cup S_{m,n}$ that satisfies certain closure properties; for example $T = \cup T_m$. The argument exploits the existential definability of the Weierstrass data as well as a difference between affinoid and quasi–affinoid rigid analytic geometry; namely, that a quasi–affinoid variety Max A in general may be covered by finitely many disjoint quasi–affinoid subdomains, just as the valuation ring K° is the union of its maximal ideal $K^{\circ\circ}$ and its multiplicative units. A crucial role is played by the theory of generalized rings of fractions developed in the first paper. The third paper, *Quasi-Affinoid Varieties*, defines the category of $S_{m,n}$–analytic varieties $X = \text{Max}\, A$ and establishes the acyclicity of quasi–affinoid covers. The proofs employ results from the first paper; in particular, the fact that the assignment $U \mapsto \mathcal{O}_X(U)$ is a presheaf of A–algebras for R–subdomains U of X. The quantifier elimination of the second paper is used to relate quasi–affinoid and affinoid covers, a key step in the proof of the Acyclicity Theorem. The fourth paper, *A Rigid Analytic Approximation Theorem*, gives a global Artin Approximation theorem between a "Henselization" $H_{m,n}$ of a ring T_{m+n} of strictly convergent power series and its "completion" $S_{m,n}$. This links the algebraic properties of affinoid and quasi–affinoid algebras.

Résumé **(Anneaux de séries séparées et géométrie quasi-affinoïde)**

Les articles de ce volume présentent une théorie de la géométrie analytique rigide sur un corps ultramétrique K qui généralise la théorie affinoïde classique au cas de la géométrie analytique rigide relative sur un polydisque « ouvert ». Cette théorie est basée sur l'étude algébrique des anneaux de séries convergentes $S_{m,n}$ développée dans le premier article, *Rings of Separated Power Series.* Les algèbres quasi-affinoïdes (les quotients $S_{m,n}/I$) partagent de nombreuses propriétés avec les algèbres affinoïdes (les quotients T_m/I d'un anneau de séries strictement convergentes). Parmi les résultats principaux signalons le Nullstellensatz pour les algèbres quasi-affinoïdes A ainsi que la Propriété Universelle pour une large classe de sous-domaines ouverts de Max X, les R-sous-domaines. Le second article, *Model Completeness and Subanalytic Sets*, contient des résultats sur la structure des images de familles de fonctions analytiques provenant par extension d'une famille quelconque de fonctions de $S = \cup S_{m,n}$ satisfaisant certaines propriétés de fermeture ; par exemple $T = \cup T_m$ est une telle famille. La preuve utilise le fait que les données de Weierstrass sont définissables ainsi que le fait, témoignant de la différence entre géométrie affinoïde et quasi-affinoïde, qu'une variété quasi-affinoïde Max A peut généralement être recouverte par un nombre fini de sous-domaines quasi-affinoïdes disjoints, de la même façon que l'anneau de valuation K° est l'union de son idéal maximal $K^{\circ\circ}$ et de ses unités multiplicatives. La théorie des anneaux généralisés de fractions développée dans le premier article joue un rôle crucial. Dans le troisième article, *Quasi-Affinoid Varieties*, on définit la catégorie des variétés $S_{m,n}$-analytiques $X = \operatorname{Max} A$ et on établit l'acyclicité des recouvrements quasi-affinoïdes. Les démonstrations emploient des résultats du premier article, notamment le fait que le foncteur $U \mapsto \mathcal{O}_X(U)$ est un préfaisceau d'A-algèbres pour des R-sous-domaines U de X. On utilise également le résultat d'élimination des quantificateurs obtenu dans le second article pour établir un rapport entre les recouvrements quasi-affinoïdes et les recouvrements affinoïdes, ce qui est une étape cruciale dans la démonstration du théorème d'acyclicité. Le quatrième article, *A Rigid Analytic Approximation Theorem*, donne un théorème d'approximation globale d'Artin entre un « hensélisé » $H_{m,n}$ d'un anneau T_{m+n} de séries strictement convergentes et son complété $S_{m,n}$. Ce résultat permet de relier les propriétés algébriques des algèbres quasi-affinoïdes et affinoïdes.

CONTENTS

INTRODUCTION

Let K be a field, complete with respect to the non-trivial ultrametric absolute value $|\cdot| : K \to \mathbb{R}_+$. By K° denote the valuation ring, by $K^{\circ\circ}$ its maximal ideal, and by $\widetilde{K}$ the residue field $K^\circ/K^{\circ\circ}$. Let K' be an algebraically closed field containing K and consider the polydisc

$$\Delta_{m,n} := ((K')^\circ)^m \times ((K')^{\circ\circ})^n .$$

In 1961, Tate introduced rings T_m of analytic functions on the closed polydiscs $\Delta_{m,0}$. These rings lift the affine algebraic geometry of the field $\widetilde{K}$. In particular, the Euclidean Division Theorem for $\widetilde{K}[\xi]$ lifts to a global Weierstrass Division Theorem for T_m. The basic properties of T_m that follow from Weierstrass Division include Noetherianness, Noether Normalization, unique factorization, and a Nullstellensatz. These results pave the way for the development of rigid (affinoid) analytic geometry.

The representation

$$\Delta_{m,n} = \varinjlim_{\varepsilon}((K')^\circ)^m \times (\varepsilon(K')^\circ)^n,$$

where $\varepsilon \in (K')^{\circ\circ}$, yields a ring of analytic functions on $\Delta_{m,n}$ by taking a corresponding inverse limit of Tate rings. This gives the polydisc $\Delta_{m,n}$ the structure of a rigid analytic variety. But its global functions are, in general, unbounded. Even if one restricts attention to those functions with finite supremum norm, the geometric behavior can be pathological.

In the first paper, *Rings of Separated Power Series*, we define rings $S_{m,n}$ of bounded analytic functions on $\Delta_{m,n}$ with a tractable algebraic and geometric behavior. Those rings share many of the nice properties of the Tate rings T_m, though the proofs are often rather more difficult. We show that the rings $S_{m,n}$ are Noetherian rings (often K-Banach algebras) of bounded analytic functions on $\Delta_{m,n}$, that satisfy a Nullstellensatz, are unique factorization domains, and are regular rings of dimension $m+n$.

We call quotients of the $S_{m,n}$ *quasi-affinoid algebras*. Quasi-affinoid algrebras share most of the properties of affinoid algebras. For example, the residue norms arising from different presentations of a quasi-affinoid algebra are all equivalent; quasi-affinoid morphisms are continuous; in characteristic zero (and often in characteristic p) the residue norms and the supremum norm on a reduced quasi-affinoid algebra are equivalent; and quasi-affinoid rational domains satisfy the appropriate universal mapping property. These results pave the way for the development of a relative rigid analytic geometry over open polydiscs.

We give three applications of the general theory. In the second paper, *Model Completeness and Subanalytic Sets*, we present a quantifier elimination theorem which lays the foundation for the theory of rigid subanalytic sets based on the Tate Rings. The third paper, *Quasi-Affinoid Varieties*, applies the results of the first two papers to treat the basic sheaf theory of quasi-affinoid varieties and to prove the quasi-affinoid Acyclicity Theorem. In the fourth paper, *A Rigid Analytic Approximation Theorem*, a global Artin Approximation Theorem is presented for the pair of rings $H_{m,n} \hookrightarrow S_{m,n}$, where $H_{m,n}$ is the algebraic closure of T_{m+n} in $S_{m,n}$. In this context the rings $S_{m,n}$ play the role of a kind of completion of the Tate rings.

Achnowledgements. — Both authors thank MSRI and the ICMS, Edinburgh for support and hospitality, Jan Denef for his encouragement in this project, and Judy Mitchell for her patience in typing numerous versions of this manuscript. The second author also gratefully acknowledges the support of the CNR and the hospitality of the University of Pisa. Diagrams were created by using `diagram.sty` by Paul Taylor of Queen Mary and Westfield College, London.

RINGS OF SEPARATED POWER SERIES

1. Introduction

Let K be a field, complete with respect to the non-trivial ultrametric absolute value $|\cdot| : K \to \mathbb{R}_+$. By K° denote the valuation ring, by $K^{\circ\circ}$ its maximal ideal, and by $\widetilde{K}$ the residue field $K^\circ/K^{\circ\circ}$. Let K' be an algebraically closed field containing K and consider the polydisc

$$\Delta_{m,n} := ((K')^\circ)^m \times ((K')^{\circ\circ})^n .$$

In 1961, Tate [**39**] introduced rings T_m of analytic functions on the closed polydiscs $\Delta_{m,0}$. These rings lift the affine algebraic geometry of the field $\widetilde{K}$. In particular, the Euclidean Division Theorem for $\widetilde{K}[\xi]$ lifts to a global Weierstrass Division Theorem for T_m. The basic properties of T_m that follow from Weierstrass Division include Noetherianness, Noether Normalization, unique factorization, and a Nullstellensatz. These results pave the way for the development of rigid analytic geometry (see [**6**] and [**10**]).

Because in its metric topology K' is totally disconnected and not locally compact, to construct rigid analytic spaces one relies on a Grothendieck topology to provide a suitable framework for sheaf theory. For example, the basic admissible open affinoids of rigid analytic geometry are obtained by an analytic process analogous to localization in algebraic geometry (see [**6**, Section 7.2.3]). The resulting domains, rational domains, satisfy a certain universal property (see [**6**, Section 7.2.2]) and therefore give a local theory of rigid analytic spaces. The local data are linked together with a notion of admissible open cover and Tate's Acyclicity Theorem. This makes it possible, for example, to endow every algebraic variety over K with an analytic structure, that of a rigid analytic variety.

The representation

$$\Delta_{m,n} = \varinjlim_{\varepsilon} ((K')^\circ)^m \times (\varepsilon (K')^\circ)^n,$$

where $\varepsilon \in (K')^{\circ\circ}$, yields a ring of analytic functions on $\Delta_{m,n}$ by taking a corresponding inverse limit of Tate rings. This gives the polydisc $\Delta_{m,n}$ the structure of a rigid analytic variety. But its global functions are, in general, unbounded. Even if one restricts attention to those functions with finite supremum norm, the geometric behavior can be pathological. For example, let $\{a_i\}_{i\in\mathbb{N}} \subset (K')^{\circ\circ}$ be a sequence such that $\lim_{i\to\infty} |a_i| = 1$. Put

$$f(\rho) := \sum a_i \rho^i.$$

Then f converges and has infinitely many zeros on $\Delta_{0,1}$. This follows by restricting to the closed subdiscs $\varepsilon \cdot \Delta_{1,0}$ and applying Weierstrass Preparation.

The rings $S_{m,n}$, defined below, represent Noetherian rings (often, K-Banach algebras) of bounded analytic functions on $\Delta_{m,n}$ with a tractable algebraic and geometric behavior. We address the issue of the corresponding sheaf theory in **[22]**.

These rings have been used in various contexts. In **[16]**, where the $S_{m,n}$ were first defined, they were used to obtain a uniform bound on the number of isolated points in fibers of affinoid maps. This result was strengthened in **[2]** to give a uniform bound on the piece numbers of such fibers. In **[11]**, rings $S_{0,n}$ were used to lift the rings $\widetilde{K}[\![\rho]\!]$ in order to obtain analytic information about local rings of algebraic varieties over $\widetilde{K}$. In **[17]** (and later in **[21]**), the $S_{m,n}$ were used to provide the basis for a theory of rigid subanalytic sets; i.e., images of K-analytic maps. This theory of rigid subanalytic sets was developed considerably further in **[21]**, **[19]**, **[18]**, **[20]**. The manuscript **[21]** (unpublished) contains a quantifier simplification theorem suitable for the development of a theory of subanalytic sets based on the Tate rings. That manuscript was produced in 1995, well before the completion of this paper, and hence it was written to be self contained. As a result the proofs were rather ad hoc. In the paper **[23]** we give a smoother and more general treatment of that quantifier simplification theorem, based on some of the machinery developed in this paper, specifically the Weierstrass Division and Preparation Theorems (Theorem 2.3.8 and Corollary 2.3.9) and the concept of "generalized ring of fractions" developed in Section 5.

(The theory of the images of semianalytic sets under proper K-analytic maps was developed by Schoutens in **[32]**–**[36]**. Recently in **[12]**, **[37]** and **[13]** Gardener and Schoutens have given a quantifier elimination in the language of Denef and van den Dries **[9]** over the Tate rings T_m, using the results of Raynaud–Mehlmann **[27]**, Berkovich **[3]**, and Hironaka, **[15]**. The proof of their elimination theorem also depends on the model completeness result of **[21]**, see **[23**, Section 4].)

The theory of the rings $S_{m,n}$ was not developed systematically in papers **[16]**, **[17]**, **[18]**, **[19]**, **[20]** and **[21]**. Instead, partial results were proved as needed. The accumulation of these partial results convinced us that a systematic theory of the rings $S_{m,n}$ would be possible and would provide a natural basis for rigid analytic geometry on the polydiscs $\Delta_{m,n}$. The theory developed in this paper has been applied in **[23]** to prove a quantifier elimination theorem which provides the basis for the theory of rigid subanalytic sets based on the Tate rings, and in **[22]** which treats the basic sheaf theory of quasi-affinoid varieties and proves the quasi-affinoid acyclicity theorem. The theory has also been applied in **[31]** to yield a global Artin Approximation Theorem for the pair of rings $H_{m,n} \hookrightarrow S_{m,n}$, where $H_{m,n}$ is the algebraic closure of T_{m+n} in $S_{m,n}$. Here the $S_{m,n}$ play the role of a kind of completion of Tate rings.

The goals of this paper are (i) to develop the commutative algebra of the power series rings $S_{m,n}$ (Section 4) and (ii) to develop the ingredients of sheaf theory for $S_{m,n}$-analytic varieties; in particular to show that rational domains in this setting (which we term quasi-affinoid) satisfy the same universal property as affinoid rational domains. This provides a foundation for a relative rigid analytic geometry over open polydiscs.

In the next few paragraphs we outline the contents of this paper.

In Section 2, we define the rings $S_{m,n}$ of separated power series, prove that they are Noetherian and prove two Weierstrass Preparation Theorems as in **[16]**, **[17]** and **[2]**, one relative to the variables ranging over closed discs, the other relative to the variables ranging over open discs. These Weierstrass Preparation Theorems were crucial in the applications mentioned above. But, because there are two types of variables, a suitably large collection of Weierstrass automorphisms does not exist. Thus these Weierstrass Preparation Theorems do not yield Noether Normalization for quotient rings of the $S_{m,n}$ (see Example 2.3.5), making the basic theory considerably more difficult to establish than in the affinoid case.

We are interested in studying properties of quotient rings $S_{m,n}/I$. In affinoid geometry, the key technique is Noether Normalization. The difficulties stemming from the failure of Noether Normalization for $S_{m,n}$ are overcome in Section 3 by a careful analysis of the behavior of restriction maps from $\Delta_{m,n}$ to closed subpolydiscs and to certain disjoint unions of open subpolydiscs.

Section 4 contains the Nullstellensatz and results on flatness, excellence, and unique factorization. The Nullstellensatz yields a supremum seminorm on the maximal ideal space of a quasi-affinoid algebra (i.e., a quotient ring of $S_{m,n}$).

In Section 5, we relate the behavior of the supremum seminorm to the residue norm derived from the Gauss norm on $S_{m,n}$, patching together uniform data that hold on affinoid algebras induced by restriction maps. The results are used to show that K-algebra homomorphisms of quasi-affinoid algebras are continuous, that all residue norms on a quasi-affinoid algebra are equivalent (i.e., the topology of a quasi-affinoid algebra is independent of presentation), and that quasi-affinoid rational domains satisfy an appropriate Universal Mapping Property. We prove when $\operatorname{Char} K = 0$, and in many cases also when $\operatorname{Char} K = p$, that on a reduced quasi-affinoid algebra the supremum norm and the residue norms are equivalent.

Section 6 contains some finiteness theorems, in particular it contains a weak analogue of Zariski's Main Theorem for quasi-finite maps, which is applied to show that quasi-affinoid subdomains are finite unions of R-subdomains.

We employ three different sorts of argument in this paper. The first sort of argument, "slicing", combines a generalization of the notion of discrete valuation ring (DVR) and a generalization of the notion of orthonormal basis. Each "level" of a formal power series ring over a DVR projects to a formal power series ring over a field, whose algebraic properties can often be lifted. Similar arguments were employed in **[14]** and in **[4]**. The second sort of argument exploits the relation between residue order and restrictions to closed polydiscs. A special case of this type of argument was used in **[5]**. To treat the case of a discretely valued ground field we must understand how generating systems of modules behave under ground field extension. Here we use the notion of stable fields (see **[6]**). The third sort of argument uses techniques of commutative algebra to extract information from completions at maximal ideals.

Following is a telegraphic summary of the principal results of this paper.

Theorem 2.1.3. — *If $\widetilde{K}$ is algebraic over $\widetilde{E}$ then*

$$S_{m,n}(E,K) = K\widehat{\otimes}_E E\langle\xi\rangle[\![\rho]\!].$$

Corollary 2.2.4. — *$S_{m,n}$ is Noetherian.*

Theorem 2.3.2 and Corollary 2.3.3. — *Weierstrass Division and Preparation Theorems for $S_{m,n}$.*

Theorem 2.3.8 and Corollary 2.3.9. — *Weierstrass Division and Preparation Theorems for $A\langle\xi\rangle[\![\rho]\!]_s$.*

Theorem 3.1.3. — *Submodules of $(S_{m,n})^\ell$ are v-strict. In particular, ideals of $S_{m,n}$ are strictly closed.*

Theorem 3.2.3. — *Strictness of a generating system is preserved under restriction to suitably large rational polydiscs.*

Corollary 3.3.2. — *For a submodule $M \subset (S_{m,n})^\ell$, and ε large enough*

$$\iota_\varepsilon^{-1}(\iota_\varepsilon(M)\cdot T_{m,n}(\varepsilon)) = M.$$

Theorems 3.4.3, 3.4.6. — *The restriction of a quasi-affinoid algebra to a suitably chosen finite union of open polydiscs is an isometry in residue norms.*

Theorem 4.1.1. — *The Nullstellensatz for $S_{m,n}$.*

Corollary 4.2.2. — *$S_{m,n}$ is a regular ring of dimension $m+n$.*

Proposition 4.2.3. — *If $\operatorname{Char} K = 0$, $S_{m,n}$ is excellent.*

Proposition 4.2.5. — *$S_{m,n}$ is often excellent when $\operatorname{Char} K = p \neq 0$.*

Theorem 4.2.7. — *$S_{m,n}$ is a UFD.*

Theorem 5.1.5. — *For a quasi-affinoid algebra, the ring of power-bounded elements is integral over the ring of elements of residue norm ≤ 1.*

Corollary 5.1.8. — *Characterization of power-boundedness, topological nilpotence and quasi-nilpotence in terms of the supremum seminorm.*

Theorem 5.2.3, Corollary 5.2.4. — *Quasi-affinoid morphisms are continuous. In particular all residue norms on a quasi-affinoid algebra are equivalent.*

Theorem 5.2.6. — *Homomorphism Extension Lemma.*

Proposition 5.3.2. — *Generalized rings of fractions are well-defined.*

Theorem 5.3.5. — *Quasi-rational domains satisfy the appropriate universal mapping property.*

Proposition 5.4.3. — *Tensor products exist in the category of quasi-affinoid algebras.*

Theorems 5.5.3, 5.5.4. — *In characteristic zero, and often in characteristic p, the residue norm and the supremum norm of a reduced quasi-affinoid algebra are equivalent.*

Theorem 6.1.2. — *A quasi-affinoid map that is finite-to-one is piecewise finite.*

Theorem 6.2.2. — *A quasi-affinoid subdomain is a finite union of R-subdomains.*

Corollary 6.2.3. — *Quasi-affinoid subdomains are open.*

2. Rings of Separated Power Series

In this section, we define the rings $S_{m,n} = S_{m,n}(E, K)$ of separated power series, prove that these rings are Noetherian (Corollary 2.2.4) and that they satisfy Weierstrass Preparation and Division theorems (Corollary 2.3.3 and Theorem 2.3.2), but not (Example 2.3.5) Noether Normalization.

2.1. Definitions. — Let K be a field, complete with respect to a non-trivial ultrametric absolute value $|\cdot|\colon K \to \mathbb{R}_+$, let K° denote the valuation ring of K, let $K^{\circ\circ}$ denote its maximal ideal and let $\sim\colon K^\circ \to \widetilde{K} := K^\circ/K^{\circ\circ}$ denote the canonical residue epimorphism. Throughout this paper, we will be concerned with power series whose coefficients lie in certain subrings B of K° called quasi-Noetherian rings.

Let B be a valued subring of K° such that each $x \in B$ with $|x| = 1$ is a unit of B (such rings are called *B-rings.*) It follows from the ultrametric inequality that B is a local ring. The ring B is called *quasi-Noetherian* iff for each ideal $\mathfrak{a}$ of B there is a zero-sequence $\{x_i\}_{i\in\mathbb{N}} \subset \mathfrak{a}$ (called a *quasi-finite generating system*) such that each

$a \in \mathfrak{a}$ can be written in the form $a = \sum_{i \geq 0} b_i x_i$ for some elements $b_i \in B$. However, not all such sums need belong to $\mathfrak{a}$. (See [**6**, Section 1.8] and [**14**].)

We will make use of the following properties of quasi-Noetherian rings without further reference. Clearly, any subring $B \subset K^\circ$ which is a DVR is quasi-Noetherian, since it is Noetherian. Let $B \subset K^\circ$ be quasi-Noetherian. For any zero sequence $\{a_i\}_{i \in \mathbb{N}} \subset K^\circ$, the local ring

$$A := B[a_0, a_1, \dots]_{\{a \in B[a_0, a_1, \dots] : |a| = 1\}}$$

is quasi-Noetherian ([**6**, Proposition 1.8.2.4]). The completion of B is itself quasi-Noetherian ([**6**, Proposition 1.8.2.2]). The value semigroup $|B \setminus \{0\}| \subset \mathbb{R}_+ \setminus \{0\}$ is discrete ([**6**, Corollary 1.8.1.3]). Therefore, there is a sequence $\{b_i\}_{i \in \mathbb{N}} \subset B \setminus \{0\}$ with $|B \setminus \{0\}| = \{|b_i|\}_{i \in \mathbb{N}}$ and $1 = |b_0| > |b_1| > \cdots$. The sequence of ideals

$$B_i := \{b \in B : |b| \leq |b_i|\},\ i \in \mathbb{N}$$

is called the *natural filtration* of B. Note that B_1 is the unique maximal ideal of B. By $\widetilde{B}$ denote the residue field B/B_1 of B. For $i \in \mathbb{N}$, put $\widetilde{B}_i := B_i/B_{i+1}$; then $\widetilde{B} = \widetilde{B}_0 \subset \widetilde{K}$. Since $B_1 \cdot B_i \subset B_{i+1}$, the B-modules $\widetilde{B}_i$ can be viewed in a canonical way as $\widetilde{B}$-vector spaces. Each $\widetilde{B}$ vector space $\widetilde{B}_i$ is finite-dimensional; in fact, this property characterizes the class of quasi-Noetherian rings ([**6**, Theorem 1.8.1.2]). For $i \in \mathbb{N}$ we may identify the $\widetilde{B}$-vector space $\widetilde{B}_i$ with the $\widetilde{B}$-vector subspace $\left(b_i^{-1} B_i\right)^{\sim}$ of $\widetilde{K}$ via the map

$$\pi_i : (a + B_{i+1}) \longmapsto \left(b_i^{-1} a\right)^{\sim}.$$

When $i > 0$, this identification of $\widetilde{B}_i$ with a $\widetilde{B}$-vector subspace of $\widetilde{K}$ is not canonical; it will, however, be used frequently.

Let R be a ring and let $\{\mathfrak{a}_\lambda\}_{\lambda \in I}$ be an inverse system of ideals of R. When we endow R with the topology induced by taking $\{\mathfrak{a}_\lambda\}_{\lambda \in I}$ to be a system of neighborhoods of 0, R is said to be a ring with a *linear topology*. In this subsection, we will assume that R is complete and Hausdorff in this linear topology. For example, let R be a subring of K°; then the topology induced on R by the absolute value $|\cdot|$ is a Hausdorff linear topology.

Let $\xi = (\xi_1, \dots, \xi_m)$ be variables. A formal power series $\sum a_\mu \xi^\mu$ with coefficients in R is called *strictly convergent* iff $\{a_\mu\}_{\mu \in \mathbb{N}^m}$ is a zero-sequence in R. By $R\langle\xi\rangle$, we denote the collection of all strictly convergent power series; it is a subring of the formal power series ring $R[\![\xi]\!]$. The ring $R\langle\xi\rangle$ is complete and Hausdorff in the *uniform topology*; i.e., in the linear topology given by the system of ideals $\{\mathfrak{a}_\lambda \cdot R\langle\xi\rangle\}_{\lambda \in I}$. In case $R = K^\circ$, by $K\langle\xi\rangle$, we denote the K-algebra $K \otimes_R R\langle\xi\rangle$ of strictly convergent power series over K.

Let $\rho = (\rho_1, \dots, \rho_n)$ be variables. Then

$$R\langle\xi\rangle[\![\rho]\!] = R[\![\rho]\!]\langle\xi\rangle$$

when we endow $R[\![\rho]\!]$ with the *product topology*; i.e., the topology induced by the inverse system of ideals

$$\left\{(\rho)^d + \sum_{|\nu|<d} \rho^\nu \cdot \mathfrak{a}_{\lambda_\nu}[\![\rho]\!]\right\}_{d\in\mathbb{N}}.$$

In case R carries the discrete topology, $R\langle\xi\rangle = R[\xi]$ and

$$R[\xi][\![\rho]\!] = R[\![\rho]\!]\langle\xi\rangle\,,$$

where $R[\![\rho]\!]$ carries the (ρ)-adic topology. If $R \subset K^\circ$ then the absolute value $|\cdot|$ on R induces a linear topology, and $|\cdot|$ extends to an R-module norm on $R\langle\xi\rangle[\![\rho]\!]$ called the *Gauss norm*, given by

$$\left\|\sum_{\mu\nu} f_{\mu\nu}\xi^\mu\rho^\nu\right\| := \sup_{\mu\nu}|f_{\mu\nu}|\,.$$

These definitions will be used in Subsection 2.3 where we discuss Weierstrass Division Theorems.

Definition 2.1.1. —Fix a complete, quasi-Noetherian subring $E \subset K^\circ$ and, if Char $K = p > 0$, assume in addition that E is a DVR. Let $\xi = (\xi_1, \dots, \xi_m)$ and $\rho = (\rho_1, \dots, \rho_n)$ be variables. We define a K-subalgebra $S_{m,n}(E, K)$ of $K[\![\xi, \rho]\!]$, called a *ring of separated power series.*

Let $\mathfrak{B}$ be the family of quasi-Noetherian subrings of K° which consists of all local rings of the form

$$\left(E[a_0, a_1, \dots]_{\{a\in E[a_0,a_1,\dots]:|a|=1\}}\right)^{\widehat{}},$$

where $\widehat{}$ denotes completion in $|\cdot|$, and where $\{a_i\}_{i\in\mathbb{N}} \subset K^\circ$ is a zero-sequence. Then put

$$\begin{aligned} S_{m,n} = S_{m,n}(E,K) &:= K \otimes_{K^\circ} \left(\varinjlim_{B\in\mathfrak{B}} B\langle\xi\rangle[\![\rho]\!]\right), \\ S_{m,n}^\circ &:= \varinjlim_{B\in\mathfrak{B}} B\langle\xi\rangle[\![\rho]\!], \\ S_{m,n}^{\circ\circ} &:= K^{\circ\circ}\cdot S_{m,n}^\circ, \\ \widetilde{S}_{m,n} &:= \varinjlim_{B\in\mathfrak{B}} \widetilde{B}[\xi][\![\rho]\!]. \end{aligned}$$

For $f = \sum a_{\mu\nu}\xi^\mu\rho^\nu \in S_{m,n}$ we define the *Gauss norm* of f by

$$\|f\| := \sup_{\mu,\nu}|a_{\mu,\nu}|.$$

Note that $S_{m,n}$ contains the *Tate ring* $T_{m+n}(K) = K\langle\xi,\rho\rangle$ and $S_{m,0}$ coincides with T_m. In case $K = \mathbb{Q}_p$, the field of p-adic numbers, we have $S_{m,n} = \mathbb{Q}_p \otimes_{\mathbb{Z}_p} \mathbb{Z}_p\langle\xi\rangle[\![\rho]\!]$, where $\mathbb{Z}_p$ denotes the ring of p-adic integers. When K is algebraically closed and E

is a DVR with $E \subset K^\circ$ and $\widetilde{E} = \widetilde{K}$, the rings $S_{m,n}(E,K)$ are the rings defined in [**17**]. Following the usage in [**17**], when E is understood, we may write

$$K\langle\xi\rangle\,[\![\rho]\!]_s := S_{m,n}(E,K).$$

(The subscript s stands for "separated".) In the case that $\widetilde{E} = \widetilde{K}$ the rings $S_{0,n}$ and their quotient rings are the formal completions considered in [**11**, Section 2.3.2,], and used to derive properties of the formal localizations. The description of these rings given in Definition 2.1.1 is due to Bartenwerfer [**2**].

The family $\mathfrak{B}$, described in Definition 2.1.1, satisfies the following properties, which we use without further reference.

(a) $\mathfrak{B}$ forms a direct system under inclusion,

(b) $\varinjlim_{B\in\mathfrak{B}} B = K^\circ$,

(c) for each $B \in \mathfrak{B}$ and $b \in B$ there is some $B' \in \mathfrak{B}$ with $(b^{-1}B \cap K^\circ) \subset B'$,

and

(d) for any $B \in \mathfrak{B}$ and any zero-sequence $\{a_i\}_{i\in\mathbb{N}} \subset K^\circ$,

$$\left(B[a_0, a_1, \dots]_{\{a\in B[a_0,a_1,\dots]:|a|=1\}}\right)^\wedge \in \mathfrak{B}.$$

If $E \subset E'$ and $K \subset K'$ then

$$S_{m,n}(E,K) \subset S_{m,n}(E',K').$$

If K' is a finite algebraic extension of K then $S_{m,n}(E,K') = K' \otimes_K S_{m,n}(E,K)$.

Remark 2.1.2. — The following are easy consequences of the properties of B-rings (*cf.* [**2**] and [**17**]).

(i) If $f = \sum a_{\mu,\nu}\xi^\mu\rho^\nu \in S_{m,n}$ then

$$\|f\| = \sup_{\mu,\nu} |a_{\mu\nu}| = \max_{\mu,\nu} |a_{\mu\nu}|,$$

i.e., the supremum is attained.

(ii) We have the following characterizations of the subring $S_{m,n}^\circ$, the ideal $S_{m,n}^{\circ\circ}$, and the residue ring $\widetilde{S}_{m,n}$:

$$\begin{aligned} S_{m,n}^\circ &= \{f \in S_{m,n} : \|f\| \le 1\}, \\ S_{m,n}^{\circ\circ} &= \{f \in S_{m,n} : \|f\| < 1\} \text{ and} \\ \widetilde{S}_{m,n} &= S_{m,n}^\circ / S_{m,n}^{\circ\circ}. \end{aligned}$$

As in [**6**, Corollary 1.5.3.2], the Gauss norm $\|\cdot\|$ is an absolute value on $S_{m,n}$ extending that on K.

The *canonical residue epimorphism* $\sim: K^\circ \to \widetilde{K}$ extends to the residue epimorphism $\sim: S_{m,n}^\circ \to \widetilde{S}_{m,n} : \sum a_{\mu\nu}\xi^\mu\rho^\nu \mapsto \sum \widetilde{a}_{\mu\nu}\xi^\mu\rho^\nu$. Let I be an ideal of $S_{m,n}$, and put $I^\circ := S_{m,n}^\circ \cap I$. Since $\sim: S_{m,n}^\circ \to \widetilde{S}_{m,n}$ is surjective, the image of I° under $\sim$ is an ideal of $\widetilde{S}_{m,n}$, which we denote by $\widetilde{I}$.

In general the $S_{m,n}(E,K)$ are not complete in $\|\cdot\|$. However, for many choices of $E \subset K$ they are. When $\widetilde{K}$ is algebraic over $\widetilde{E}$, we will show that

$$S_{m,n}(E,K) = K\widehat{\otimes}_E E\langle\xi\rangle[\![\rho]\!],$$

where $\widehat{\otimes}_E$ denotes the complete tensor product of normed E-modules (see [**6**, Section 2.1.7]). This situation is clarified in the next theorem. Observe that the natural map

$$\sigma : K \otimes_E E\langle\xi\rangle[\![\rho]\!] \longrightarrow K[\![\xi,\rho]\!] : \sum \alpha_i \otimes f_i \longmapsto \sum a_i f_i$$

is injective. Indeed, it is easy to see that the field of fractions $Q(E)$ of E is a flat E-algebra. Hence, $K[\![\xi,\rho]\!]$, being a $Q(E)$-vector space, is also a flat E-algebra. It now follows from [**25**, Theorem 7.6], that $\operatorname{Ker}\sigma = (0)$. The image of σ is contained in $S_{m,n}(E,K)$. Moreover, since σ is contractive, it extends to a map

$$\widehat{\sigma} : K\widehat{\otimes}_E E\langle\xi\rangle[\![\rho]\!] \longrightarrow K[\![\xi,\rho]\!].$$

It is not hard to see that the image of $\widehat{\sigma}$ is contained in $S_{m,n}(E,K)$, when $S_{m,n}(E,K)$ is complete (see below).

Theorem 2.1.3. — *Let $n > 0$.*

(i) *$S_{m,n}(E,K)$ is $\|\cdot\|$-complete if, and only if, $\widetilde{K}$ has finite transcendence degree over $\widetilde{E}$. In that case let $E' \subset K^\circ$ be a finitely generated extension of E such that $\widetilde{K}$ is algebraic over $\widetilde{E}'$. Then*

$$S_{m,n}(E,K) = S_{m,n}(E',K) = K\widehat{\otimes}_{E'} E'\langle\xi\rangle[\![\rho]\!],$$

where $\widehat{\otimes}_{E'}$ denotes complete tensor product of normed E'-modules (see [**6**, Section 2.1.7]*).*

(ii) *There is a quasi-Noetherian ring E', $E \subset E' \subset K^\circ$, such that $S_{m,n}(E',K)$ is $\|\cdot\|$-complete (and contains $S_{m,n}(E,K)$).*

(iii) *$\widetilde{S}_{m,n}(E,K)$ is (ρ)-adically complete if, and only if, $\widetilde{K}$ is a finitely generated field extension of $\widetilde{E}$.*

(iv) *$S^\circ_{m,n}(E,K)$ is (ρ)-adically complete if, and only if, $\widetilde{K}$ is a finitely generated field extension of $\widetilde{E}$ and K is discretely valued. (In which case we may take $E = K^\circ$.)*

Proof

(i) Suppose that $\widetilde{K}$ has infinite transcendence degree over $\widetilde{E}$. Let $t_i \in K^\circ$, $i \in \mathbb{N}$, be such that the $\widetilde{t}_i$ are algebraically independent over $\widetilde{E}$. Let $f_i = \sum_{j=1}^{\infty} t_i^j \rho_1^j \in S_{0,1} \subset S_{m,n}$ $(n > 0)$. Choose $a \in K^{\circ\circ}$ (i.e., $|a| < 1$). The series $f = \sum_{i=1}^{\infty} a^i f_i$ is Cauchy in $\|\cdot\|$ but does not belong to $S_{m,n}$. Indeed for any $B \in \mathfrak{B}$, $\widetilde{B}$ is a finitely generated field extension of $\widetilde{E}$ and for $i \geq 1$, $\widetilde{B}_i$ is a finite dimensional vector space over $\widetilde{B}$. Hence $f \notin B[\![\rho_1]\!]$.

For the converse, assume that $\widetilde{K}$ is of finite transcendence degree over $\widetilde{E}$. Note that if $E' \in \mathfrak{B}$ then $S_{m,n}(E,K) = S_{m,n}(E',K)$. Hence we may assume that $\widetilde{K}$ is algebraic over $\widetilde{E}$. Let $f_i \in S^\circ_{m,n}$ with $\|f_i\| \to 0$. There are $a_i \in K^\circ$ with $|a_i| = \|f_i\|$ and $B^{(i)} \in \mathfrak{B}$ such that $\frac{1}{a_i} f_i \in B^{(i)}\langle\xi\rangle[\![\rho]\!]$, i.e., $f_i \in a_i B^{(i)}\langle\xi\rangle[\![\rho]\!]$. Let

$$B^{(i)} = B^{(i)}_0 \supset B^{(i)}_1 \supset \cdots$$

be the natural filtration of $B^{(i)}$. Since $\widetilde{K}$ is algebraic over $\widetilde{E}$, each field $\widetilde{B}^{(i)}_0 = \widetilde{B}^{(i)}$, and hence each $\widetilde{B}^{(i)}_j$, is a finite-dimensional $\widetilde{E}$-vector space. Let $\widetilde{B}^{(i)}_j$ be generated over $\widetilde{E}$ by the residues modulo $B^{(i)}_{j+1}$ of $b_{ijk} \in B^{(i)}_j$, $k = 1, \ldots, \dim \widetilde{B}^{(i)}_j$. Let $\{c_i\}_{i\in\mathbb{N}}$ be a rearrangement of $\{a_i b_{ijk} : i \in \mathbb{N}, j \in \mathbb{N}, k = 1, \ldots, \dim \widetilde{B}^{(i)}_j\}$ in non-increasing size. (Recall that $a_i \to 0$.) Putting

$$B := (E[c_0, c_1, \ldots]_{\{a\in E[c_0,c_1,\ldots]:|a|=1\}})^\wedge \in \mathfrak{B}$$

yields $a_i B^{(i)} \subset B$ for all i and $\sum_i f_i \in B\langle\xi\rangle[\![\rho]\!]$. Hence $S_{m,n}(E, K)$ is complete.

As we observed above, there is a map $\widehat{\sigma} : K\widehat{\otimes}_E E\langle\xi\rangle[\![\rho]\!] \to S_{m,n}$. If $\widetilde{K}$ is algebraic over $\widetilde{E}$ then for every $B \in \mathfrak{B}$, $\widetilde{B}$ and the $\widetilde{B}_i$ are all finite-dimensional $\widetilde{E}$ vector spaces. Hence for each $B \in \mathfrak{B}$, there is a map

$$\tau : B\langle\xi\rangle[\![\rho]\!] \to K\widehat{\otimes}_E E\langle\xi\rangle[\![\rho]\!],$$

which is a left inverse of $\widehat{\sigma}$.

(ii) Repeated use of [**6**, Proposition 1.8.2.3 and Theorem 1.8.1.2], shows that there is a quasi-Noetherian ring E', $E \subset E' \subset K^\circ$, such that $\widetilde{K}$ is an algebraic extension of $\widetilde{E}'$. Hence $S_{m,n}(E, K) \subset S_{m,n}(E', K)$ and by (i) $S_{m,n}(E', K)$ is complete.

(iii) If $\widetilde{K}$ is a finitely generated field extension of $\widetilde{E}$ then replacing E by a suitable finitely generated extension we may assume that $\widetilde{E} = \widetilde{K}$. But then

$$\widetilde{S}_{m,n} = \widetilde{E}[\xi][\![\rho]\!],$$

which is (ρ)-adically complete.

If, on the other hand, there are $\widetilde{t}_i \in \widetilde{K}$ such that $\widetilde{t}_{i+1} \notin \widetilde{E}(\widetilde{t}_1, \ldots, \widetilde{t}_i)$ then $f := \sum \widetilde{t}_i \rho_1^i \notin \widetilde{S}_{m,n}$, since for every $B \in \mathfrak{B}$, $\widetilde{B}$ is a finitely generated field extension of $\widetilde{E}$.

(iv) If K is not discretely valued there are $a_i \in K^\circ$ with $|a_i| < |a_{i+1}| < 1$ for $i = 0, 1, 2, \ldots$. Then $\sum_i a_i \rho_1^i \notin S_{m,n}$. On the other hand, if $\widetilde{K}$ is a finitely generated extension of $\widetilde{E}$ and K is discretely valued, then $K^\circ \in \mathfrak{B}$. □

Remark 2.1.4

(i) Suppose $\operatorname{Char} K = p \neq 0$. In this case we require E to be a complete DVR. By the Cohen Structure Theorem ([**25**, Theorem 29.4]), E has a coefficient field (i.e., an isomorphic copy of $\widetilde{E} \subset E$) which we also denote by $\widetilde{E}$. If π is a prime of E then $\widetilde{E} \subset E = \widetilde{E}[\pi]^\wedge$. Thus $S_{m,n}(E, K) = S_{m,n}(\widetilde{E}, K)$. Hence we could have required in the equicharacteristic p case that $E \subset K$ be a field, without loss of generality.

(ii) Let K be a perfect field of characteristic p, and let $E \subset K^\circ$ be a subfield. Then there is a field E', $E \subset E' \subset K^\circ$, with E' perfect and $\widetilde{K}$ algebraic over $\widetilde{E}'$. Hence, using (i) above, for any DVR $E \subset K^\circ$ there is a field $E' \subset K^\circ$ such that $S_{m,n}(E, K) \subset S_{m,n}(E', K)$, $S_{m,n}(E', K)$ is complete in $\|\cdot\|$ and $S_{m,n}(E', K)$ is a finite $S_{m,n}(E',K)^p$–module. (The monomials $\xi^\mu\rho^\nu$ with $0 \le \mu_i < p$, $0 \le \nu_j < p$, form a basis.)

By definition, $S^\circ_{m,n}$ is the direct limit of complete rings (the $B\langle\xi\rangle[\![\rho]\!]$). Next we show that while $S_{m,n}$ may not be a complete K-algebra it is the direct limit of complete F-algebras for some complete, nontrivially valued subfield F of K. This decomposition will be used in Subsection 5.2.

Let F be a complete subfield of K such that F° is a DVR and $\widetilde{F}$ is finitely generated as a field. (For example, in the mixed characteristic case let $F = \mathbb{Q}_p$, the field of p-adic numbers, and in the equicharacteristic case let F be the fraction field of $\mathbb{Q}[\![t]\!]$ or $\mathbb{F}_p[\![t]\!]$, depending on the characteristic of K, where $t \in K^{\circ\circ}$.) Let $B' \in \mathfrak{B}$. There is a $B \in \mathfrak{B}$ such that $B' \cup F^\circ \subset B$. Consider the F-algebra

$$F\widehat{\otimes}_{F^\circ} B\langle\xi\rangle[\![\rho]\!].$$

By the definition of the complete tensor product $\widehat{\otimes}$ this is an F-Banach algebra (i.e., is complete in $\|\cdot\|$). In general there is no $B'' \in \mathfrak{B}$ such that $(F\widehat{\otimes}_{F^\circ} B\langle\xi\rangle[\![\rho]\!])^\circ \subset B''\langle\xi\rangle[\![\rho]\!]$. However, the natural map

$$\sigma : F \otimes_{F^\circ} B\langle\xi\rangle[\![\rho]\!] \longrightarrow S_{m,n} : \quad \sum \alpha_i \otimes f_i \longmapsto \sum \alpha_i f_i$$

is an isometry because $F^\circ \otimes_{F^\circ} B\langle\xi\rangle[\![\rho]\!] = B\langle\xi\rangle[\![\rho]\!]$. The next proposition shows that σ extends to $F\widehat{\otimes}_{F^\circ} B\langle\xi\rangle[\![\rho]\!]$.

Proposition 2.1.5. — *With the above notation,*

$$F\widehat{\otimes}_{F^\circ} B\langle\xi\rangle[\![\rho]\!] \subset S_{m,n}(E,K).$$

Indeed

$$S_{m,n} = \varinjlim_{F^\circ \subset B \in \mathfrak{B}} F\widehat{\otimes}_{F^\circ} B\langle\xi\rangle[\![\rho]\!].$$

Proof. — It is sufficient to show that if $f \in F\widehat{\otimes}_{F^\circ} B\langle\xi\rangle[\![\rho]\!]$ and $\|f\| \le 1$ then there is a $B'' \in \mathfrak{B}$ such that $f \in B''\langle\xi\rangle[\![\rho]\!]$. Let $f \in F\widehat{\otimes}_{F^\circ} B\langle\xi\rangle[\![\rho]\!]$ with $\|f\| \le 1$. Then there are $f_i \in B\langle\xi\rangle[\![\rho]\!]$ and $m_i \in \mathbb{N}$ such that $f = \sum \pi^{-m_i} f_i$, where π is a prime of F°, and $\|\pi^{-m_i} f_i\| \to 0$. Hence for each i there is a nullsequence $\{a_{ij}\}_{j\in\mathbb{N}}$ with $\pi^{-m_i} f_i \in B'\langle\xi\rangle[\![\rho]\!]$, where

$$B' := \left(B[a_{ij} : j \in \mathbb{N}]_{\{a \in B[a_{ij} : j\in\mathbb{N}] : |a|=1\}}\right)^{\widehat{}}$$

and $|a_{ij}| \le \|\pi^{-m_i} f_i\|$ for all i and j. Since $\|\pi^{-m_i} f_i\| \to 0$, any rearrangement of the double sequence $\{a_{ij}\}_{i,j\in\mathbb{N}}$ as a sequence will be a null-sequence. Let $\{c_i\}_{i\in\mathbb{N}}$ be such a rearrangement. Then if

$$B'' := \left(B[c_0, c_1, \ldots]_{\{a \in B[c_0,c_1,\ldots] : |a|=1\}}\right)^{\widehat{}},$$

$f \in B''\langle\xi\rangle[\![\rho]\!]$. □

In general the F-Banach Algebras $F\widehat{\otimes}_{F^\circ}B\langle\xi\rangle[\![\rho]\!] \subset S_{m,n}$ constructed above are not Noetherian and the Weierstrass Preparation and Division Theorems need not hold in them. An argument similar to the proof of Proposition 2.1.5 shows that we can write

$$S_{m,n}(E,K) = \varinjlim_{B\in\mathfrak{B}} (K\cdot B\langle\xi\rangle[\![\rho]\!])^{\widehat{}}$$

as the direct limit of K-Banach Algebras. These K-Banach algebras likewise may fail to satisfy the Weierstrass Preparation and Division Theorems of Subsection 2.3.

Remark 2.1.6

(i) The rings $S_{m,n} = S_{m,n}(E,K)$ can have quite different properties depending on the choice of E. As we saw in Theorem 2.1.3, if $\widetilde{E}$ is large enough the $S_{m,n}(E,K)$ will be complete and the $\widetilde{S}_{m,n}$ may even be (ρ)-adically complete. On the other hand if $\widetilde{E} \subset \widetilde{K}$ is small, the $S_{m,n}$ will be far from complete and the $\widetilde{S}_{m,n}$ far from (ρ)-adically complete. Nevertheless, for all choices of E, $S^\circ_{m,n}$ is, by definition, the direct limit of the $\|\cdot\|$-complete and (ρ)-adically complete rings $B\langle\xi\rangle[\![\rho]\!]$, and this key property allows the development of the theory.

(ii) There is a larger class of power series rings in which many of the results and proofs of this paper remain valid. This larger class is defined as follows. Fix a family $\mathfrak{B}$ of complete, quasi-Noetherian subrings $B \subset K^\circ$ that satisfy the properties (a), (b), (c) and (d) listed after Definition 2.1.1, and put

$$S_{m,n} = S_{m,n}(\mathfrak{B},K) := K\otimes_{K^\circ} \varinjlim_{B\in\mathfrak{B}} B\langle\xi\rangle[\![\rho]\!].$$

Example 2.1.7 shows that this definition is more general.

(iii) If we wished to work over complete rings we could also have proceeded as follows: Form the rings $S_{m,n}(E,K)$ as in Definition 2.1.1, or the rings $S_{m,n}(\mathfrak{B},K)$ defined above, and then take their completions $\widehat{S_{m,n}} = S_{m,n}(E,K)^{\widehat{}}$ or $S_{m,n}(\mathfrak{B},K)^{\widehat{}}$. In general the rings $S_{m,n}(E,K)^{\widehat{}}$ would be different from the rings $S_{m,n}(E',K)$ for any E'. However all the results of the paper are true for these rings $\widehat{S_{m,n}}$. The proofs that use "slicing" arguments may be modified as follows. Though an arbitrary $f \in (\widehat{S_{m,n}})^\circ$ need not belong to $B\langle\xi\rangle[\![\rho]\!]$ for any $B\in\mathfrak{B}$, there is an increasing sequence $B^{(0)} \subset B^{(1)} \subset \ldots$ from $\mathfrak{B}$ and $f^{(i)} \in B^{(i)}\langle\xi\rangle[\![\rho]\!]$ such that $\|f - f^{(i)}\| \to 0$.

Example 2.1.7. — We give an example of a $\mathfrak{B}$, as in Remark 2.1.6(ii), such that there is no E with $S_{m,n}(\mathfrak{B},K) \subset S_{m,n}(E,K)$. Consider $F = \mathbb{F}_p(t_1,t_2,\ldots)(z)$ with absolute value derived from the (z)-adic valuation and let K be the completion of the algebraic closure of F. Let $\{\alpha_i\}$ be a sequence of positive rationals converging to zero, and define inductively

$$\begin{aligned} E_0 &:= \mathbb{F}_p(t_i + z^{\alpha_i}, i\in\mathbb{N}) \\ E_i &:= \left(E_{i-1}[t_i^{p^{-n}} : n\in\mathbb{N}]_{\{a\in E_{i-1}[t_i^{p^{-n}}\,:\,n\in\mathbb{N}]\,:\,|a|=1\}}\right)^{\widehat{}}. \end{aligned}$$

Let $\mathfrak{B}_i$ be the family of all quasi-Noetherian rings of the form

$$\left(E_i[a_0, a_1, \dots]_{\{a \in E_i[a_0, a_1, \dots]:|a|=1\}}\right)^\frown$$

where $\{a_i\}_{i \in \mathbb{N}}$ is a null sequence from K°, and let

$$\mathfrak{B} := \cup_i \mathfrak{B}_i.$$

We will show that for $n > 0$ there is no complete DVR $E \subset K^\circ$ such that

$$S_{m,n}(\mathfrak{B}, K) \subset S_{m,n}(E, K).$$

Suppose that $S_{m,n}(\mathfrak{B}, K) \subset S_{m,n}(E, K)$. Since K is algebraically closed, by Remark 2.1.4 we may assume that $E \subset K^\circ$ is a field and that $\widetilde{E} = \widetilde{K}$.

Note that E_i has a countable dense subset $\{c_0, c_1, \dots\}$. Hence

$$\sum c_i \rho_1^i \in S_{m,n}(\mathfrak{B}, K) \subset S_{m,n}(E, K).$$

Therefore for each $i \in \mathbb{N}$ there is a zero sequence $\{a_1, a_2, \dots\}$ from K° such that

$$E_i \subset \left(E[a_1, a_2, \dots]_{\{a \in E[a_1, a_2, \dots]:|a|=1\}}\right)^\frown =: E_i'.$$

Since $\widetilde{E} = \widetilde{K}$ we may assume that $|a_j| < 1$ for all j. Since $t_i^{p^{-n}} \in E_i$, there are $e_{nj} \in E_i'$ with $e_{n0} \in E$ such that

$$t_i^{p^{-n}} = e_{n0} + \sum_{j=1}^{\infty} e_{nj} a_j.$$

Then

$$t_i = e_{n0}^{p^n} + \sum_{j=1}^{\infty} e_{nj}^{p^n} a_j^{p^n}.$$

Since $|a_j| < 1$ for all j, we see that the sequence $e_{n0}^{p^n}$ converges to t_i. Since $E \subset K^\circ$ is a field the absolute value is trivial on E and hence $t_i \in E$. The quasi-Noetherian ring E_0' contains both E and E_0. Thus it contains the elements z^{α_i}, $i \in \mathbb{N}$. Since $|z^{\alpha_i}| = p^{-\alpha_i}$ this contradicts the discreteness of the value semigroup of E_0'. One can construct a similar counterexample in characteristic zero.

Remark 2.1.8. — We will use the term *affinoid* to refer to objects defined over the Tate rings and the term *quasi-affinoid* to refer to objects defined over rings of separated power series. Hence, for example, an *affinoid algebra* is a quotient of a T_m and a *quasi-affinoid algebra* is a quotient of an $S_{m,n}$.

2.2. Noetherianness. — In this subsection, we lift the Noetherian property of the residue rings $\widetilde{S}_{m,n}$ to the $S_{m,n}$ by lifting generators of ideals. This also yields the property that ideals of $S_{m,n}$ are strictly closed in $\|\cdot\|$, a property that will be further analyzed in Subsection 3.1.

Lemma 2.2.1. — *Suppose $A = \varinjlim A_\lambda$ is a Noetherian ring which is the direct limit of the rings A_λ. Put $\mathcal{A} := \varinjlim A_\lambda[\![\rho]\!] \subset A[\![\rho]\!]$. The following are equivalent:*

(i) *$\mathcal{A}$ is Noetherian.*
(ii) *$A[\![\rho]\!]$ is a flat $\mathcal{A}$-algebra.*
(iii) *$A[\![\rho]\!]$ is a faithfully flat $\mathcal{A}$-algebra.*
(iv) *Each ideal of $\mathcal{A}$ is closed in the (ρ)-adic topology.*

If each A_λ is Noetherian and if for every λ there is some $\mu \geq \lambda$ such that A is a flat A_μ-algebra, then $A[\![\rho]\!]$ is a flat $\mathcal{A}$-algebra.

Proof. — It is no loss of generality to assume that each $A_\lambda \subset A$. We first show (i) $\Rightarrow$ (ii) $\Rightarrow$ (iii) $\Rightarrow$ (iv) $\Rightarrow$ (i).

(i) $\Rightarrow$ (ii). Let I be the ideal of $\mathcal{A}$ generated by the variables $\rho_1, \dots, \rho_n$. Since $A[\![\rho]\!]$ is Noetherian and since $I \cdot A[\![\rho]\!]$ is contained in the Jacobson radical of $A[\![\rho]\!]$, $A[\![\rho]\!]$ is I-adically ideal separated as an $\mathcal{A}$-module. Since for every $\ell \in \mathbb{N}$

$$\mathcal{A}/I^\ell = A[\![\rho]\!]/(\rho)^\ell,$$

(ii) follows from (i) by the Local Flatness Criterion ([**25**, Theorem 22.3]).

(ii) $\Rightarrow$ (iii). Let I be any ideal of $\mathcal{A}$; then $I \cdot A[\![\rho]\!]$ is the unit ideal if, and only if, for some $f_1, \dots, f_\ell \in I$ and $\alpha_1, \dots, \alpha_\ell \in A$, the constant term of $\sum \alpha_i f_i$ is a unit. The latter condition holds if, and only if, I generates the unit ideal of $\mathcal{A}$. Therefore (iii) follows from (ii) by [**25**, Theorem 7.2].

(iii) $\Rightarrow$ (iv). Since $A[\![\rho]\!]$ is Noetherian and since $(\rho) \cdot A[\![\rho]\!]$ is contained in the Jacobson radical, each ideal of $A[\![\rho]\!]$ is closed in the (ρ)-adic topology by the Krull Intersection Theorem ([**25**, Theorem 8.10 (i)]). Let I be any ideal of $\mathcal{A}$; then the (ρ)-adic closure of I in $\mathcal{A}$ is equal to $I \cdot A[\![\rho]\!] \cap \mathcal{A}$. Hence to prove (iv), we must show that $I = I \cdot A[\![\rho]\!] \cap \mathcal{A}$. If $A[\![\rho]\!]$ is faithfully flat over $\mathcal{A}$, this follows from [**25**, Theorem 7.5].

(iv) $\Rightarrow$ (i). Let I be an ideal of $\mathcal{A}$. Since $A[\![\rho]\!]$ is Noetherian, there are finitely many elements $f_1, \dots, f_\ell$ of I which generate the ideal $I \cdot A[\![\rho]\!]$. Let J be the ideal of $\mathcal{A}$ generated by $f_1, \dots, f_\ell$. To prove (i), we show that $J = I$. If each ideal of $\mathcal{A}$ is closed in the (ρ)-adic topology, then, as above,

$$\begin{aligned} I &= \mathcal{A} \cap I \cdot A[\![\rho]\!] \\ &= \mathcal{A} \cap J \cdot A[\![\rho]\!] \\ &= J, \end{aligned}$$

proving (i).

Now suppose that each A_λ is Noetherian and that for every λ there is some $\mu \geq \lambda$ such that A is a flat A_μ-algebra. We show that $A[\![\rho]\!]$ is a flat $\mathcal{A}$-algebra.

If A is a flat A_μ-algebra then

$$A[\rho] = A \otimes_{A_\mu} A_\mu[\rho]$$

is a flat $A_\mu[\rho]$-algebra. Since, in addition, A is Noetherian, by the Artin-Rees Lemma ([**25**, Theorem 8.6]), the $A_\mu[\rho]$-module $A[\rho]$ is (ρ)-adically ideal-separated. Since $A_\mu[\rho]$ is Noetherian, by the Local Flatness Criterion ([**25**], Theorem 22.3), for every

$\ell \in \mathbb{N}$, $A[\rho]/(\rho)^\ell$ is a flat $A_\mu[\rho]/(\rho)^\ell$-algebra. Since $A[\![\rho]\!]/(\rho)^\ell = A[\rho]/(\rho)^\ell$ and $A_\mu[\![\rho]\!]/(\rho)^\ell = A_\mu[\rho]/(\rho)^\ell$, and since $\rho_1, \ldots, \rho_n$ are contained in the Jacobson radical of $A[\![\rho]\!]$, by another application of the local flatness criterion, $A[\![\rho]\!]$ is a flat $A_\mu[\![\rho]\!]$-algebra. To show that $A[\![\rho]\!]$ is a flat $\mathcal{A}$-algebra, we use **[25]**, Theorem 7.6. Suppose $f_1, \ldots, f_\ell \in \mathcal{A}$; then for some μ such that $A[\![\rho]\!]$ is a flat $A_\mu[\![\rho]\!]$-algebra, $f_1, \ldots, f_\ell \in A_\mu[\![\rho]\!]$. Suppose, furthermore, for some $g_1, \ldots, g_\ell \in A[\![\rho]\!]$ that $\sum g_i f_i = 0$. Since $A[\![\rho]\!]$ is a flat $A_\mu[\![\rho]\!]$-algebra, there are $r \in \mathbb{N}$, $\varphi_{ij} \in A_\mu[\![\rho]\!]$ and $\gamma_j \in A[\![\rho]\!]$, $1 \le i \le \ell$, $1 \le j \le r$, such that

$$\sum_i f_i \varphi_{ij} = 0 \text{ for all } j, \text{ and } g_i = \sum_j \varphi_{ij}\gamma_j \text{ for all } i.$$

Since $A_\mu[\![\rho]\!] \subset \mathcal{A}$, it follows immediately that $A[\![\rho]\!]$ is a flat $\mathcal{A}$-algebra. □

The following is an immediate consequence of Lemma 2.2.1, taking the A_λ to be the $\widetilde{B}[\xi]$, $B \in \mathfrak{B}$.

Corollary 2.2.2. — *The residue rings $\widetilde{S}_{m,n}$ are Noetherian; each ideal of $\widetilde{S}_{m,n}$ is closed in the (ρ)-adic topology.*

The next lemma allows us to lift generators of an ideal $\widetilde{I}$ of $\widetilde{S}_{m,n}$ to generators of the ideal I of $S_{m,n}$.

Lemma 2.2.3. — *Let $I \subset S_{m,n}$ be an ideal and let $g_1, \ldots, g_r \in I^\circ$ be such that $\{\widetilde{g}_1, \ldots, \widetilde{g}_r\}$ generates $\widetilde{I}$. Let $f \in S^\circ_{m,n}$ and choose $B \in \mathfrak{B}$ such that $f, g_1, \ldots, g_r \in B\langle\xi\rangle[\![\rho]\!]$. Suppose that $\|f - h\| < \|f\|$ for some $h \in I$. Then there are $f_1, \ldots, f_r \in B\langle\xi\rangle[\![\rho]\!]$ with*

$$\left\| f - \sum_{i=1}^{r} f_i g_i \right\| < \|f\| \tag{2.2.1}$$

and $\|f\| = \max_{1\le i\le r} \|f_i\|$.

Proof. — Let $B = B_0 \supset B_1 \supset \cdots$ be the natural filtration of B, and suppose

$$f \in B_p\langle\xi\rangle[\![\rho]\!] \setminus B_{p+1}\langle\xi\rangle[\![\rho]\!].$$

Find $b_p \in B$ with $B_p = \{b \in B : |b| \le |b_p|\}$, let $\pi_p : B_p \to \widetilde{B}_p \subset \widetilde{K}$ be the B-module residue epimorphism $a \mapsto (b_p^{-1}a)^\sim$, and write

$$\widetilde{K} = \widetilde{B}_p \oplus V$$

for some $\widetilde{B}$-vector space V. This implies that

$$\widetilde{K}[\xi][\![\rho]\!] = \widetilde{B}_p[\xi][\![\rho]\!] \oplus V[\xi][\![\rho]\!] \tag{2.2.2}$$

as $\widetilde{B}[\xi][\![\rho]\!]$-modules. (This useful decomposition can be found in **[14]**.)

Since $\|f - h\| < \|f\|$ for some $h \in I$, we have $\pi_p(f) \in \widetilde{I}$. Since $\widetilde{g}_1, \ldots, \widetilde{g}_r$ generate $\widetilde{I}$, we have

$$\pi_p(f) = \sum_{i=1}^{r} \widetilde{f}_i \widetilde{g}_i \in \widetilde{B}_p[\xi][\![\rho]\!]$$

for some $\widetilde{f}_1, \ldots, \widetilde{f}_r \in \widetilde{K}[\xi][\![\rho]\!]$. By (2.2.2), we may assume $\widetilde{f}_1, \ldots, \widetilde{f}_r \in \widetilde{B}_p[\xi][\![\rho]\!]$. Thus there are $f_1, \ldots, f_r \in B_p\langle\xi\rangle[\![\rho]\!]$ corresponding to $\widetilde{f}_1, \ldots, \widetilde{f}_r$ under the residue map π_p. Clearly, $\|f - \sum f_j g_j\| < \|f\|$. □

Since each $B \in \mathfrak{B}$ has discrete value semigroup and since $B\langle\xi\rangle[\![\rho]\!]$ is complete in $\|\cdot\|$, Lemma 2.2.3 implies that the separated power series rings are Noetherian.

***Corollary 2.2.4* (*cf.* [17, Proposition 2.6.2]).** — *The rings $S_{m,n}$ are Noetherian. Indeed, let $I \subset S_{m,n}$ be an ideal and suppose the residues of $g_1, \ldots, g_r \in I^\circ$ generate $\widetilde{I}$ in $\widetilde{S}_{m,n}$. Then for every $f \in I$ there are $f_1, \ldots, f_r \in S_{m,n}$ with*

$$f = \sum_{i=1}^{r} f_i g_i,$$

and $\|f\| = \max_{1 \le i \le r} \|f_i\|$. Moreover, if for some $B \in \mathfrak{B}$, $f, g_1, \ldots, g_r \in B\langle\xi\rangle[\![\rho]\!]$, then $f_1, \ldots, f_r$ may also be taken to lie in $B\langle\xi\rangle[\![\rho]\!]$.

In fact, Lemma 2.2.3 yields the slightly stronger result, Corollary 2.2.6.

***Definition 2.2.5* (*cf.* [6, Definition 1.1.5.1]).** — Let (A, v) be a multiplicatively valued ring. An ideal I of A is called *strictly closed* in v iff for every $f \in A$ there is some $g \in I$ such that $v(f - g) \le v(f - h)$ for every $h \in I$.

Corollary 2.2.6. — *Ideals of $S_{m,n}$ are strictly closed in $\|\cdot\|$. Indeed, let $I \subset S_{m,n}$ be an ideal and suppose the residues of $g_1, \ldots, g_r \in I^\circ$ generate $\widetilde{I}$ in $\widetilde{S}_{m,n}$. Then for every $f \in S_{m,n}$ there are $f_1, \ldots, f_r \in S_{m,n}$ with*

$$\left\| f - \sum_{i=1}^{r} f_i g_i \right\| \le \|f - h\|$$

for every $h \in I$, and $\|f\| \ge \max_{1 \le i \le r} \|f_i\|$. Moreover, if for some

$$B \in \mathfrak{B}, \quad f, g_1, \ldots, g_r \in B\langle\xi\rangle[\![\rho]\!],$$

then $f_1, \ldots, f_r$ may be taken to lie in $B\langle\xi\rangle[\![\rho]\!]$.

Taking $n = 0$ in the above, we obtain [6, Corollary 5.2.7.8].

In Subsection 3.1, we will be interested in some refinements of Corollary 2.2.6.

Definition 2.2.7. — Let I be an ideal of $S_{m,n}$. For $f \in S_{m,n}$, we define the *residue norm*

$$\|f\|_I := \inf\{\|f - h\| : h \in I\}.$$

From Corollary 2.2.6, it follows that there is some $h \in I$ such that $\|f\|_I = \|f - h\|$.

The direct sum $(S_{m,n}/I)^\ell$ is a normed $(S_{m,n}/I)$-module via

$$\|\cdot\|_I\colon (S_{m,n}/I)^\ell \to \mathbb{R}_+ : (f_1, \ldots, f_\ell) \mapsto \max_{1\leq i\leq \ell} \|f_i\|_I.$$

We will be concerned with submodules M of $(S_{m,n}/I)^\ell$, which will be endowed with the norm $\|\cdot\|_I$. Residue modules play an important role.

Definition 2.2.8. — Let $(M, |\cdot|)$ be a normed K-module. By M° and $M^{\circ\circ}$ denote, respectively, the K°-modules

$$M^\circ := \{f \in M\colon |f| \leq 1\} \quad \text{and}$$
$$M^{\circ\circ} := \{f \in M\colon |f| < 1\}.$$

We define the *residue module* $\widetilde{M}$ by

$$\widetilde{M} := M^\circ / M^{\circ\circ}.$$

It is a $\widetilde{K}$-module.

From Corollary 2.2.6, it follows that

$$(S_{m,n}/I)^\circ = S^\circ_{m,n}/I^\circ \text{ and } (S_{m,n}/I)^\sim = \widetilde{S}_{m,n}/\widetilde{I}.$$

2.3. Weierstrass Division Theorems. — We recall in Theorem 2.3.2 the Weierstrass Division Theorems for the rings $S_{m,n}$ (see [**16**] and [**17**]) in the form given in [**2**, Section 1.2]. These will be used in Section 4 and extensively in Section 5. In Theorem 2.3.8, we prove an extension of these division theorems to handle Weierstrass divisors with coefficients in a quasi-affinoid algebra. The statement and proof of Theorem 2.3.8 rely on results of Sections 4 and 5, but the theorem itself is only used in Section 6 and in [**23**].

***Definition 2.3.1* (*cf.* [17, Sections 2.3 and 2.4]).** — An element $f \in \widetilde{S}_{m,n}$ is *regular in ξ_m of degree s* iff for some $c \in \widetilde{K}$, cf is congruent modulo $(\rho) \cdot \widetilde{S}_{m,n}$ to a monic polynomial in ξ_m of degree s. An element $f \in \widetilde{S}_{m,n}$ is *regular in ρ_n of degree s* iff $f(\xi, 0, \ldots, 0, \rho_n) = \rho_n^s \cdot g(\xi, \rho_n)$ for some unit $g \in \widetilde{K}[\xi][\![\rho_n]\!]$. An element $f \in S_{m,n} \setminus \{0\}$ is *regular of degree s in ξ_m* (respectively, ρ_n) iff for some $c \in K$, $(cf)^\sim \in \widetilde{S}_{m,n}$ is regular of degree s in ξ_m (respectively, ρ_n).

The formal power series ring $\widetilde{B}[\xi][\![\rho]\!]$, whence $\widetilde{S}_{m,n}$, has the usual local Weierstrass Division Theorem for elements regular in ρ, as in [**41**, Theorem VI.1.5]. As in [**1**, Section 2.2] or in [**17**, Proposition 2.4.1], this lifts to the complete, linearly topologized ring $B\langle\xi\rangle[\![\rho]\!]$. As explained in Subsection 2.1, $\widetilde{B}[\xi][\![\rho]\!]$ is equal to the strictly convergent power series ring $\widetilde{B}[\![\rho]\!]\langle\xi\rangle$. The Euclidean Division Theorem for $\widetilde{B}[\xi]$ lifts to a Weierstrass Division Theorem in $\widetilde{B}[\![\rho]\!]\langle\xi\rangle$ for elements regular in ξ, as in [**6**, Theorem 5.2.1.2]. This may be lifted to $B\langle\xi\rangle[\![\rho]\!]$ as in [**17**, Proposition 2.3.1], or as in [**2**, Section 1.2], using the Hensel's Lemma of [**8**, Section 4]. This yields the following theorem.

Theorem 2.3.2* (Weierstrass Division Theorem, *cf. [**17**, Propositions 2.3.1 and 2.4.1])
Let $f, g \in S^\circ_{m,n}$ with $\|f\| = 1$.

(i) *If f is regular in ξ_m of degree s, then there exist unique $q \in S^\circ_{m,n}$ and $r \in S^\circ_{m-1,n}[\xi_m]$ of degree at most $s-1$ such that $g = qf + r$. If $g \in I \cdot S^\circ_{m,n}$ for some (closed) ideal I of $S^\circ_{m-1,n}$, then $q, r \in I \cdot S^\circ_{m,n}$.*
(ii) *If f is regular in ρ_n of degree s, then there exist unique $q \in S^\circ_{m,n}$ and $r \in S^\circ_{m,n-1}[\rho_n]$ of degree at most $s-1$ such that $g = qf + r$. If $g \in I \cdot S^\circ_{m,n}$ for some (closed) ideal I of $S^\circ_{m,n-1}$, then $q, r \in I \cdot S^\circ_{m,n}$.*

Moreover, if $f, g \in B\langle\xi\rangle[\![\rho]\!]$ for some $B \in \mathfrak{B}$, also, $q, r \in B\langle\xi\rangle[\![\rho]\!]$.

Dividing ξ_m^s (or ρ_n^s) by an element $f \in S_{m,n}$ regular in ξ_m (or ρ_n) of degree s, we obtain the following corollary.

***Corollary 2.3.3* (Weierstrass Preparation Theorem).** — *Let $f \in S^\circ_{m,n}$ with $\|f\| = 1$.*

(i) *If f is regular in ξ_m of degree s, then there exist a unique unit u of $S^\circ_{m,n}$ and a unique monic polynomial $P \in S^\circ_{m-1,n}[\xi_m]$ of degree s such that $f = u \cdot P$; in addition, P is regular in ξ_n of degree s.*
(ii) *If f is regular in ρ_n of degree s, then there exist a unique unit u of $S^\circ_{m,n}$ and a unique monic polynomial $P \in S^\circ_{m,n-1}[\rho_n]$ of degree s such that $f = u \cdot P$; in addition, P is regular in ρ_n of degree s.*

Moreover, if $f \in B\langle\xi\rangle[\![\rho]\!]$ for some $B \in \mathfrak{B}$, also $u, P \in B\langle\xi\rangle[\![\rho]\!]$.

Unlike the rings $B[\![\xi, \rho]\!]$ and $B\langle\xi, \rho\rangle$, there may be no automorphism of $S_{m,n}$ under which a given element f with $\|f\| = 1$ becomes regular (see Example 2.3.5).

Definition 2.3.4* (*cf. [**17**, Section 3.12]). — An element $f = \sum f_\mu(\rho)\xi^\mu \in \widetilde{S}_{m,n}$ is *preregular in ξ of degree μ_0* iff $f_{\mu_0} \not\equiv 0$ modulo $(\rho) \cdot \widetilde{S}_{m,n}$ and $f_\mu \equiv 0$ modulo $(\rho) \cdot \widetilde{S}_{m,n}$ for all μ lexicographically larger than μ_0. An element $f = \sum f_\nu(\xi)\rho^\nu \in \widetilde{S}_{m,n}$ is *preregular in ρ of degree ν_0* iff $f_{\nu_0} \in \widetilde{K} \setminus \{0\}$ and for all lexicographically smaller indices ν, $f_\nu = 0$. An element $f \in S_{m,n} \setminus \{0\}$ is *preregular in ξ of degree μ_0* (respectively, *in ρ of degree ν_0*) iff for some $c \in K$, $(cf)^\sim \in \widetilde{S}_{m,n}$ is preregular of the same degree.

If f is preregular in ξ (respectively, ρ) then after an automorphism of the form $\rho \mapsto \rho$, $\xi_m \mapsto \xi_m$, $\xi_i \mapsto \xi_i + \xi_m^{c_i}$ (respectively, $\xi \mapsto \xi$, $\rho_n \mapsto \rho_n$, $\rho_j \mapsto \rho_j + \rho_n^{c_j}$) f becomes regular in ξ_m (respectively, ρ_n) of some degree s. Such automorphisms are called *Weierstrass automorphisms*.

Example 2.3.5. — The element $\xi\cdot\rho \in S_{1,1}$ is not preregular. Indeed, there is no finite monomorphism $S_{m,n} \to S_{1,1}/(\xi\rho)$ for any $m, n \in \mathbb{N}$. Since the map

$$S_{1,0} \oplus S_{0,1} \to S_{1,1}/(\xi\rho)\colon (f,g) \mapsto f+g$$

is surjective and $\dim S_{1,0} = \dim S_{0,1} = 1$ (see Corollary 4.2.2), we must have

$$\dim(S_{1,1}/(\xi\rho)) = 1.$$

Thus, if there were a finite monomorphism

$$\varphi : S_{m,n} \to S_{1,1}/(\xi\rho),$$

either $m = 1$ and $n = 0$, or $m = 0$ and $n = 1$. We treat the case $m = 1$ and $n = 0$. Let

$$\alpha : S_{1,1}/(\xi\rho) \to S_{0,1} = S_{1,1}/(\xi\rho, \xi)$$

be the canonical projection. Since α is surjective,

$$\alpha \circ \varphi : S_{1,0} \to S_{0,1}$$

is finite. Since $\dim S_{0,1} = 1$, $\alpha \circ \varphi$ must be injective. By [**6**, Proposition 3.8.1.7], we can reduce modulo $K^{\circ\circ}$ to obtain a finite $\widetilde{K}$-algebra homomorphism

$$(\alpha\circ\varphi)^{\sim} : \widetilde{K}[\xi] \to \widetilde{S}_{0,1}.$$

But such a map cannot exist, since the transcendence degree of $\widetilde{S}_{0,1}$ over $\widetilde{K}$ is infinite.

Remark 2.3.6. — For every nonzero $f \in S_{0,n}$, there is a Weierstrass automorphism of $S_{0,n}$ under which f becomes regular in ρ_n of some degree. Therefore, arguing as in [**6**, Theorem 6.1.2.1], one proves the following version of Noether Normalization: Let d be the Krull dimension of $S_{0,n}/I$; then there is a finite K-algebra monomorphism $\varphi : S_{0,d} \to S_{0,n}/I$.

In Definition 5.2.7, we will define the ring $A\langle\xi\rangle[\![\rho]\!]_s \subset A[\![\xi,\rho]\!]$ of separated power series with coefficients in a quasi-affinoid algebra A. Using the results of Subsection 5.2, we state and prove here relative Weierstrass Division Theorems for such rings. These theorems will be used only in Section 6 and in [**23**].

Definition 2.3.7. — Let A be a quasi-affinoid algebra. By the Extension Lemma, Theorem 5.2.6, for each $x \in \operatorname{Max} A$, there is a unique homomorphism

$$\varepsilon_x : A\langle\xi_1,\dots,\xi_m\rangle[\![\rho_1,\dots,\rho_n]\!]_s \to S_{m,n}(E, A/x)$$

extending the map $A \to A/x$ and preserving the variables ξ and ρ. An element $f \in A\langle\xi\rangle[\![\rho]\!]_s$ is *regular in* ξ_m (respectively, ρ_m) *of degree* s iff for each $x \in \operatorname{Max} A$, $\varepsilon_x(f) \in S_{m,n}(E, A/x)$ is regular in ξ_m (respectively, ρ_n) of degree s. *Preregular* elements are defined similarly.

***Theorem 2.3.8* (Weierstrass Division Theorem).** — *Let A be a quasi-affinoid algebra, and let $f, g \in A\langle\xi\rangle[\![\rho]\!]_s$.*

(i) *If f is regular in ξ_m of degree s, then there exist unique $q \in A\langle\xi\rangle[\![\rho]\!]_s$ and $r \in A\langle\xi'\rangle[\![\rho]\!]_s[\xi_m]$ of degree at most $s-1$ such that $g = qf + r$ (where $\xi' = (\xi_1, \ldots, \xi_{m-1})$.)*

(ii) *If f is regular in ρ_n of degree s, then there exist unique $q \in A\langle\xi\rangle[\![\rho]\!]_s$ and $r \in A\langle\xi\rangle[\![\rho']\!]_s[\rho_n]$ of degree at most $s-1$ such that $g = qf + r$ (where $\rho' = (\rho_1, \ldots, \rho_{n-1})$.)*

Proof

(i) *Existence.* Write

$$f = \sum_{\mu,\nu} a_{\mu\nu}\xi^\mu\rho^\nu = \sum_{i\geq 0} f_i\xi_m^i.$$

Since f is regular in ξ_m of degree s, $\varepsilon_x(f_s)$ is a unit of $S_{m-1,n}(E, A/x)$ for each $x \in \operatorname{Max} A$. It follows by the Nullstellensatz, Theorem 4.1.1, that f_s is a unit of $A\langle\xi\rangle[\![\rho]\!]_s$. Since $\varepsilon_x(f_s^{-1}) \cdot \varepsilon_x(f)$ is regular in ξ_m of degree s for each $x \in \operatorname{Max} A$, we may therefore take $f_s = 1$. It follows that

$$\varepsilon_x(f_i) \in S^\circ_{m-1,n}(E, A/x), \quad i < s,$$

and

$$\varepsilon_x(f_i) \in (\rho)S^\circ_{m-1,n}(E, A/x) + S^{\circ\circ}_{m-1,n}(E, A/x), \quad i > s,$$

for every $x \in \operatorname{Max} A$. By Corollary 5.1.8, f_i is power-bounded for $i < s$ and f_i is quasi-nilpotent for $i > s$.

Write $A = S_{m',n'}/I$ and consider the canonical projection

$$\varphi : S_{m+m',n+n'} \to A\langle\xi\rangle[\![\rho]\!]_s$$

modulo $I \cdot S_{m+m',n+n'}$. Let

$$F = \sum F_i\xi_m^i$$

be a preimage of f, where each $F_i \in S_{m-1+m',n+n'}$. By Lemma 3.1.6, there is an r so that for $i > s$,

$$F_i = \sum_{j=1}^r H_{ij}F_{s+j},$$

where $\|H_{i1}\|, \ldots, \|H_{ir}\| \leq 1$.

By the Extension Lemma, Theorem 5.2.6, there is a K-algebra homomorphism ψ such that

$$\begin{array}{ccc} S_{m+m',n+n'} & \hookrightarrow & S_{m+m'+s,n+n'+r} \\ {\scriptstyle\varphi}\downarrow & \swarrow{\scriptstyle\psi} & \\ A\langle\xi\rangle[\![\rho]\!]_s & & \end{array}$$

commutes, and

$$\psi(\xi_i) = \xi_i, \quad 1 \le i \le m; \qquad \psi(\xi_{m+i}) = \varphi(\xi_{m+i}), \quad 1 \le i \le m';$$
$$\psi(\xi_{m+m'+i}) = f_{i-1}, \quad 1 \le i \le s,$$

and

$$\psi(\rho_i) = \rho_i, \quad 1 \le i \le n; \qquad \psi(\rho_{n+i}) = \varphi(\rho_{n+i}), \quad 1 \le i \le n';$$
$$\psi(\rho_{n+n'+i}) = f_{s+i}, \quad 1 \le i \le r.$$

Note that f is the image under ψ of

$$f^* := \sum_{i=0}^{s-1} \xi_{m+m'+i+1}\xi_m^i + \xi_m^s + \sum_{i>s} \xi_m^i \left(\sum_{j=1}^{r} H_{ij}\rho_{n+n'+j} \right)$$

and $f^* \in S_{m+m'+s,n+n'+r}$ is regular in ξ_m of degree s.

Let $G \in S_{m+m'+s,n+n'+r}$ be a preimage of g under ψ. By Theorem 2.3.2, there are unique $Q \in S_{m+m'+s,n+n'+r}$ and $R \in S_{m-1+m'+s,n+n'+r}[\xi_m]$ of degree at most $s-1$ with

$$G = Qf^* + R.$$

Putting $q = \psi(Q)$ and $r = \psi(R)$ satisfies the existence assertion of part (i).

Uniqueness. Let $q \in A\langle\xi\rangle[\![\rho]\!]_s$ and let $r \in A\langle\xi'\rangle[\![\rho]\!]_s[\xi_m]$ be of degree at most $s-1$. Suppose

$$0 = qf + r;$$

we must show that $q = r = 0$. Let

$$Q \in S_{m+m'+s,n+n'+r} \quad \text{and} \quad R \in S_{m-1+m'+s,n+n'+r}[\xi_m]$$

with $\deg R \le s-1$ be preimages under ψ of q and r, respectively. Then

$$G := Qf^* + R \in \operatorname{Ker}\psi = I \cdot S_{m+m'+s,n+n'+r}.$$

The ideal I is closed by Corollary 2.2.6; hence by Theorem 2.3.2 (i), $Q, R \in \operatorname{Ker}\psi$, as desired.

(ii) The proof of this part is entirely analogous to the above. □

The corresponding Weierstrass Preparation Theorem follows in the usual way.

***Corollary 2.3.9* (Weierstrass Preparation Theorem).** — *Let A be a quasi-affinoid algebra, and let $f \in A\langle\xi\rangle[\![\rho]\!]_s$.*

(i) *If f is regular in ξ_m of degree s, then there exist unique unit $u \in A\langle\xi\rangle[\![\rho]\!]_s$ and monic polynomial $P \in A\langle\xi'\rangle[\![\rho]\!][\xi_m]$ of degree s such that $f = uP$. Furthermore P is regular in ξ_m of degree s.*

(ii) *If f is regular in ρ_n of degree s, then there exist unique unit $u \in A\langle\xi\rangle[\![\rho]\!]_s$ and monic polynomial $P \in A\langle\xi\rangle[\![\rho']\!]_s[\rho_n]$ of degree s such that $f \in uP$. Furthermore P is regular in ρ_n of degree s.*

3. Restrictions to Polydiscs

In this section, we study the restriction maps from $\Delta_{m,n}$ (see Introduction) to "closed" (and to "open") sub-polydiscs, and show how to transfer information from their (quasi-)affinoid function algebras back to $S_{m,n}$.

The closed subpolydiscs with which we are concerned in this section are Cartesian products where the first m factors are closed unit discs and the next n factors are closed discs of radius $\varepsilon \in \sqrt{|K \setminus \{0\}|}$. Such products are K-affinoid varieties, and we denote their corresponding rings of K-affinoid functions by $T_{m,n}(\varepsilon, K)$.

To transfer algebraic information from the affinoid algebras $T_{m,n}(\varepsilon)$ to $S_{m,n}$, we analyze the metric behavior of the inclusions $\iota_\varepsilon : S_{m,n} \hookrightarrow T_{m,n}(\varepsilon)$ as $\varepsilon \to 1$. We carry out our computations by reducing to the case that $\varepsilon \in |K \setminus \{0\}|$. In the case that K is discretely valued, this entails working with certain algebraic extensions K' of K and understanding the inclusion $S_{m,n}(E, K) \hookrightarrow S_{m,n}(E, K')$. The reader interested only in the case that K is algebraically closed may omit the complications arising from field extensions.

We are interested in studying properties of quotient rings $S_{m,n}/I$. We study such quotient rings by studying metric properties (e.g., pseudo-Cartesian and strict) of generating systems of submodules of $(S_{m,n})^\ell$, and how they transform under restriction maps to rational sub-polydiscs.

In Subsection 3.1, we introduce metric properties of generating systems of submodules of $(S_{m,n})^\ell$ and of $(\widetilde{S}_{m,n})^\ell$. In particular we introduce a valuation, the total value v, on $S_{m,n}$ which lifts the (ρ)-adic valuation on $\widetilde{S}_{m,n}$ and refines the Gauss norm on $S_{m,n}$. This allows us to formulate the "slicing" arguments whereby (ρ)-adic properties of $\widetilde{S}_{m,n}$ are seen to lift to $S_{m,n}$. The valuations $\|\cdot\|$ and v induce norms $\|\cdot\|_M$ and v_M on a quotient module $(S_{m,n})^\ell/M$. We prove a number of estimates.

In Subsection 3.2, we study restrictions to closed subpolydiscs. The main result is Theorem 3.2.3, which says that if ε is suitably large, then a strict generating system remains strict under restriction.

In Subsection 3.3, we transfer information from $T_{m,n}(\varepsilon)$ back to $S_{m,n}$. The main results are Theorem 3.3.1 and its corollaries, which show, roughly speaking, how to replace powers of ε with powers of (ρ) for ε near 1. More precisely, they establish a key relation between v_M and $\|\cdot\|_{\iota_\varepsilon(M)\cdot T_{m,n}(\varepsilon)}$ uniformly in ε for ε suitably large, which is used extensively in the rest of this paper. This is how we overcome the difficulties stemming from the failure of Noether normalization for $S_{m,n}$.

In Subsection 3.4 we study restrictions from $\Delta_{m,n}$ to certain disjoint unions of open subpolydiscs. When the centers of the polydiscs are K-rational, these maps have the form $\varphi : S_{m,n} \to \oplus_{j=0}^{r} S_{0,n+m}$. In the case of non-$K$-rational centers, the restriction maps are only slightly more complicated. We show in Theorems 3.4.3 and 3.4.6 that such restrictions are isometries in the residue norms derived from $\|\cdot\|$ and respectively I and $\varphi(I)$, provided the finite collection of open polydiscs is chosen appropriately. Theorems 3.4.3 and 3.4.6 will be used in Subsection 5.5 to derive the fact that on certain reduced quotients $S_{m,n}/I$, the residue and supremum norms are equivalent from the simpler case of reduced quotients $S_{0,n+m}/I$.

3.1. Strict and Pseudo-Cartesian Modules. — We introduce metric properties of generating systems of submodules of $(S_{m,n})^\ell$ and $(\widetilde{S}_{m,n})^\ell$ and their quotients. We introduce a valuation, the total value v, on $S_{m,n}$ which lifts the (ρ)-adic valuation on $\widetilde{S}_{m,n}$ and refines the Gauss norm on $S_{m,n}$. The lemmas of this subsection show how certain metric properties of generating systems of modules lift from residue modules and transform under maps and ground field extension.

Let (A, v) be a multiplicatively valued ring, and let (N, w) be a normed A-module; i.e.,

$$w(an) \leq v(a)w(n)$$

for all $a \in A$, $n \in N$. Let M be an A-submodule of N. A finite generating system $\{g_1, \ldots, g_r\}$ of M is called *w-strict* iff for all $f \in N$ there exist $a_1, \ldots, a_r \in A$ such that

$$\begin{aligned} & w(f) \geq \max_{1\leq i\leq r} v(a_i)w(g_i), \text{ and} \\ (3.1.1) \qquad & w\left(f - \sum_{i=1}^{r} a_i g_i\right) \leq w(f-h) \text{ for all } h \in M. \end{aligned}$$

The generating system $\{g_1, \ldots, g_r\}$ is called *w-pseudo-Cartesian* iff (3.1.1) is only assumed to hold for all $f \in M$; i.e., iff for all $f \in M$ there exist $a_1, \ldots, a_r \in A$ such that

$$\begin{aligned} w(f) &\geq \max_{1\leq i\leq r} v(a_i)w(g_i), \text{ and} \\ f &= \sum_{i=1}^{r} a_i g_i. \end{aligned}$$

An A-module $M \subset N$ is called *w-strict* (*w-pseudo-Cartesian*) iff it has a w-strict (w-pseudo-Cartesian) generating system. Usually, N will be a quotient of the ℓ-fold norm-direct sum of $S_{m,n}$.

Along with the Gauss norm, we will be interested primarily in two other valuations. One, the residue order, is a rank-one additive valuation on $\widetilde{S}_{m,n}$. The other, the total value, is a rank-two multiplicative valuation on $S_{m,n}$. These valuations are defined below.

Assume $n \geq 1$, and define the map $\widetilde{\mathrm{o}} : \widetilde{S}_{m,n} \to \mathbb{Z} \cup \{\infty\}$ as follows. Put $\widetilde{\mathrm{o}}(0) := \infty$, and for $f \in \widetilde{S}_{m,n} \setminus \{0\}$, put $\widetilde{\mathrm{o}}(f) := \ell$, where $f \in (\rho)^\ell \setminus (\rho)^{\ell+1}$. It will not lead to confusion if we also define the map $\widetilde{\mathrm{o}} : S_{m,n} \to \mathbb{Z} \cup \{\infty\}$ by $\widetilde{\mathrm{o}}(0) := \infty$, and for $f \in S_{m,n} \setminus \{0\}$, $\widetilde{\mathrm{o}}(f) := \widetilde{\mathrm{o}}((cf)^\sim)$, where $c \in K$ satisfies $\|cf\| = 1$. The map $\widetilde{\mathrm{o}}$ is called the *residue order*. The residue order is an additive valuation on $\widetilde{S}_{m,n}$.

Consider $(\mathbb{R}_+ \setminus \{0\})^2$ as an ordered group with coordinatewise multiplication and lexicographic order. Define a map $v : S_{m,n} \to (\mathbb{R}_+ \setminus \{0\})^2 \cup \{(0,0)\}$ as follows. Put $v(0) := (0,0)$, and for $f \in S_{m,n} \setminus \{0\}$, put

$$v(f) := \left(\|f\|, 2^{-\widetilde{\mathrm{o}}(f)}\right).$$

Then v is a multiplicative valuation on $S_{m,n}$, called the *total value*. Note that v extends the absolute value on K in an obvious sense.

The total value yields information on elements $f(\xi, \rho) \in S_{m,n}$ as $|\rho| \to 1$, in a sense to be made precise in Subsections 3.2 and 3.3. Our aim in this subsection is to establish an analogue of Corollary 2.2.6 for the total value. This analogue will be established by lifting a similar result for the residue order from the residue ring $\widetilde{S}_{m,n}$.

Let $M \subset (S_{m,n})^\ell$ be a submodule. Put $M^\circ := (S^\circ_{m,n})^\ell \cap M$ and let $\widetilde{M}$ be the image of M° under the canonical residue epimorphism $\sim: (S^\circ_{m,n})^\ell \to (\widetilde{S}_{m,n})^\ell$.

The next lemma establishes a basic lifting property of $\widetilde{\mathrm{o}}$-strict generating systems. The lemma ensures that the lifting behaves well with respect to restrictions. More precisely,

$$\|a_i(\xi, c \cdot \rho)\| = |c|^{\widetilde{\mathrm{o}}(a_i)} \|a_i\|$$

for any $c \in K^\circ \setminus \{0\}$ and any $a_i \in S_{m,n}$ that satisfies condition (i). Condition (ii) stems from the definition of strictness. And condition (iii) says that we've done the whole slice.

Lemma 3.1.1. — *Let M be a submodule of $(S_{m,n})^\ell$. Let $B \in \mathfrak{B}$ and let $\{g_1, \ldots, g_r\} \subset (B\langle\xi\rangle[[\rho]])^\ell \cap M$ satisfy $\|g_i\| = 1$ for $i = 1, \ldots, r$. Suppose $\{\widetilde{g}_1, \ldots, \widetilde{g}_r\}$ is an $\widetilde{\mathrm{o}}$-strict generating system of $\widetilde{M}$. Let $B = B_0 \supset B_1 \supset \cdots$ be the natural filtration of B and suppose $f \in (B_p\langle\xi\rangle[[\rho]])^\ell \setminus (B_{p+1}\langle\xi\rangle[[\rho]])^\ell$. Then there are $a_1, \ldots, a_r \in B_p\langle\xi\rangle[[\rho]]$ such that*

(i) *for $i = 1, \ldots, r$ if $a_i \neq 0$ then $a_i \in (\rho)^{\widetilde{\mathrm{o}}(a_i)} B_p\langle\xi\rangle[[\rho]] \setminus B_{p+1}\langle\xi\rangle[[\rho]]$,*
(ii) *$v(f) \geq \max_{1 \leq i \leq r} v(a_i g_i)$, and*
(iii) *if $v(f - h) < v(f - \sum_{i=1}^r a_i g_i)$ for some $h \in M$, then $\|f - \sum_{i=1}^r a_i g_i\| < \|f\|$.*

(When condition (i) *holds, to verify* (ii)*, it suffices to verify*

(ii)′ $\widetilde{\mathrm{o}}(f) \leq \min_{1 \leq i \leq r} \widetilde{\mathrm{o}}(a_i g_i)$,

since $a_1, \ldots, a_r \in B_p\langle\xi\rangle[\![\rho]\!]$.)

Proof. — Let $\pi_p : B_p \to \widetilde{B}_p \subset \widetilde{K}$ be the B-module residue epimorphism $a \mapsto (b_p^{-1}a)^\sim$ and write $\widetilde{K} = \widetilde{B}_p \oplus V$ for some $\widetilde{B}$-vector space V. Then

$$\widetilde{K}[\xi][[\rho]] = \widetilde{B}_p[\xi][[\rho]] \oplus V[\xi][[\rho]] \tag{3.1.2}$$

as $\widetilde{B}[\xi][[\rho]]$-modules, and $\widetilde{\mathrm{o}}(a+b) = \min\{\widetilde{\mathrm{o}}(a), \widetilde{\mathrm{o}}(b)\}$ when $a \in \widetilde{B}_p[\xi][[\rho]]$ and $b \in V[\xi][[\rho]]$. Since $\{\widetilde{g}_1, \ldots, \widetilde{g}_r\}$ is $\widetilde{\mathrm{o}}$-strict, there are $\widetilde{c}_1, \ldots, \widetilde{c}_r \in \widetilde{S}_{m,n}$ so that

$$\widetilde{\mathrm{o}}(\pi_p(f)) \leq \min_{1\leq i\leq r} \widetilde{\mathrm{o}}(\widetilde{c}_i\widetilde{g}_i) \quad \text{and} \quad \widetilde{\mathrm{o}}\left(\pi_p(f) - \sum_{i=1}^{r} \widetilde{c}_i\widetilde{g}_i\right) \geq \widetilde{\mathrm{o}}(f-h) \tag{3.1.3}$$

for all $h \in \widetilde{M}$.

By (3.1.2), we may write $\widetilde{c}_i = \widetilde{a}_i + \widetilde{b}_i$ where $\widetilde{a}_i \in \widetilde{B}_p[\xi][[\rho]]$ and $\widetilde{b}_i \in V[\xi][[\rho]]$, $1 \leq i \leq r$. Since $\widetilde{g}_1, \ldots, \widetilde{g}_r \in (\widetilde{B}[\xi][[\rho]])^\ell$, by (3.1.2)

$$\widetilde{\mathrm{o}}\left(\pi_p(f) - \sum \widetilde{a}_i\widetilde{g}_i\right) \geq \widetilde{\mathrm{o}}\left(\pi_p(f) - \sum \widetilde{c}_i\widetilde{g}_i\right) \text{ and}$$
$$\min_{1\leq i\leq r} \widetilde{\mathrm{o}}(\widetilde{a}_i\widetilde{g}_i) \geq \min_{1\leq i\leq r} \widetilde{\mathrm{o}}(\widetilde{c}_i\widetilde{g}_i).$$

Thus, (3.1.3) holds with $\widetilde{a}_i$ in place of $\widetilde{c}_i$. Now for any $\widetilde{a} \in \widetilde{B}_p[\xi][[\rho]]$, if $\widetilde{a} \neq 0$ then $\widetilde{a} \in (\rho)^{\widetilde{\mathrm{o}}(\widetilde{a})}\widetilde{B}_p[\xi][[\rho]]$. Hence there are $a_1, \ldots, a_r \in B_p\langle\xi\rangle[[\rho]]$ such that for $1 \leq i \leq r$, $\pi_p(a_i) = \widetilde{a}_i$, $a_i = 0$ if $\widetilde{a}_i = 0$ and $a_i \in (\rho)^{\widetilde{\mathrm{o}}(\widetilde{a}_i)}B_p\langle\xi\rangle[[\rho]]$ if $\widetilde{a}_i \neq 0$. It is clear that $a_1, \ldots, a_r$ satisfy the lemma. □

We show in Theorem 3.1.3 that every submodule of $(S_{m,n})^\ell$ is v-strict. In light of Lemma 3.1.1, the next lemma reduces this to showing that every submodule of $(\widetilde{S}_{m,n})^\ell$ is $\widetilde{\mathrm{o}}$-strict.

Lemma 3.1.2. — *Let M be a submodule of $(S_{m,n})^\ell$ and suppose $\{g_1, \ldots, g_r\} \subset M^\circ$ satisfies $\widetilde{g}_1, \ldots, \widetilde{g}_r \neq 0$. Then $\{g_1, \ldots, g_r\}$ is a v-strict generating system of M if and only if $\{\widetilde{g}_1, \ldots, \widetilde{g}_r\}$ is an $\widetilde{\mathrm{o}}$-strict generating system of $\widetilde{M}$. Moreover*

(i) *if $\{g_1, \ldots, g_r\}$ is v-strict and $f, g_1, \ldots, g_r \in (B\langle\xi\rangle[\![\rho]\!])^\ell$ then there are $h_1, \ldots, h_r \in B\langle\xi\rangle[\![\rho]\!]$ such that*

$$v\left(f - \sum_{i=1}^{r} h_ig_i\right) \leq v(f-h)$$

for all $h \in M$ and

$$v(f) \geq \max_{1\leq i\leq r} v(h_ig_i),$$

and

(ii) *if $\{\widetilde{g}_1, \ldots, \widetilde{g}_r\}$ is $\widetilde{\mathrm{o}}$-strict and $\widetilde{f}, \widetilde{g}_1, \ldots, \widetilde{g}_r \in (\widetilde{B}[\xi][\![\rho]\!])^\ell$ then there are $\widetilde{h}_1, \ldots, \widetilde{h}_r \in \widetilde{B}[\xi][\![\rho]\!]$ such that*

$$\widetilde{\mathrm{o}}\left(\widetilde{f} - \sum_{i=1}^{r} \widetilde{h}_i\widetilde{g}_i\right) \geq \widetilde{\mathrm{o}}(\widetilde{f} - \widetilde{h})$$

for all $\widetilde{h} \in \widetilde{M}$ *and*

$$\widetilde{\mathrm{o}}(\widetilde{f}) \leq \min_{1\leq i\leq r} \widetilde{\mathrm{o}}(\widetilde{h}_i\widetilde{g}_i).$$

Proof

($\Rightarrow$) Let $\widetilde{f} \in (\widetilde{S}_{m,n})^\ell \setminus \{0\}$ and lift $\widetilde{f}$ to an element $f \in (S^\circ_{m,n})^\ell$. Find $a_1, \dots, a_r \in S^\circ_{m,n}$ such that $v(f) \geq \max_{1\leq i\leq r} v(a_i g_i)$ and

$$v\left(f - \sum_{i=1}^r a_i g_i\right) \leq v(f-h) \tag{3.1.4}$$

for every $h \in M$. Since $\|f\| = 1$, we must have that

$$\widetilde{\mathrm{o}}(f) \leq \min\left\{\widetilde{\mathrm{o}}(a_i g_i) : \|a_i g_i\| = 1\right\}.$$

Thus $\widetilde{\mathrm{o}}(f) \leq \min_{1\leq i\leq r} \widetilde{\mathrm{o}}(\widetilde{a}_i\widetilde{g}_i)$. If $\|f - \sum_{i=1}^r a_i g_i\| < 1$ then $\widetilde{f} = \sum_{i=1}^r \widetilde{a}_i\widetilde{g}_i \in \widetilde{M}$ and we are done. Otherwise, assume $\|f - \sum_{i=1}^r a_i g_i\| = 1$. Let $\widetilde{h} \in \widetilde{M}$ and lift $\widetilde{h}$ to $h \in M^\circ$. Hence, by (3.1.4), $\|f - h\| = 1$ and

$$\widetilde{\mathrm{o}}\left(\widetilde{f} - \sum_{i=1}^r \widetilde{a}_i\widetilde{g}_i\right) = \widetilde{\mathrm{o}}\left(f - \sum_{i=1}^r a_i g_i\right) \geq \widetilde{\mathrm{o}}(f-h) = \widetilde{\mathrm{o}}(\widetilde{f} - \widetilde{h}),$$

and we have proved that $\{\widetilde{g}_1, \dots, \widetilde{g}_r\}$ is $\widetilde{\mathrm{o}}$-strict.

($\Leftarrow$) Parts (i) and (ii), as well as ($\Leftarrow$) follow immediately from Lemma 3.1.1 using the facts that $\|S_{m,n}\| = |K|$, $|B\setminus\{0\}| \subset \mathbb{R}_+ \setminus \{0\}$ is discrete and $B\langle\xi\rangle[[\rho]]$ is complete in $\|\cdot\|$ for every $B \in \mathfrak{B}$. □

Now the proof of Theorem 3.1.3 reduces to a computation involving the Artin-Rees Lemma for the (ρ)-adic topology on $(\widetilde{S}_{m,n})^\ell$.

Theorem 3.1.3. — *Each submodule of* $(S_{m,n})^\ell$ *is* v*-strict. Each submodule of* $(\widetilde{S}_{m,n})^\ell$ *is* $\widetilde{\mathrm{o}}$*-strict.*

Proof. — By Lemma 3.1.2, we need only prove the last assertion. Let $M \subset (\widetilde{S}_{m,n})^\ell$ be a submodule.

***Claim* (A).** — *If* $\{g_1, \dots, g_r\}$ *is an* $\widetilde{\mathrm{o}}$*-pseudo-Cartesian generating system of* M *then it is* $\widetilde{\mathrm{o}}$*-strict.*

The ideal (ρ) is contained in the Jacobson radical of $\widetilde{S}_{m,n} = \varinjlim \widetilde{B}[\xi][[\rho]]$. Hence by the Krull Intersection Theorem ([**25**, Theorem 8.10]), the $\widetilde{\mathrm{o}}$-topology on $(\widetilde{S}_{m,n})^\ell$ is separated and M is a closed set.

Let $f \in (\widetilde{S}_{m,n})^\ell$. Since M is closed and since $\widetilde{\mathrm{o}}((\widetilde{S}_{m,n})^\ell) = \mathbb{N} \cup \{\infty\}$ there is some $f_0 \in M$ such that

$$\widetilde{\mathrm{o}}(f - f_0) \geq \widetilde{\mathrm{o}}(f - h)$$

for all $h \in M$. Putting $h = 0$ in the above we have $\widetilde{o}(f_0) \geq \widetilde{o}(f)$ by the ultrametric inequality. There are $a_1, \ldots, a_r \in \widetilde{S}_{m,n}$ such that

$$\widetilde{o}(f_0) = \min_{1 \leq i \leq r} \widetilde{o}(a_i g_i) \quad \text{and} \quad f_0 = \sum_{i=1}^{r} a_i g_i.$$

Thus, we have that $\widetilde{o}(f) \leq \widetilde{o}(f_0) = \min_{1 \leq i \leq r} \widetilde{o}(a_i g_i)$ and

$$\widetilde{o}\left(f - \sum_{i=1}^{r} a_i g_i\right) \geq \widetilde{o}(f - h)$$

for all $h \in M$. This proves the claim.

For $i \in \mathbb{N}$, put

$$M_i := \{f \in M : \widetilde{o}(f) \geq i\}.$$

We have $M = M_0 \supset M_1 \supset \cdots$. By the Artin-Rees Lemma ([**25**, Theorem 8.5]) there is some $c \in \mathbb{N}$ such that for all $i > c$

$$M_i = (\rho)^{i-c} M_c. \tag{3.1.5}$$

Each quotient M_i/M_{i+1} is a finite module over $\widetilde{S}_{m,n}/(\rho) = \widetilde{T}_m$. Find $r \in \mathbb{N}$ sufficiently large so that each M_i/M_{i+1} can be generated by r elements for $0 \leq i \leq c$. By $\pi_i : M_i \to M_i/M_{i+1}$, denote the canonical projection. For each $1 \leq i \leq c$, choose $g_{ij} \in M_i \setminus M_{i+1}$, $1 \leq j \leq r$, so that $\pi_i(g_{i1}), \ldots, \pi(g_{ir})$ generate the $\widetilde{T}_m$-module M_i/M_{i+1}.

***Claim* (B).** — *$\{g_{ij}\}$ is an $\widetilde{o}$-strict generating system of M.*

By Claim A, it suffices to show that $\{g_{ij}\}$ is an $\widetilde{o}$-pseudo-Cartesian generating system.

Let $f \in M$, and let $B \in \mathfrak{B}$ be such that $\{f\} \cup \{g_{ij}\} \subset (\widetilde{B}[\xi][[\rho]])^\ell$. Write $\widetilde{K} = \widetilde{B} \oplus V$ for some $\widetilde{B}$-vector space V. Then

$$\widetilde{K}[\xi][[\rho]] = \widetilde{B}[\xi][[\rho]] \oplus V[\xi][[\rho]] \tag{3.1.6}$$

as $\widetilde{B}[\xi][\![\rho]\!]$-modules, and $\widetilde{o}(a+b) = \min\{\widetilde{o}(a), \widetilde{o}(b)\}$ when $a \in \widetilde{B}[\xi][\![\rho]\!]$ and $b \in V[\xi][[\rho]]$. Put $N := (\widetilde{B}[\xi][[\rho]])^\ell \cap M$; and for $i \in \mathbb{N}$, put

$$N_i := \{h \in N : \widetilde{o}(h) \geq i\} = (\widetilde{B}[\xi][[\rho]])^\ell \cap M_i.$$

It follows from (3.1.6) that $\pi_i(g_{i1}), \ldots, \pi_i(g_{ir})$ generate the $\widetilde{B}[\xi]$-module N_i/N_{i+1} for $0 \leq i \leq c$. Furthermore, by (3.1.5), $\{\pi_i(\rho^\nu g_{cj})\}_{1 \leq j \leq r, |\nu| = i-c}$ generates the $\widetilde{B}[\xi]$-module N_i/N_{i+1} for $i > c$. Since $\widetilde{o}(g_{ij}) = i$ and since $\widetilde{B}[\xi][[\rho]]$ is complete in $\widetilde{o}$, the claim follows. □

Lemma 3.1.4. — *Let M be a submodule of $(S_{m,n})^\ell$ and suppose that $\{g_1, \dots, g_r\} \subset M^\circ$ satisfy $\widetilde{g}_1, \dots, \widetilde{g}_r \neq 0$. Then $\{g_1, \dots, g_r\}$ is a $\|\cdot\|$-strict generating system of M if, and only if, $\{\widetilde{g}_1, \dots, \widetilde{g}_r\}$ generate $\widetilde{M}$. In particular, since $\widetilde{S}_{m,n}$ is Noetherian, each submodule of $(S_{m,n})^\ell$ is $\|\cdot\|$-strict.*

Proof. — As in Lemmas 3.1.1 and 3.1.2. □

It follows from Theorem 3.1.3 and Lemma 3.1.4 that we may make the following definitions.

Definition 3.1.5 (cf. Definition 2.2.7). — Let M be a submodule of $(S_{m,n})^\ell$. For $f \in (S_{m,n})^\ell$ we define the *residue norms*

$$\begin{aligned} v_M(f) &:= \inf\{v(f-h) \colon h \in M\}, \text{ and} \\ \|f\|_M &:= \inf\{\|f-h\| \colon h \in M\}. \end{aligned}$$

There is some $h \in M$ such that $v_M(f) = v(f-h)$ and $\|f\|_M = \|f-h\|$. Let M be a submodule of $(\widetilde{S}_{m,n})^\ell$. For $f \in (\widetilde{S}_{m,n})^\ell$ we define

$$\widetilde{o}_M(f) := \sup\{\widetilde{o}(f-h) \colon h \in M\}.$$

There is some $h \in M$ such that $\widetilde{o}_M(f) = \widetilde{o}(f-h)$.

It follows from Lemma 3.1.4 that $\|\cdot\|_M$ is a norm on $(S_{m,n})^\ell/M$. If E is such that $S_{m,n} = S_{m,n}(E,K)$ is complete in $\|\cdot\|$ (see Theorem 2.1.3) then $(S_{m,n})^\ell/M$ is complete in $\|\cdot\|_M$.

The following lemma is an application of Theorem 3.1.3. It is used in Theorem 2.3.8. In the statement of the lemma, the set A will usually consist of the coefficients f_i of a power series

$$F = \sum_{i \geq 0} f_i(\xi, \rho)\lambda^i \in B\langle \xi, \lambda \rangle [\![\rho]\!] \text{ (respectively, } B\langle \xi \rangle [\![\rho, \lambda]\!]).$$

The lemma allows us to write all the coefficients of F as linear combinations of the first few:

$$F = \sum_{i \geq 0} \sum_{j=1}^{r} h_{ij} f_j \lambda^i$$

in such a way that each power series

$$F_j := \sum_{i \geq 0} h_{ij}\lambda^i \in B'\langle \xi, \lambda \rangle [\![\rho]\!] \text{ (respectively, } B'\langle \xi \rangle [\![\rho, \lambda]\!]),$$

for some $B \subset B' \in \mathfrak{B}$. Although $B\langle \xi \rangle [\![\rho]\!]$ is not in general Noetherian, we are still able to do this. The estimate in the lemma is sufficient to guarantee convergence of F_j in the $(B_1 + (\rho))$-adic (respectively, $(B_1 + (\rho, \lambda))$-adic) topology.

Lemma 3.1.6. — *Let* $B \in \mathfrak{B}$ *and* $A \subset B\langle\xi\rangle[\![\rho]\!]$. *Then there are*

$$f_1, \ldots, f_r \in A, \quad \ell_0, c, e \in \mathbb{N}, \text{ and } B \subset B' \in \mathfrak{B}$$

with the following property. Let $B' = B'_0 \supset B'_1 \supset \cdots$ *be the natural filtration of* B'. *For each* $f \in A$ *there are* $h_1, \ldots, h_r \in B'\langle\xi\rangle[\![\rho]\!]$ *such that*

$$f = \sum_{i=1}^{r} h_i f_i.$$

If, in addition,

$$f \in B'_\ell\langle\xi\rangle[\![\rho]\!] + (\rho)^{2\ell e+c} B'\langle\xi\rangle[\![\rho]\!]$$

for some $\ell > \ell_0$, *then we may choose* $h_1, \ldots, h_r$ *such that*

$$h_1, \ldots, h_r \in B'_\ell\langle\xi\rangle[\![\rho]\!] + (\rho)^{\ell e} B'\langle\xi\rangle[\![\rho]\!].$$

Proof. — Put $I := A \cdot S_{m,n}$, and let $\{g_1, \ldots, g_d\} \subset S_{m,n} \setminus \{0\}$ be a v-strict generating system of I. Since $S_{m,n}$ is Noetherian, there are $f_1, \ldots, f_s \in A$ and $h_{ij} \in S_{m,n}$ such that

$$g_i = \sum_{j=1}^{s} h_{ij} f_j, \quad 1 \le i \le d.$$

Without loss of generality, we may assume that all $g_i, h_{ij} \in S^\circ_{m,n}$ and

$$\|g_1\| = \cdots = \|g_d\| = |\alpha|,$$

for some $\alpha \in K^\circ \setminus \{0\}$. Find $B \subset B' \in \mathfrak{B}$ such that

$$\frac{1}{\alpha} g_1, \ldots, \frac{1}{\alpha} g_d \in B'\langle\xi\rangle[\![\rho]\!].$$

Let $B' = B'_0 \supset B'_1, \ldots$ be the natural filtration of B' and find ℓ_0 so that

$$\alpha \in B'_{\ell_0} \setminus B'_{\ell_0+1}.$$

Put

$$e := \max_{1 \le i \le d} \widetilde{\mathrm{o}}(g_i).$$

To find a suitable $c \in \mathbb{N}$, consider the ideal

$$J := A \cdot (B'/B'_{\ell_0})[\xi][\![\rho]\!].$$

The ring $(B'/B'_{\ell_0})[\xi][\![\rho]\!]$ is Noetherian, so the Artin–Rees Lemma, [**25**, Theorem 8.5], yields a $c \in \mathbb{N}$ such that for all $q \ge c$,

$$J \cap (\rho)^q \subset (\rho)^{q-c} \cdot J.$$

Find $f_{s+1}, \ldots, f_r \in A$ so that the images of $f_1, \ldots, f_r$ in $(B'/B'_{\ell_0})[\xi][\![\rho]\!]$ generate J.

Let $f \in A$ with

$$f \in B'_\ell\langle\xi\rangle[\![\rho]\!] + (\rho)^{2\ell e+c} B'\langle\xi\rangle[\![\rho]\!].$$

There are $H_1, \dots, H_r \in B'\langle\xi\rangle[\![\rho]\!]$ such that

$$f - \sum_{i=1}^{r} H_i f_i =: f' \in B'_{\ell_0}\langle\xi\rangle[\![\rho]\!].$$

By choice of c, if $\ell > \ell_0$, we may assume that

$$H_1, \dots, H_r \in (\rho)^{2\ell e} \cdot B'\langle\xi\rangle[\![\rho]\!].$$

We have

$$f' \in B'_{\ell_0}\langle\xi\rangle[\![\rho]\!]$$

and if $\ell > \ell_0$, we have moreover that

$$f' \in B'_{\ell}\langle\xi\rangle[\![\rho]\!] + (\rho)^{2\ell e} B'_{\ell_0}\langle\xi\rangle[\![\rho]\!].$$

Let

$$\tau_{\ell_0} : B'_{\ell_0} \to \widetilde{B}'_{\ell_0} \subset \widetilde{K}$$

be any residue epimorphism. Note, by choice of B', that

$$\{(\alpha^{-1}g_1)^{\sim}, \dots, (\alpha^{-1}g_d)^{\sim}\} \subset \widetilde{B}'[\xi][\![\rho]\!]$$

is an $\widetilde{\mathrm{o}}$–strict generating system of $\widetilde{I}$. Thus by Lemma 3.1.2, there are

$$\widetilde{H}'_{11}, \widetilde{H}'_{21}, \dots, \widetilde{H}'_{d1} \in \widetilde{B}'_{\ell_0}[\xi][\![\rho]\!]$$

such that

$$\pi_{\ell_0}(f') = \sum_{i=1}^{d} \widetilde{H}'_{i1}(\alpha^{-1}g_i)^{\sim}.$$

If $\ell > \ell_0$, we have, moreover, that

$$\widetilde{H}'_{11}, \dots, \widetilde{H}'_{d1} \in (\rho)^{2\ell e - c}\widetilde{B}'_{\ell_0}[\xi][\![\rho]\!].$$

Lift $\widetilde{H}'_{11}, \dots, \widetilde{H}'_{d1}$ to elements $H'_{11}, \dots, H'_{d1} \in B'_{\ell_0}\langle\xi\rangle[\![\rho]\!]$ such that for each i,

$$H'_{i1} \in (\rho)^{\widetilde{\mathrm{o}}(\widetilde{H}'_{i1})} B'_{\ell_0}\langle\xi\rangle[\![\rho]\!].$$

Put

$$f'' := f' - \sum_{i=1}^{d} H'_{i1} g_i \in B'_{\ell_0+1}\langle\xi\rangle[\![\rho]\!],$$

and observe that if $\ell > \ell_0$

$$f'' \in B'_{\ell}\langle\xi\rangle[\![\rho]\!] + (\rho)^{2\ell e - c} B'_{\ell_0+1}\langle\xi\rangle[\![\rho]\!].$$

Iterating this procedure $\ell - \ell_0$ times, we obtain sequences

$$H'_{ij} \in (\rho)^{2\ell e - jc} B'_{\ell_0+j}\langle\xi\rangle[\![\rho]\!]$$

such that

$$f''' := f' - \sum_{i=1}^{d} \sum_{j=1}^{\ell-\ell_0} H'_{ij} g_i \in B'_\ell\langle\xi\rangle[\![\rho]\!].$$

Finally, since $\{g_1, \ldots, g_d\}$ is a $\|\cdot\|$-strict generating system for I, by Lemma 3.1.2, there are $H''_1, \ldots, H''_d \in B'_\ell\langle\xi\rangle[\![\rho]\!]$ such that

$$f''' = \sum H''_i g_i.$$

Put

$$h_i := H_i + \sum_{p,j} (H'_{pj} + H''_p) h_{pi}.$$

□

The next five lemmas give criteria under which a generating system of a module is strict and under which strictness is preserved by contractive homomorphisms and field extensions. For technical reasons, we work over a quotient ring $S_{m,n}/I$. The modules M we consider will carry the residue norm $\|\cdot\|_I$. We will also consider residue modules $\widetilde{M}$ (see Definition 2.2.8).

Lemma 3.1.7. — *Let M be a submodule of $(S_{m,n})^\ell/N$ and suppose that $g_1, \ldots, g_r \in M^\circ$ satisfy $\widetilde{g}_1, \ldots, \widetilde{g}_r \neq 0$. Then:*

(i) *$\{g_1, \ldots, g_r\}$ is a $\|\cdot\|_N$-strict generating system of M if, and only if, $\{\widetilde{g}_1, \ldots, \widetilde{g}_r\}$ generates $\widetilde{M}$.*

(ii) *$\{g_1, \ldots, g_r\}$ is a v_N-strict generating system of M if, and only if, $\{\widetilde{g}_1, \ldots, \widetilde{g}_r\}$ is an $\widetilde{o}_N$-strict generating system of $\widetilde{M}$.*

Hence each submodule of $(S_{m,n})^\ell/N$ is $\|\cdot\|_N$-strict and v_N-strict. Each submodule of $(\widetilde{S}_{m,n})^\ell/\widetilde{N}$ is $\widetilde{o}_{\widetilde{N}}$-strict.

Proof

(i) ($\Rightarrow$) Lift an element $\widetilde{f} \in \widetilde{M} \setminus \{0\}$ to an element $f \in M$ with $\|f\|_N = 1$. Since $\{g_1, \ldots, g_r\}$ is $\|\cdot\|_N$-strict, there are $h_1, \ldots, h_r \in S_{m,n}$ with

$$f = \textstyle\sum_{i=1}^r g_i h_i \quad \text{and}$$
$$1 = \|f\|_N = \max_{1 \le i \le r} \|g_i\|_N \|h_i\| = \max_{1 \le i \le r} \|h_i\|.$$

Hence $\widetilde{f} = \sum_{i=1}^r \widetilde{g}_i \widetilde{h}_i$; i.e., $\{\widetilde{g}_1, \ldots, \widetilde{g}_r\}$ generates $\widetilde{M}$.

($\Leftarrow$) Put

$$\mathcal{M} := \{f \in (S_{m,n})^\ell : f + N \in M\}.$$

Find $A_1, \ldots, A_s \in N^\circ$ and $G_1, \ldots, G_r \in \mathcal{M}$ such that $\{\widetilde{A}_1, \ldots, \widetilde{A}_s\}$ generates $\widetilde{N}$ and $g_i = G_i + N$, $1 \le i \le r$. By Lemma 3.1.4, we may assume that $\|G_i\| = \|g_i\|_N = 1$, $1 \le i \le r$. It follows that $\{\widetilde{A}_1, \ldots, \widetilde{A}_s, \widetilde{G}_1, \ldots, \widetilde{G}_r\}$ generates $\widetilde{\mathcal{M}}$; hence by Lemma 3.1.4, $\{A_1, \ldots, A_s, G_1, \ldots, G_r\}$ is a $\|\cdot\|$-strict generating system of $\mathcal{M}$.

Let $f \in M$. By Lemma 3.1.4, there is a $F \in \mathcal{M}$ such that $f = F + N$ and $\|F\| = \|f\|_N$. We may write

$$F = \sum_{i=1}^{r} G_i h_i + \sum_{i=1}^{s} A_i h_{r+i}$$

for some $h_1, \ldots, h_{r+s} \in S_{m,n}$ with

$$\|F\| = \|f\|_N = \max_{1 \le i \le r+s} \|h_i\|.$$

Hence

$$f = \sum_{i=1}^{r} g_i h_i \quad \text{and} \quad \|f\|_N = \max_{1 \le i \le r} \|g_i\|_N \|h_i\|,$$

as desired.

(ii) ($\Rightarrow$) Lift an element $\widetilde{f} \in \widetilde{M} \setminus \{0\}$ to an element $f \in M$ with $\|f\|_N = 1$. Since $\{g_1, \ldots, g_r\}$ is v_N-strict, there are $h_1, \ldots, h_r \in S^{\circ}_{m,n}$ such that

$$(3.1.7) \qquad \begin{aligned} &v_N(f) \ge \max_{1 \le i \le r} v_N(g_i) \cdot v(h_i) \quad \text{and} \\ &v_N\left(f - \sum_{i=1}^{r} g_i h_i\right) \le v_N(f - h) \end{aligned}$$

for every $h \in M$. Since $v_N(f) = (\|f\|_N, 2^{-\widetilde{\mathrm{o}}_{\widetilde{N}}(f)})$ and $\|f\|_N = 1$, we have

$$\widetilde{\mathrm{o}}_{\widetilde{N}}(f) \le \min\{\widetilde{\mathrm{o}}_{\widetilde{N}}(g_i) + \widetilde{\mathrm{o}}(h_i) \colon \|h_i\| = 1\}.$$

Thus, $\widetilde{\mathrm{o}}_{\widetilde{N}}(\widetilde{f}) \le \min_{1 \le i \le r}(\widetilde{\mathrm{o}}_{\widetilde{N}}(\widetilde{g}_i) + \widetilde{\mathrm{o}}(\widetilde{h}_i))$. If $\|f - \sum_{i=1}^{r} g_i h_i\|_N < 1$ then $\widetilde{f} = \sum_{i=1}^{r} \widetilde{g}_i \widetilde{h}_i \in \widetilde{M}$, and we are done. Otherwise, $\|f - \sum_{i=1}^{r} g_i h_i\| = 1$. Let $\widetilde{h} \in \widetilde{M}$ and lift $\widetilde{h}$ to an element $h \in M^{\circ}$ with $\|h\|_N = 1$. By (3.1.7), $\|f - h\|_N = 1$ and

$$\widetilde{\mathrm{o}}_{\widetilde{N}}\left(\widetilde{f} - \sum_{i=1}^{r} \widetilde{g}_i \widetilde{h}_i\right) = \widetilde{\mathrm{o}}_N\left(f - \sum_{i=1}^{r} g_i h_i\right) \ge \widetilde{\mathrm{o}}_{\widetilde{N}}(f - h) = \widetilde{\mathrm{o}}_{\widetilde{N}}(\widetilde{f} - \widetilde{h}),$$

and we are done.

($\Leftarrow$) Put

$$\mathcal{M} := \{f \in (S_{m,n})^{\ell} \colon f + N \in M\}.$$

Find $A_1, \ldots, A_s \in N^{\circ}$ and $G_1, \ldots, G_r \in \mathcal{M}$ such that $\{\widetilde{A}_1, \ldots, \widetilde{A}_s\}$ is an $\widetilde{\mathrm{o}}$-strict generating system of $\widetilde{N}$ and $g_i = G_i + N$, $1 \le i \le r$. By Theorem 3.1.3, we may assume that $v(G_i) = v_N(g_i)$, $1 \le i \le r$. As in part (i), it suffices to show that $\{A_1, \ldots, A_s, G_1, \ldots, G_r\}$ is a v-strict generating system of $\mathcal{M}$. By Lemma 3.1.2, this reduces to showing that $\{\widetilde{A}_1, \ldots, \widetilde{A}_s, \widetilde{G}_1, \ldots, \widetilde{G}_r\}$ is an $\widetilde{\mathrm{o}}$-strict generating system of $\widetilde{\mathcal{M}}$. Let $F \in (\widetilde{S}_{m,n})^{\ell}$ and put $f := F + \widetilde{N}$. Since $\{\widetilde{g}_1, \ldots, \widetilde{g}_r\}$ is an $\widetilde{\mathrm{o}}_{\widetilde{N}}$-strict generating system of $\widetilde{M}$, there are $h_1, \ldots, h_r \in \widetilde{S}_{m,n}$ such that

$$\widetilde{\mathrm{o}}_{\widetilde{N}}(f) \leq \min_{1\leq i\leq r} (\widetilde{\mathrm{o}}_{\widetilde{N}}(g_i) + \widetilde{\mathrm{o}}(h_i)) \quad \text{and}$$

$$\widetilde{\mathrm{o}}_{\widetilde{N}}\left(f - \sum_{i=1}^{r} g_i h_i\right) \geq \widetilde{\mathrm{o}}_{\widetilde{N}}(f - h)$$

for every $h \in \widetilde{M}$. Since $\{\widetilde{A}_1, \ldots, \widetilde{A}_s\}$ is an $\widetilde{\mathrm{o}}$-strict generating system, there are $h_{r+1}, \ldots, h_{r+s} \in \widetilde{S}_{m,n}$ such that

$$\widetilde{\mathrm{o}}\left(F - \sum_{i=1}^{r} \widetilde{G}_i h_i\right) \leq \min_{1\leq i\leq s} \widetilde{\mathrm{o}}(\widetilde{A}_i h_{r+i}) \quad \text{and}$$

$$\widetilde{\mathrm{o}}_{\widetilde{N}}\left(f - \sum_{i=1}^{r} g_i h_i\right) = \widetilde{\mathrm{o}}\left(F - \sum_{i=1}^{r} \widetilde{G}_i h_i - \sum_{i=1}^{s} \widetilde{A}_i h_{r+i}\right).$$

Let $H \in \widetilde{\mathcal{M}}$, and put $h := H + \widetilde{N}$. We have

$$\begin{aligned} \widetilde{\mathrm{o}}\left(F - \sum_{i=1}^{r} \widetilde{G}_i h_i - \sum_{i=1}^{s} \widetilde{A}_i h_{r+i}\right) &= \widetilde{\mathrm{o}}_{\widetilde{N}}\left(f - \sum_{i=1}^{r} g_i h_i\right) \\ &\geq \widetilde{\mathrm{o}}_{\widetilde{N}}(f - h) \\ &\geq \widetilde{\mathrm{o}}(F - H), \end{aligned}$$

as desired.

To prove the last assertions of the Lemma, observe that by part (i), each submodule of $(S_{m,n})^\ell/N$ is $\|\cdot\|_N$-strict because $(\widetilde{S}_{m,n})^\ell/\widetilde{N}$ is Noetherian (Corollary 2.2.2). The fact that each submodule M of $(\widetilde{S}_{m,n})^\ell/\widetilde{N}$ is $\widetilde{\mathrm{o}}_{\widetilde{N}}$-strict follows from the fact that we may include in an $\widetilde{\mathrm{o}}$-strict generating system of the inverse image submodule $\mathcal{M}$ of $(\widetilde{S}_{m,n})^\ell$ an $\widetilde{\mathrm{o}}$-strict generating system of $\widetilde{N}$ (use Theorem 3.1.3). Finally, to see that each submodule of $(S_{m,n})^\ell/N$ is v_N-strict, we apply part (ii). □

Lemma 3.1.8. — *Let M be a submodule of $(S_{m,n})^\ell/N$ and let $g_1, \ldots, g_r$ be generators with $\|g_1\|_N = \cdots = \|g_r\|_N = 1$. Put*

$$\Phi := \{(h_1, \ldots, h_r) \in (S_{m,n})^r : \sum_{i=1}^{r} g_i h_i = 0\} \quad \textit{and}$$

$$\Psi := \{(h_1, \ldots, h_r) \in (\widetilde{S}_{m,n})^r : \sum_{i=1}^{r} \widetilde{g}_i h_i = 0\}.$$

Then $\{g_1, \ldots, g_r\}$ is a $\|\cdot\|_N$-strict generating system of M if, and only if, $\widetilde{\Phi} = \Psi$.

Proof

($\Rightarrow$) Assume $\{g_1,\dots,g_r\}$ is a $\|\cdot\|_N$-strict generating system of M. Let $\widetilde{h} = (\widetilde{h}_1,\dots,\widetilde{h}_r) \in \Psi \setminus \{0\}$ and find $h \in (S_{m,n})^r$ that lifts $\widetilde{h}$. We have:

$$\left\| \sum_{i=1}^{r} g_i h_i \right\|_N < \max_{1\le i\le r} \|h_i\|.$$

Since $\{g_1,\dots,g_r\}$ is $\|\cdot\|_N$-strict, there is an $h' = (h'_1,\dots,h'_r) \in (S_{m,n})^r$ such that

$$\sum_{i=1}^{r} g_i h_i = \sum_{i=1}^{r} g_i h'_i \text{ and } \max_{1\le i\le r} \|h'_i\| = \left\| \sum_{i=1}^{r} g_i h_i \right\|_N < \max_{1\le i\le r} \|h_i\| = 1.$$

Put $H := h - h' \in \Phi$, and note that $\widetilde{H} = \widetilde{h}$. This proves $\widetilde{\Phi} = \Psi$.

($\Leftarrow$) By Lemma 3.1.4, there are $G_1,\dots,G_r \in (S_{m,n})^\ell$ with $\|G_i\| = 1$ and $g_i = G_i + N$, $1 \le i \le r$. Put

$$\mathcal{M} := \{f \in (S_{m,n})^\ell : f + N \in M\}.$$

Let $\{A_1,\dots,A_s\}$ be a $\|\cdot\|$-strict generating system of N with $\|A_1\| = \cdots = \|A_s\| = 1$. Since M has a $\|\cdot\|_N$-strict generating system by Lemma 3.1.7, it suffices to show that $\{g_1,\dots,g_r\}$ is $\|\cdot\|_N$-pseudo-Cartesian. Indeed, since for any $f \in M$ there is an $F \in \mathcal{M}$ with $f = F + N$ and $\|F\| = \|f\|_N$, it suffices to show that $\{G_1,\dots,G_r,A_1,\dots,A_s\}$ is a $\|\cdot\|$-pseudo-Cartesian generating system of $\mathcal{M}$.

Let $F \in \mathcal{M}$ and write

$$F = \sum_{i=1}^{r} G_i h_i + \sum_{i=1}^{s} A_i h_{r+i} \tag{3.1.8}$$

for some $h_1,\dots,h_{r+s} \in S_{m,n}$. Since $\{A_1,\dots,A_s\}$ is $\|\cdot\|$-strict, we may always assume that

$$\max_{r+1\le i\le r+s} \|h_i\| \le \max\{\|F\|, \|h_1\|,\dots,\|h_r\|\}. \tag{3.1.9}$$

If $\|F\| \ge \max_{1\le i\le r} \|h_i\|$, then by (3.1.9) we are done. Therefore, assume that

$$0 \ne \|F\| < \max_{1\le i\le r} \|h_i\| \le 1. \tag{3.1.10}$$

Let $\{C_1,\dots,C_t\}$ be a $\|\cdot\|$-strict generating system of Φ with $\|C_1\| = \cdots = \|C_t\| = 1$. Find $B \in \mathfrak{B}$ such that

$$\begin{gathered} h_1,\dots,h_{r+s} \in B\langle\xi\rangle[\![\rho]\!], \\ G_1,\dots,G_r,A_1,\dots,A_s \in (B\langle\xi\rangle[\![\rho]\!])^\ell, \\ C_1,\dots,C_t \in (B\langle\xi\rangle[\![\rho]\!])^r. \end{gathered}$$

Using (3.1.9) and the fact that $|B \setminus \{0\}|$ is discrete, it suffices to find $h'_i \in B\langle\xi\rangle[\![\rho]\!]$ with

$$F = \sum_{i=1}^{r} G_i h'_i + \sum_{i=1}^{s} A_i h'_{r+i} \quad \text{and} \qquad (3.1.11)$$
$$\max_{1\le i\le r} \|h'_i\| < \max_{1\le i\le r} \|h_i\|.$$

Let $B = B_0 \supset B_1 \supset \cdots$ be the natural filtration of B, and suppose

$$(h_1, \ldots, h_r) \in (B_p\langle\xi\rangle[\![\rho]\!])^r \setminus (B_{p+1}\langle\xi\rangle[\![\rho]\!])^r.$$

By (3.1.9),

$$h_1, \ldots, h_{r+s} \in B_p\langle\xi\rangle[\![\rho]\!].$$

Let

$$\pi_p\colon B_p \to \widetilde{B}_p = (b_p^{-1}B_p)^{\sim} \subset \widetilde{K}$$

be the projection.

Write $\widetilde{K} = \widetilde{B}_p \oplus V$ for some $\widetilde{B}$-vector space V. Then

$$\widetilde{K}[\xi][\![\rho]\!] = \widetilde{B}_p[\xi][\![\rho]\!] \oplus V[\xi][\![\rho]\!] \qquad (3.1.12)$$

as $\widetilde{B}[\xi][\![\rho]\!]$-modules. By (3.1.8) and (3.1.10),

$$\pi_p((h_1, \ldots, h_r)) \in \Psi = \widetilde{\Phi}.$$

Thus for some $\widetilde{e}_1, \ldots, \widetilde{e}_t \in \widetilde{K}[\xi][\![\rho]\!]$,

$$\pi_p((h_1, \ldots, h_r)) = \sum_{i=1}^{t} \widetilde{C}_i \widetilde{e}_i.$$

By (3.1.12), we may assume $\widetilde{e}_1, \ldots, \widetilde{e}_t \in \widetilde{B}_p[\xi][\![\rho]\!]$. Find $e_1, \ldots, e_t \in B_p\langle\xi\rangle[\![\rho]\!]$ with $\pi_p(e_i) = \widetilde{e}_i$, $1 \le i \le t$. Put

$$e := \sum_{i=1}^{t} C_i e_i \in \Phi,$$

and

$$(h'_1, \ldots, h'_r) := (h_1, \ldots, h_r) - e.$$

Note that (3.1.11) is satisfied because $\pi_p(e) = \pi_p((h_1, \ldots, h_r))$. □

Lemma 3.1.9. — *Let M be a submodule of $(\widetilde{S}_{m,n})^\ell/N$ and suppose $g_1, \ldots, g_r$ generate M. Put*

$$\Psi := \left\{ (h_1, \ldots, h_r) \in (\widetilde{S}_{m,n})^r : \sum_{i=1}^{r} g_i h_i = 0 \right\},$$

and for each $i \in \mathbb{N}$, *put*

$$\begin{aligned} M_i &:= \{f \in M : \widetilde{o}_N(f) \geq i\} \text{ and} \\ \Psi_i &:= \left\{(h_1, \ldots, h_r) \in (\widetilde{S}_{m,n})^r : \widetilde{o}_N\left(\sum_{i=1}^r g_i h_i\right) \geq e + i\right\} \end{aligned}$$

where

$$e := \max_{1 \leq i \leq r} \widetilde{o}_N(g_i).$$

Then:

(i) *If* $\{g_1, \ldots, g_r\}$ *is an* $\widetilde{o}_N$*-strict generating system of* M, *then*

$$\Psi_i = \Psi + \bigoplus_{j=1}^r (\rho)^{i+e-\widetilde{o}_N(g_j)} \widetilde{S}_{m,n}$$

for all i.

Conversely:

(ii) *By the Artin-Rees Lemma (*[**25**, Theorem 8.5]*) there is some* $c \in \mathbb{N}$ *such that for all* $i > c$,

$$M_i = (\rho)^{i-c} M_c.$$

If

$$\Psi_i = \Psi + \bigoplus_{j=1}^r (\rho)^{i+e-\widetilde{o}_N(g_j)} \widetilde{S}_{m,n}$$

for $1 \leq i \leq c - e$, *then* $\{g_1, \ldots, g_r\}$ *is an* $\widetilde{o}_N$*-strict generating system of* M.

Proof

(i) Assume $\{g_1, \ldots, g_r\}$ is an $\widetilde{o}_N$-strict generating system of M. Clearly, $\Psi + \oplus_{j=1}^r (\rho)^{i+e-\widetilde{o}_N(g_j)} \widetilde{S}_{m,n} \subset \Psi_i$. Let $h = (h_1, \ldots, h_r) \in \Psi_i$; we wish to find $H \in \Psi$ and $h' \in \oplus_{j=1}^r (\rho)^{i+e-\widetilde{o}_N(g_j)} \widetilde{S}_{m,n}$ such that

$$h = H + h'. \tag{3.1.13}$$

Since $h \in \Psi_i$, we have

$$\widetilde{o}_N\left(\sum_{j=1}^r g_j h_j\right) \geq e + i.$$

Since $\{g_1, \ldots, g_r\}$ is $\widetilde{o}_N$-strict, there is an $h' = (h'_1, \ldots, h'_r) \in (\widetilde{S}_{m,n})^r$ such that

$$\sum_{j=1}^r g_j h'_j = \sum_{j=1}^r g_j h_j \text{ and}$$

$$\min_{1 \leq j \leq r} (\widetilde{o}_N(g_j) + \widetilde{o}(h'_j)) = \widetilde{o}_N\left(\sum_{j=1}^r g_j h_j\right) \geq e + i.$$

Thus $h'_j \in (\rho)^{i+e-\widetilde{o}_N(g_j)}\widetilde{S}_{m,n}$. Put $H := h - h' \in \Psi$. We have

$$h = H + h' \in \Psi + \bigoplus_{j=1}^{r} (\rho)^{i+e-\widetilde{o}_N(g_j)}\widetilde{S}_{m,n},$$

satisfying (3.1.13).

(ii) Since M is $\widetilde{o}_N$-strict by Lemma 3.1.7, it suffices to show that $\{g_1, \ldots, g_r\}$ is $\widetilde{o}_N$-pseudo-Cartesian. Let

$$f = \sum_{i=1}^{r} g_i h_i \in M.$$

***Case* (A).** — $\widetilde{o}_N(f) \leq c$.

By assumption,

$$(h_1, \ldots, h_r) \in \Psi_{\widetilde{o}_N(f)-e} = \Psi + \bigoplus_{j=1}^{r} (\rho)^{\widetilde{o}_N(f)-\widetilde{o}_N(g_j)}\widetilde{S}_{m,n};$$

i.e.,

$$(h_1, \ldots, h_r) = H + h'$$

for some $H \in \Psi$ and $h' \in \oplus_{j=1}^{r} (\rho)^{\widetilde{o}_N(f)-\widetilde{o}_N(g_j)}\widetilde{S}_{m,n}$. Write $h' = (h'_1, \ldots, h'_r)$. Since $H \in \Psi$,

$$f = \sum_{i=1}^{r} g_i h'_i \text{ and } \min_{1 \leq i \leq r} (\widetilde{o}_N(g_i) + \widetilde{o}(h'_i)) \geq \widetilde{o}_N(f),$$

as desired.

***Case* (B).** — $\widetilde{o}_N(f) > c$.

By choice of c,

$$f \in M_{\widetilde{o}_N(f)} = (\rho)^{\widetilde{o}_N(f)-c} M_c \;;$$

i.e.,

$$f = \sum_{|\nu| = \widetilde{o}_N(f)-c} \rho^\nu f_\nu, \quad f_\nu \in M_c.$$

Now apply Case A to the f_ν. □

Let K' be a complete, valued field extension of K, write $S_{m,n} := S_{m,n}(E, K)$ and $S'_{m',n'} := S_{m',n'}(E', K')$, and suppose I is an ideal of $S_{m,n}$ and J is an ideal of $S'_{m',n'}$. Put

$$A := S_{m,n}/I \quad \text{and} \quad B := S'_{m',n'}/J,$$

and by $\|\cdot\|_I$ and $\|\cdot\|_J$ denote the respective residue norms on A and B, as in Definition 3.1.5. Suppose

$$\varphi : A \to B$$

is a K-algebra homomorphism such that

$$\|\varphi(f)\|_J \leq \|f\|_I$$

for all $f \in A$. Then φ induces a K°-algebra homomorphism

$$\varphi^\circ : A^\circ \to B^\circ,$$

where

$$A^\circ = S^\circ_{m,n}/I^\circ \quad \text{and} \quad B^\circ = (S'_{m',n'})^\circ/J^\circ.$$

In addition, φ induces a $\widetilde{K}$-algebra homomorphism

$$\widetilde{\varphi} : \widetilde{A} \to \widetilde{B},$$

where

$$\widetilde{A} = \widetilde{S}_{m,n}/\widetilde{I} \quad \text{and} \quad \widetilde{B} = \widetilde{S}'_{m',n'}/\widetilde{J}.$$

Lemma 3.1.10. — *With notation as above, let M be a submodule of A^ℓ and put $N := \varphi(M) \cdot B \subset B^\ell$. Suppose $\widetilde{\varphi}$ is flat. Then:*

(i) *If $\{g_1, \ldots, g_r\}$ is a $\|\cdot\|_I$-strict generating system of M, then $\{\varphi(g_1), \ldots, \varphi(g_r)\}$ is a $\|\cdot\|_J$-strict generating system of N.*
(ii) *φ is flat.*
(iii) *φ° is flat.*

Proof

(i) We may assume that $\|g_1\|_I = \cdots = \|g_r\|_I = 1$. Put

$$\Phi_A := \left\{ (h_1, \ldots, h_r) \in A^r : \sum_{i=1}^r g_i h_i = 0 \right\},$$

$$\Phi_B := \left\{ (h_1, \ldots, h_r) \in B^r : \sum_{i=1}^r \varphi(g_i) h_i = 0 \right\},$$

$$\Psi_A := \left\{ (h_1, \ldots, h_r) \in \widetilde{A}^r : \sum_{i=1}^r \widetilde{g}_i h_i = 0 \right\},$$

$$\Psi_B := \left\{ (h_1, \ldots, h_r) \in \widetilde{B}^r = \sum_{i=1}^r \widetilde{\varphi}(\widetilde{g}_i) h_i = 0 \right\}.$$

By Lemma 3.1.8, $\widetilde{\Phi}_A = \Psi_A$. Since $\widetilde{\varphi}$ is flat, by [**25**, Theorem 7.6], $\Psi_B = \widetilde{B} \cdot \widetilde{\varphi}(\Psi_A)$. We have:

$$\Psi_B = \widetilde{B} \cdot \widetilde{\varphi}(\Psi_A) = \widetilde{B} \cdot \widetilde{\varphi}(\widetilde{\Phi}_A) \subset \widetilde{\Phi}_B \subset \Psi_B;$$

i.e., $\widetilde{\Phi}_B = \Psi_B$. Part (i) now follows from Lemma 3.1.8.

(ii) Let $\mathfrak{a}$ be an ideal of A. By [**25**, Theorem 7.6], we must show that the canonical map

$$\mathfrak{a} \otimes_A B \to A \otimes_A B \tag{3.1.14}$$

is injective.

Let $\{g_1, \ldots, g_r\}$ be a $\|\cdot\|_I$-strict generating system of $\mathfrak{a}$ with $\|g_1\| = \cdots = \|g_r\| = 1$. Define Φ_A, Φ_B, Ψ_A, Ψ_B as in part (i). To prove that (3.1.14) is injective, it suffices to show that $\Phi_B = B \cdot \varphi(\Phi_A)$. By Lemma 3.1.7, it is enough to show that $\widetilde{\Phi}_B$ is generated by $\widetilde{\varphi}(\widetilde{\Phi}_A)$. By part (i), and Lemma 3.1.8 $\widetilde{\Phi}_B = \Psi_B$. Since $\widetilde{\varphi}$ is flat, $\Psi_B = \widetilde{B} \cdot \widetilde{\varphi}(\Psi_A)$. Finally, by Lemma 3.1.8, $\Psi_A = \widetilde{\Phi}_A$. This proves part (ii).

(iii) Let $g_1, \ldots, g_r \in A^\circ$ and define Φ_A and Φ_B as in part (i). By [**25**, Theorem 7.6], we must show that

$$\Phi_B^\circ = B^\circ \cdot \varphi^\circ(\Phi_A^\circ).$$

This follows immediately from parts (i) and (ii) since there is a $\|\cdot\|_I$-strict generating system of the A°-module Φ_A°. □

It is often convenient to work over an extension field of K. The next lemma shows that $S_{m,n}$ and the total value v behave well with respect to ground field extension.

Lemma 3.1.11. — *Let K' be a complete, valued field extension of K, let $E' \subset (K')^\circ$ be a complete, quasi-Noetherian ring, and put*

$$S_{m,n} := S_{m,n}(E, K), \quad S'_{m,n} := S_{m,n}(E', K').$$

Assume $S'_{m,n} \supset S_{m,n}$; e.g., take $E' \supset E$. Let M be a submodule of $(S_{m,n})^\ell$ and put $M' := M \cdot S'_{m,n}$.

(i) *$\widetilde{S}'_{m,n}$ is a faithfully flat $\widetilde{S}_{m,n}$-algebra.*
(ii) *Suppose $\{g_1, \ldots, g_r\} \subset M$ is a v-strict generating system of M, then $\{g_1, \ldots, g_r\}$ is also a v-strict generating system of M', and for every $f \in (S_{m,n})^\ell$, $v_M(f) = v_{M'}(f)$. In particular $\|f\|_M = \|f\|_{M'}$.*
(iii) *$S_{m,n}(E', K')$ is a faithfully flat $S_{m,n}(E, K)$-algebra.*
(iv) *$S_{m,n}(E', K')^\circ$ is a faithfully flat $S_{m,n}(E, K)^\circ$-algebra.*

Proof

(i) By Corollary 2.2.2, both $\widetilde{S}_{m,n}$ and $\widetilde{S}'_{m,n}$ are Noetherian. Since $(\rho) \subset \operatorname{rad} \widetilde{S}'_{m,n}$, $\widetilde{S}'_{m,n}$ is (ρ)-adically ideal-separated. For each $\ell \in \mathbb{N}$,

$$\widetilde{S}_{m,n}/(\rho)^\ell = \widetilde{K}[\xi, \rho]/(\rho)^\ell \to \widetilde{K}'[\xi, \rho]/(\rho)^\ell = \widetilde{S}'_{m,n}/(\rho)^\ell$$

is flat. Hence by the Local Flatness Criterion [**25**, Theorem 22.3], $\widetilde{S}'_{m,n}$ is a flat $\widetilde{S}_{m,n}$-algebra. Let $\mathfrak{m}$ be a maximal ideal of $\widetilde{S}_{m,n}$. By [**25**, Theorem 7.2], to prove that $\widetilde{S}'_{m,n}$ is faithfully flat over $\widetilde{S}_{m,n}$, we must show that $\mathfrak{m} \cdot \widetilde{S}'_{m,n} \neq \widetilde{S}'_{m,n}$. Since $(\rho) \subset \mathfrak{m}$, this follows from the faithful flatness of $\widetilde{K}'[\xi]$ over $\widetilde{K}[\xi]$.

(ii) We may assume that $\|g_i\| = 1$, $1 \leq i \leq r$. Put

$$\begin{aligned} N &:= \left\{(h_1, \ldots, h_r) \in (\widetilde{S}_{m,n})^r : \sum_{i=1}^r \widetilde{g}_i h_i = 0\right\}, \\ N' &:= \left\{(h_1, \ldots, h_r) \in (\widetilde{S}'_{m,n})^r : \sum_{i=1}^r \widetilde{g}_i h_i = 0\right\}, \end{aligned}$$

and for each $i \in \mathbb{N}$, put

$$\begin{aligned} N_i &:= \left\{(h_1, \ldots, h_r) \in (\widetilde{S}_{m,n})^r : \widetilde{\mathrm{o}}\left(\sum_{i=1}^r \widetilde{g}_i h_i\right) \geq e + i\right\}, \\ N'_i &:= \left\{(h_1, \ldots, h_r) \in (\widetilde{S}'_{m,n})^r : \widetilde{\mathrm{o}}\left(\sum_{i=1}^r \widetilde{g}_i h_i\right) \geq e + i\right\}, \end{aligned}$$

where $e := \max_{1 \leq i \leq r} \widetilde{\mathrm{o}}(g_i)$. By Lemma 3.1.2, $\{\widetilde{g}_1, \ldots, \widetilde{g}_r\}$ is an $\widetilde{\mathrm{o}}$-strict generating system of $\widetilde{M}$. Hence by Lemma 3.1.9(i),

$$N_i = N + \bigoplus_{j=1}^r (\rho)^{i+e-\widetilde{\mathrm{o}}_N(g_j)} \widetilde{S}_{m,n}$$

for all $i \in \mathbb{N}$. By part (i),

$$N'_i = \widetilde{S}'_{m,n} \otimes_{\widetilde{S}_{m,n}} N_i \text{ and } N' = \widetilde{S}'_{m,n} \otimes_{\widetilde{S}_{m,n}} N.$$

Hence,

$$N'_i = N' + \bigoplus_{j=1}^r (\rho)^{i+e-\widetilde{\mathrm{o}}_N(g_j)} \widetilde{S}'_{m,n}$$

for all $i \in \mathbb{N}$. Finally, by applying Lemmas 3.1.9 and 3.1.2 again, we see that $\{g_1, \ldots, g_r\}$ is a v-strict generating system of M'. The last assertions of part (ii) follow from Lemma 3.1.1 as in the proof of Lemma 3.1.2.

(iii) First we prove that $S'_{m,n}$ is a flat $S_{m,n}$-algebra. The faithful flatness will follow from part (iv) by faithfully flat base change; i.e., $S'_{m,n} = (S'_{m,n})^{\circ} \otimes_{S^{\circ}_{m,n}} S_{m,n}$. Of course, the proof of part (iv) makes use only of the assertion that $S'_{m,n}$ is flat over $S_{m,n}$.

Let I be an ideal of $S_{m,n}$. By [**25**, Theorem 7.7], we must show that the canonical map

$$I \otimes_{S_{m,n}} S'_{m,n} \to S_{m,n} \otimes_{S_{m,n}} S'_{m,n} \tag{3.1.15}$$

is injective.

Let $g_1, \ldots, g_r \in S_{m,n}$ be a v-strict generating system of I with $\|g_1\| = \cdots = \|g_r\| = 1$. Put

$$\begin{aligned} N &:= \left\{(h_1, \ldots, h_r) \in (S_{m,n})^r : \sum_{i=1}^r g_i h_i = 0\right\} \\ N' &:= \left\{(h_1, \ldots, h_r) \in (S'_{m,n})^r : \sum_{i=1}^r g_i h_i = 0\right\} \\ P &:= \left\{(h_1, \ldots, h_r) \in (\widetilde{S}_{m,n})^r : \sum_{i=1}^r \widetilde{g}_i h_i = 0\right\} \\ P' &:= \left\{(h_1, \ldots, h_r) \in (\widetilde{S}'_{m,n})^r : \sum_{i=1}^r \widetilde{g}_i h_i = 0\right\}. \end{aligned}$$

To prove that (3.1.15) is injective, it suffices to show that $N' = S'_{m,n} \cdot N$. By Lemma 3.1.8, $\widetilde{N} = P$, by part (ii) and Lemma 3.1.8, $(N')^\sim = P'$, and by part (i), $P' = \widetilde{S}'_{m,n} \cdot P$. Hence

$$P' = \widetilde{S}'_{m,n} \cdot P = \widetilde{S}'_{m,n} \cdot \widetilde{N} = (N')^\sim.$$

After an application of Lemma 3.1.4, one sees that $N' = S'_{m,n} \cdot N$, as desired.

(iv) Let $g_1, \ldots, g_r \in S^\circ_{m,n}$ and define N, N' as in the proof of part (iii), above. We must show that

$$(N')^\circ = (S'_{m,n})^\circ \cdot N^\circ.$$

This follows immediately from the existence of a v-strict generating system for N, from part (ii) and from the fact that $S'_{m,n}$ is flat over $S_{m,n}$. Since $K^{\circ\circ}$, $(\rho) \subset \operatorname{rad} S^\circ_{m,n}$, the faithfulness follows from that of

$$\widetilde{K}[\xi] \to ((K')^\circ / K^{\circ\circ} \cdot (K')^\circ)[\xi].$$

□

3.2. Restrictions to Rational Polydiscs. — Let $\varepsilon \in \sqrt{|K \setminus \{0\}|}$ with $1 > \varepsilon > 0$. Put

$$T_{m,n}(\varepsilon) = T_{m,n}(\varepsilon, K) := \left\{\sum a_{\mu\nu} \xi^\mu \rho^\nu \in K[\![\xi, \rho]\!] : \lim_{|\mu|+|\nu| \to \infty} \varepsilon^{|\nu|} |a_{\mu\nu}| = 0\right\}.$$

By [**6**, Theorem 6.1.5.4], $T_{m,n}(\varepsilon)$ is K-affinoid. Define a modified Gauss norm $\|\cdot\|_\varepsilon$ on $T_{m,n}(\varepsilon)$ by

$$\left\|\sum a_{\mu\nu} \xi^\mu \rho^\nu\right\|_\varepsilon := \max_{\mu,\nu} \varepsilon^{|\nu|} |a_{\mu\nu}|$$

(see [**6**, Proposition 6.1.5.2]). By [**6**, Proposition 6.1.5.5], $\|\cdot\|_\varepsilon = \|\cdot\|_{\sup}$ on $T_{m,n}(\varepsilon)$. In this subsection we make extensive use of $\|\cdot\|_{\sup}$ on affinoid algebras. Quasi-affinoid algebras also possess supremum seminorms, but we will not make use of them until after we prove the quasi-affinoid Nullstellensatz, Theorem 4.1.1.

By ι_ε denote the natural inclusion

$$\iota_\varepsilon : S_{m,n} \hookrightarrow T_{m,n}(\varepsilon),$$

which corresponds to the *restriction to the rational polydisc* $\operatorname{Max} T_{m,n}(\varepsilon)$. In the case that $\varepsilon \in |K|$ with $1 > \varepsilon > 0$, fix $c \in K$ with $|c| = \varepsilon$. Then the K-affinoid map

$$\varphi_\varepsilon : T_{m,n}(\varepsilon) \to T_{m+n}$$

given by $\xi \mapsto \xi$ and $\rho \mapsto c \cdot \rho$ identifies $T_{m,n}(\varepsilon)$ with T_{m+n}, and for $f \in T_{m,n}(\varepsilon)$, we have $\|f\|_{\sup} = \|\varphi_\varepsilon(f)\|$. By ι'_ε we denote the inclusion

$$\iota'_\varepsilon := \varphi_\varepsilon \circ \iota_\varepsilon : S_{m,n} \hookrightarrow T_{m+n};$$

thus $\iota'_\varepsilon(f) = f(\xi, c \cdot \rho)$ for $f \in S_{m,n}$. Note that the morphisms φ_ε and ι'_ε depend on the choice of c.

We are interested in the uniform behavior of the inclusions ι_ε as $\varepsilon \to 1$. In particular, we show in Theorem 3.2.3 that the image under ι_ε of a strict generating system remains strict for ε sufficiently large.

For this purpose we define a map $\sigma : S_{m,n} \to \mathbb{R}_+$ as follows (assuming that $n \geq 1$). Let $f = \sum f_\nu(\xi)\rho^\nu \in S_{m,n}$ and put $i := \widetilde{\mathrm{o}}(f)$. If $i = 0, \infty$ put $\sigma(f) := 0$. Otherwise, put

$$\sigma(f) := \max_{|\nu|<i} \left(\frac{\|f_\nu\|}{\|f\|} \right)^{1/(i-|\nu|)}.$$

Note that $0 \leq \sigma(f) < 1$. The number $\sigma(f)$ is called the *spectral radius* of f.

The following observations are useful in computations involving the spectral radius:

$$\|\iota_\varepsilon(f)\|_{\sup} \geq \varepsilon^{\widetilde{\mathrm{o}}(f)} \, \|f\| \, ,$$

with equality when $1 > \varepsilon \geq \sigma(f)$, and

$$\sigma(f) = \inf\{|c| : c \in (K')^\circ \text{ and } \widetilde{\mathrm{o}}(f(\xi, c \cdot \rho)) = \widetilde{\mathrm{o}}(f)\},$$

where $K' \supset K$ is algebraically closed. Hence if $f \cdot g \neq 0$,

$$\sigma(f \cdot g) = \max\{\sigma(f), \sigma(g)\}.$$

It is suggestive to compare the spectral radius with the *spectral value* of a monic polynomial defined in [**6**, Section 1.5.4].

We define the *spectral radius* of a submodule M of $(S_{m,n})^\ell$, $n \geq 1$ by

$$\sigma(M) := \inf_{\{g_1, \ldots, g_r\} \in \mathcal{M}} \max\{\sigma(g_1), \ldots, \sigma(g_r)\},$$

where $\mathcal{M}$ is the collection of all v-strict generating systems $\{g_1, \ldots, g_r\}$ of M.

Remark 3.2.1

(i) Let $\varepsilon \in |K|$ with $1 > \varepsilon > 0$. We have the following commutative diagram

$$\begin{array}{ccc} & T_{m,n}(\varepsilon) & \\ {\scriptstyle \iota_\varepsilon}\nearrow & & \searrow{\scriptstyle \varphi_\varepsilon} \\ S_{m,n} & \xrightarrow[\iota'_\varepsilon]{} & T_{m+n} \end{array}$$

and φ_ε is an isometric isomorphism. Since φ_ε is an isometry, this yields an identification of $\widetilde{T}_{m,n}(\varepsilon)$ with $\widetilde{K}[\xi,\rho] = \widetilde{T}_{m+n}$, where $\widetilde{T}_{m,n}(\varepsilon)$ is the quotient of the subring of power-bounded elements of $T_{m,n}(\varepsilon)$ modulo its ideal of topologically nilpotent elements (see [**6**, Section 6.3]).

(ii) Let $\varepsilon \in \sqrt{|K \setminus \{0\}|}$ with $1 > \varepsilon > 0$. Let K' be a finite algebraic extension of K and suppose $\{c_1, \ldots, c_s\}$ is a K-Cartesian basis of K' (see [**6**, Definition 2.4.1.1]). Then $\{c_1, \ldots, c_s\}$ is also a $\|\cdot\|_{\sup}$-Cartesian basis for the $T_{m,n}(\varepsilon)$-module $T'_{m,n}(\varepsilon) := T_{m,n}(\varepsilon, K')$. This is easily seen using the modified Gauss norm $\|\cdot\|_\varepsilon$, as follows. Let $f \in T'_{m,n}(\varepsilon)$; then $f = \sum_{i=1}^{s} c_i f_i$ with each $f_i \in T_{m,n}(\varepsilon)$ and $\|f\|_\varepsilon = \max_{1 \le i \le s} |c_i| \, \|f_i\|_\varepsilon$.

(iii) Using the notation of part (ii), observe that $\{c_1/c_1, \ldots, c_s/c_1\}$ is a K-Cartesian basis of K'; hence we may assume that $c_1 = 1$. Let M be a submodule of $(T_{m,n}(\varepsilon))^\ell$ and put $M' := T'_{m,n}(\varepsilon) \cdot M$. Let $f \in (T_{m,n}(\varepsilon))^\ell$; then $\|f\|_M = \|f\|_{M'}$ (see Definition 3.1.5). This is proved as follows. By Lemma 3.1.4, there is a $g \in M'$ such that $\|f - g\| = \|f\|_{M'}$. We may write $g = \sum_{i=1}^{s} c_i g_i$ with each $g_i \in M$. By part (ii),

$$\begin{aligned} \|f - g\|_\varepsilon &= \max\{\|f - g_1\|_\varepsilon, |c_2| \, \|g_2\|_\varepsilon, \ldots, |c_s| \, \|g_s\|_\varepsilon\} \\ &\geq \|f - g_1\|_\varepsilon \\ &\geq \|f\|_M . \end{aligned}$$

Since $\|f\|_{M'} \leq \|f\|_M$, we have $\|f\|_M = \|f\|_{M'}$.

Our immediate goal, Theorem 3.2.3, is to show that a strict generating system remains strict upon restriction to a suitably large rational polydisc. Lemma 3.2.2 is the inductive step of the slicing argument involved. It makes special use of condition (i) of Lemma 3.1.1.

Lemma 3.2.2. — *Let M be a submodule of $(S_{m,n})^\ell$, let $g_1, \ldots, g_r \in M$ with $\|g_1\| = \cdots = \|g_r\| = 1$, and suppose that $\{\widetilde{g}_1, \ldots, \widetilde{g}_r\}$ is an $\widetilde{\mathrm{o}}$-strict generating system of $\widetilde{M}$. Suppose $B \in \mathfrak{B}$ satisfies $\{g_1, \ldots, g_r\} \subset (B\langle\xi\rangle[[\rho]])^\ell \cap M$, and let $B = B_0 \supset B_1 \supset \cdots$ be the natural filtration of B. Let $\varepsilon \in \sqrt{|K \setminus \{0\}|}$ be such that $1 > \varepsilon \geq \max\{\sigma(g_1), \ldots, \sigma(g_r)\}$. Suppose*

$$f \in M \cap \left((B_p\langle\xi\rangle[[\rho]])^\ell \setminus (B_{p+1}\langle\xi\rangle[[\rho]])^\ell\right).$$

Then there are $a_1, \ldots, a_r \in \{0\} \cup (B_p\langle\xi\rangle[[\rho]] \setminus B_{p+1}\langle\xi\rangle[[\rho]])$ such that

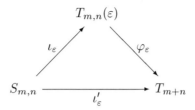

(i) $\|\iota_\varepsilon(f)\|_{\sup} \geq \max\limits_{1\leq i\leq r} \|\iota_\varepsilon(a_i g_i)\|_{\sup}$ *(recall* $\|\cdot\|_{\sup} = \|\cdot\|_\varepsilon$ *on* $T_{m,n}(\varepsilon)$*) and*

(ii) $\|f - \sum_{i=1}^r a_i g_i\| < \|f\|$.

Proof. — Choose $a_1, \ldots, a_r \in \{0\} \cup (B_p\langle\xi\rangle[[\rho]] \setminus B_{p+1}\langle\xi\rangle[[\rho]])$ as in Lemma 3.1.1. By Lemma 3.1.1 (i), $\sigma(a_i g_i) \leq \varepsilon$, so

$$\|\iota_\varepsilon(a_i g_i)\|_{\sup} = \varepsilon^{\widetilde{\mathrm{o}}(a_i g_i)}\|a_i g_i\| \leq \varepsilon^{\widetilde{\mathrm{o}}(a_i g_i)}\|f\|.$$

By Lemma 3.1.1 (ii)$'$, we get

$$\|\iota_\varepsilon(a_i g_i)\|_{\sup} \leq \varepsilon^{\widetilde{\mathrm{o}}(a_i g_i)}\|f\| \leq \varepsilon^{\widetilde{\mathrm{o}}(f)}\|f\| \leq \|\iota_\varepsilon(f)\|_{\sup},$$

which yields (i). Since $f \in M$, (ii) follows from Lemma 3.1.1 (iii). □

Theorem 3.2.3. — *Let M be a submodule of $(S_{m,n})^\ell$, $n \geq 1$, with v-strict generating system $\{g_1, \ldots, g_r\} \subset M^\circ$. Let $\varepsilon \in \sqrt{|K \setminus \{0\}|}$ with $1 > \varepsilon \geq \max_{1\leq i\leq r} \sigma(g_i)$, and assume either that K is a stable field (see* [**6**, Definition 3.6.1.1]*) or that $\varepsilon \in |K|$. Then $\{\iota_\varepsilon(g_1), \ldots, \iota_\varepsilon(g_r)\}$ is a $\|\cdot\|_{\sup}$-strict generating system of the $T_{m,n}(\varepsilon)$-module $\iota_\varepsilon(M) \cdot T_{m,n}(\varepsilon) \subset (T_{m,n}(\varepsilon))^\ell$.*

Proof. — Suppose first that $\varepsilon \in |K|$. Then by Remark 3.2.1 (i), we have the following commutative diagram,

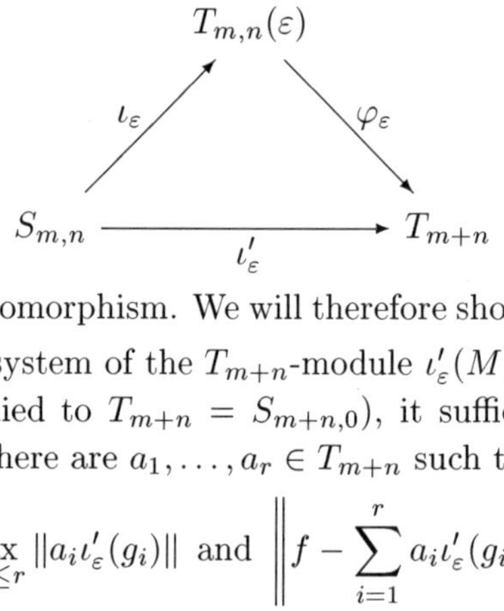

where φ_ε is an isometric isomorphism. We will therefore show that $\{\iota'_\varepsilon(g_1), \ldots, \iota'_\varepsilon(g_r)\}$ is a $\|\cdot\|$-strict generating system of the T_{m+n}-module $\iota'_\varepsilon(M) \cdot T_{m+n} \subset (T_{m+n})^\ell$.

By Lemma 3.1.4 (applied to $T_{m+n} = S_{m+n,0}$), it suffices to show for each $f \in \iota'_\varepsilon(M) \cdot T_{m+n} \setminus \{0\}$ that there are $a_1, \ldots, a_r \in T_{m+n}$ such that

$$\|f\| = \max_{1\leq i\leq r} \|a_i \iota'_\varepsilon(g_i)\| \text{ and } \left\| f - \sum_{i=1}^r a_i \iota'_\varepsilon(g_i) \right\| < \|f\|. \tag{3.2.1}$$

Write $f = \sum\limits_{i=1}^r f_i \iota'_\varepsilon(g_i)$ for some $f_1, \ldots, f_r \in T_{m+n}$. Find polynomials $f'_1, \ldots, f'_r \in K[\xi, \rho]$ such that each $\|f'_i - f_i\| < \|f\|$. Then

$$\left\| \sum_{i=1}^r f_i \iota'_\varepsilon(g_i) - \sum_{i=1}^r f'_i \iota'_\varepsilon(g_i) \right\| < \|f\|,$$

since $\|\iota'_\varepsilon(g_i)\| \leq 1$ for all i. Put $f' := \sum_{i=1}^r f'_i \iota'_\varepsilon(g_i)$. It suffices to prove (3.2.1) for f'.

Since the f'_i are polynomials, $f' = \iota'_\varepsilon(F)$ for some $F \in M$. We wish to apply Lemma 3.2.2. Since $\|S_{m,n}\| = |K|$, we may assume $\|F\|, \|g_1\|, \ldots, \|g_r\| = 1$. Hence by Lemma 3.1.2, $\{\widetilde{g}_1,\ldots,\widetilde{g}_r\}$ is an $\widetilde{o}$-strict generating system of $\widetilde{M}$. Choose $B\in\mathfrak{B}$ such that $F,g_1,\ldots,g_r\in(B\langle\xi\rangle[[\rho]])^\ell\cap M$. By iterated application of Lemma 3.2.2 (recall that $\varepsilon\in|K|$, hence $T_{m,n}(\varepsilon)$ and T_{m+n} are isometrically isomorphic) we obtain a sequence $\{a_{ij}\}\subset B\langle\xi\rangle[[\rho]]$ such that $a_{10},\ldots,a_{r0}=0$ and for every $s\in\mathbb{N}$,

(i) $\left\|\iota'_\varepsilon(F-\sum_{\substack{1\le i\le r\\0\le j\le s}}a_{ij}g_i)\right\|\ge\|\iota'_\varepsilon(a_{is+1}g_i)\|$, and

(ii) $\left\|F-\sum_{\substack{1\le i\le r\\0\le j\le s}}a_{ij}g_i\right\|>\left\|F-\sum_{\substack{1\le i\le r\\0\le j\le s+1}}a_{ij}g_i\right\|$.

Since $B\langle\xi\rangle[\![\rho]\!]$ is complete in $\|\cdot\|$ and $|B\setminus\{0\}|\subset\mathbb{R}_+\setminus\{0\}$ is discrete, by (ii),

$$F-\sum_{i=1}^r a_ig_i=0,\quad\text{where}\quad a_i:=\sum_{j\ge0}a_{ij}.$$

Hence $\|f'-\sum_{i=1}^r\iota'_\varepsilon(a_i)\iota'_\varepsilon(g_i)\|=0<\|f'\|$. It follows from (i) that $\|f'\|=\|\iota'_\varepsilon(F)\|\ge\max_{i,j}\|\iota'_\varepsilon(a_{ij}g_i)\|$ and hence that

$$\|f'\|=\max_{1\le i\le r}\|\iota'_\varepsilon(a_ig_i)\|\,.$$

This concludes the proof in case $\varepsilon\in|K\setminus\{0\}|$.

It remains to treat the case that K is a stable field. Let K' be a finite algebraic extension of K with $\varepsilon\in|K'|$. Let $S'_{m,n}:=S_{m,n}(E,K')$ and let $M':=M\cdot S'_{m,n}$. By Lemma 3.1.11, $\{g_1,\ldots,g_r\}$ is a v-strict generating system of M'. Therefore, by the preceding case, $\{\iota_\varepsilon(g_1),\ldots,\iota_\varepsilon(g_r)\}$ is a $\|\cdot\|_{\sup}$-strict generating system of the $T'_{m,n}(\varepsilon)$-module $\iota_\varepsilon(M)\cdot T'_{m,n}(\varepsilon)$.

Let $\{1=c_1,\ldots,c_s\}$ be a K-Cartesian basis of K', and let $f\in(T_{m,n}(\varepsilon))^\ell\subset(T'_{m,n}(\varepsilon))^\ell$. By the previous case there are $a_1,\ldots,a_r\in T'_{m,n}(\varepsilon)$ such that

$$\left\|f-\sum_{i=1}^r a_i\iota_\varepsilon(g_i)\right\|_{\sup}=\|f\|_{\iota_\varepsilon(M)\cdot T'_{m,n}(\varepsilon)},\ \text{and}$$
$$\|f\|_{\sup}\ge\max_{1\le i\le r}\|a_i\iota_\varepsilon(g_i)\|_{\sup}\,.$$

For $i=1,\ldots,r$, write

$$a_i=\sum_{j=1}^s c_ja_{ij}\ \text{with}\ a_{ij}\in T_{m,n}(\varepsilon).$$

Then as in Remark 3.2.1 (iii),

$$\left\|f-\sum_{i=1}^r a_{i1}\iota_\varepsilon(g_i)\right\|_{\sup}=\|f\|_{\iota_\varepsilon(M)\cdot T_{m,n}(\varepsilon)},\ \text{and}$$
$$\|f\|_{\sup}\ge\max_{1\le i\le r}\|a_{i1}\iota_\varepsilon(g_i)\|_{\sup}\,.$$

Thus $\{\iota_\varepsilon(g_1), \dots, \iota_\varepsilon(g_r)\}$ is a $\|\cdot\|_{\sup}$-strict generating system of the $T_{m,n}(\varepsilon)$-module $\iota_\varepsilon(M) \cdot T_{m,n}(\varepsilon)$. □

Let M be a submodule of $(S_{m,n})^\ell$. Lemma 3.2.5 uses Theorem 3.2.3 to relate the structure of $\widetilde{M}$ to that of $(\iota_\varepsilon(M) \cdot T_{m,n}(\varepsilon))^\sim$ for ε large enough. Lemma 3.2.6 will be used in Section 4 to prove that $S_{m,n}$ is a UFD.

Definition 3.2.4. — Let M be a submodule of $(S_{m,n})^\ell$, $n \geq 1$, and consider $\widetilde{M} \subset (\widetilde{S}_{m,n})^\ell$. Note that each $f \in (\widetilde{S}_{m,n})^\ell$ can be written uniquely as $f = \sum_{|\nu| \geq \widetilde{\mathrm{o}}(f)} f_\nu(\xi)\rho^\nu$, where each $f_\nu \in (\widetilde{K}[\xi])^\ell$. Define $\Lambda(M)$, the *uniform residue module* of M, to be the $\widetilde{K}[\xi,\rho]$-submodule of $(\widetilde{K}[\xi,\rho])^\ell$ generated by the elements $\sum_{|\nu|=\widetilde{\mathrm{o}}(f)} f_\nu(\xi)\rho^\nu$ for $f \in \widetilde{M}$.

The name uniform residue module is justified by the following lemma.

Lemma 3.2.5. — *Let M be a submodule of $(S_{m,n})^\ell$, $n \geq 1$, and let K' be a complete extension field of K. Suppose $\varepsilon \in |K'|$ with $1 > \varepsilon > \sigma(M)$. Put $N := \iota_\varepsilon(M) \cdot T_{m,n}(\varepsilon, K') \subset (T_{m,n}(\varepsilon, K'))^\ell$. Then $\widetilde{N} = \widetilde{K}' \cdot \Lambda(M)$, where we have identified $\widetilde{T}_{m,n}(\varepsilon, K')$ with $\widetilde{K}'[\xi,\rho]$.*

Proof. — Let $S'_{m,n} := S_{m,n}(E, K')$ and let $M' := S'_{m,n} \cdot M$. Choose a v-strict generating system $\{g_1, \dots, g_r\}$ of M with $\varepsilon > \max_{1 \leq i \leq r} \sigma(g_i)$. By Lemma 3.1.11 (ii), $\{g_1, \dots, g_r\}$ is a v-strict generating system of M'. Hence by Theorem 3.2.3,

$$\{\iota_\varepsilon(g_1), \dots, \iota_\varepsilon(g_r)\}$$

is a $\|\cdot\|_{\sup}$-strict generating system of $\iota_\varepsilon(M) \cdot T_{m,n}(\varepsilon, K') = N$. Put $G_i := c^{-\widetilde{\mathrm{o}}(g_i)}\iota_\varepsilon(g_i)$ where $c \in K'$ is chosen with $|c| = \varepsilon$. By Lemma 3.1.4, $\{\widetilde{G}_1, \dots, \widetilde{G}_r\}$ generates $\widetilde{N}$. □

Lemma 3.2.6. — *Let $I \subset S_{m,n}$ be an ideal. Suppose $\Lambda(I)$ is principal; then I is principal.*

Proof. — For $h \in \widetilde{S}_{m,n}$, let h° denote the leading form in ρ of the power series h. Note that $(hg)^\circ = h^\circ g^\circ$. Choose $h_1, \dots, h_s \in \widetilde{I}$ such that $\{h_1^\circ, \dots, h_s^\circ\}$ generates $\Lambda(I)$. Suppose $g \in \widetilde{K}[\xi,\rho]$ generates $\Lambda(I)$. Since each h_i° is a multiple of g, $\deg_\rho g \leq \min_{1 \leq i \leq s}(\deg_\rho h_i^\circ) =: d$. Since g is a linear combination of the h_i°, $\widetilde{\mathrm{o}}(g) \geq \min_{1 \leq i \leq s} \widetilde{\mathrm{o}}(h_i^\circ) = d$. Hence g is homogeneous in ρ of degree d, and $g = G^\circ$ for some $G \in \widetilde{I}$. By Corollary 2.2.4, it suffices to show that G generates $\widetilde{I}$.

Let $\widetilde{J}$ be the ideal of $\widetilde{S}_{m,n}$ generated by G. Clearly $\widetilde{I} \supset \widetilde{J}$; we will show that $\widetilde{I} = \widetilde{J}$. Suppose there is some $f \in \widetilde{I} \setminus \widetilde{J}$. By Theorem 3.1.3, we may assume that

$$\widetilde{\mathrm{o}}(f-h) \leq \widetilde{\mathrm{o}}(f) \tag{3.2.2}$$

for all $h \in \widetilde{J}$. Since $f^\circ \in \Lambda(I)$, there is some $a \in \widetilde{K}[\xi,\rho]$ such that $f^\circ = ag = (ag)^\circ = a^\circ G^\circ = (aG)^\circ$, contradicting (3.2.2). □

3.3. Contractions from Rational Polydiscs. — In this subsection, we transfer information from $T_{m,n}(\varepsilon)$ back to $S_{m,n}$. The main results are Theorem 3.3.1 and its Corollaries, which show, roughly speaking, how to replace powers of ε with powers of (ρ) for ε near 1. Of course, when K is discretely valued, ε cannot, in general, belong to $|K|$. It is therefore sometimes necessary to extend the ground field as we did in Subsection 3.2.

For $f \in K\langle\xi,\rho\rangle = T_{m+n}$, $n \geq 1$, let $\widetilde{d}(f) := \infty$ if $f = 0$. Otherwise, write $f(\xi) = \Sigma f_\nu(\xi)\rho^\nu$ and let $\widetilde{d}(f)$ be the largest $\ell \in \mathbb{N}$ such that for some ν with $|\nu| = \ell$ we have $\|f\| = \|f_\nu\|$. We call $\widetilde{d}(f)$ the *residue degree* of f. Note that if $\|f\| = 1$, $\widetilde{d}(f)$ is the total degree of $\widetilde{f}$ as a polynomial in ρ.

Let (A, v) be a normed ring and let $f = \Sigma f_\nu\rho^\nu$, $g = \Sigma g_\nu\rho^\nu \in A[\![\rho]\!]$. We say g is a *majorant* of f iff $v(f_\nu) \leq v(g_\nu)$ for all ν.

Let $c \in A$ with $v(c) \leq 1$, and suppose

$$\sum_{|\nu|\leq a} \rho^\nu + \sum_{|\nu|>a} c^{|\nu|-a}\rho^\nu$$

is a majorant of f and

$$\sum_{|\nu|\leq b} \rho^\nu + \sum_{|\nu|>b} c^{|\nu|-b}\rho^\nu$$

is a majorant of g. Put $e := \max\{a, b\}$. Then

(i) $\displaystyle\sum_{|\nu|\leq e} \rho^\nu + \sum_{|\nu|>e} c^{|\nu|-e}\rho^\nu$ is a majorant of $f + g$, and

(ii) $\displaystyle\sum_{|\nu|\leq a+b} \rho^\nu + \sum_{|\nu|>a+b} c^{|\nu|-(a+b)}\rho^\nu$ is a majorant of fg.

Note, for any $f \in S_{m,n}$ with $\|f\| = 1$ and any $c \in K^\circ$, that $f(\xi, c\cdot\rho)$ is majorized by $\sum c^{|\nu|}\rho^\nu$. This fact will be used in the proof of the next theorem, which, for $f \in (S_{m,n})^\ell$ and M a submodule of $(S_{m,n})^\ell$, relates $v_M(f)$ and $\|\iota_\varepsilon(f)\|_{\iota_\varepsilon(M)\cdot T_{m,n}(\varepsilon)}$, when ε is sufficiently large. The proof shows, via the concept of majorization, that if the "slicing" in $(T_{m,n}(\varepsilon))^\ell$ is done carefully, then it pulls back to $(S_{m,n})^\ell$.

Theorem 3.3.1. — *Let M be a submodule of $(S_{m,n})^\ell$, $n \geq 1$, let $\varepsilon \in \sqrt{|K \setminus \{0\}|}$ with $1 > \varepsilon > \sigma(M)$. Then for every $f \in (S_{m,n})^\ell$,*

$$v_M(f) \leq (\|f\|, 2^{-\alpha}),$$

where $\alpha \in \mathbb{N} \cup \{\infty\}$ is the least element such that $\varepsilon^\alpha\|f\| \leq \|\iota_\varepsilon(f)\|_{\iota_\varepsilon(M)\cdot T_{m,n}(\varepsilon)}$. If $\alpha = \infty$, then $v_M(f) = (0, 0)$.

Proof. — Let K' be the completion of the algebraic closure of K, and put $S'_{m,n} := S_{m,n}(E, K')$, $T'_{m,n}(\varepsilon) := T_{m,n}(\varepsilon, K')$ and $M' := S'_{m,n}\cdot M$. By Lemma 3.1.11, $\sigma(M') \leq \sigma(M)$ and $v_{M'}(f) = v_M(f)$. Certainly,

$$\|\iota_\varepsilon(f)\|_{\iota_\varepsilon(M')\cdot T'_{m,n}(\varepsilon)} \leq \|\iota_\varepsilon(f)\|_{\iota_\varepsilon(M)\cdot T_{m,n}(\varepsilon)}\,.$$

Therefore, we may assume $K = K'$, so that, in particular, $\varepsilon \in |K|$ and $T_{m,n}(\varepsilon)$ is isometrically isomorphic to T_{m+n}. Choose $c \in K$ with $|c| = \varepsilon$. We may replace ι_ε by ι'_ε as in Remark 3.2.1 (i).

Since $\varepsilon^{\widetilde{o}(f)}\|f\| \leq \|\iota'_\varepsilon(f)\|$, if $\|\iota'_\varepsilon(f)\| = \|\iota'_\varepsilon(f)\|_{\iota'_\varepsilon(M)\cdot T_{m+n}}$ there is nothing to show. Therefore, we may assume that

$$\|\iota'_\varepsilon(f)\|_{\iota'_\varepsilon(M)\cdot T_{m+n}} < \|\iota'_\varepsilon(f)\|. \tag{3.3.1}$$

We may further assume that $\|f\| = 1$.

Let $\alpha \in \mathbb{N}\cup\{\infty\}$ be the least element such that $\varepsilon^\alpha \leq \|\iota'_\varepsilon(f)\|_{\iota'_\varepsilon(M)\cdot T_{m+n}}$. By (3.3.1), $\alpha > 0$. Fix $\beta \in \mathbb{N}$, $\beta < \alpha$. We must show that

$$v_M(f) < (\|f\|, 2^{-\beta}).$$

Let $\{g_1, \ldots, g_r\}$ be a v-strict generating system of M with $\|g_1\| = \cdots = \|g_r\| = 1$ and $\varepsilon > \max_{1\leq i\leq r} \sigma(g_i)$. For $1 \leq i \leq r$, put $G_i := c^{-\widetilde{o}(g_i)}\iota'_\varepsilon(g_i)$, where $c \in K$ with $|c| = \varepsilon$, and find $B \in \mathfrak{B}$ such that $\iota'_\varepsilon(f), G_1, \ldots, G_r \in (B\langle\xi,\rho\rangle)^\ell$. Let $B = B_0 \supset B_1 \supset \cdots$ be the natural filtration of B.

***Claim* (A).** — *Let $F \in (B_p\langle\xi,\rho\rangle)^\ell \setminus (B_{p+1}\langle\xi,\rho\rangle)^\ell$ and suppose for some $h \in \iota'_\varepsilon(M)\cdot T_{m+n}$ that $\|F - h\| < \|F\|$. Then there are polynomials $h_i \in B_p[\xi,\rho]$ such that*

(i) $\left\| F - \sum_{i=1}^r h_i G_i \right\| < \|F\|$, *and*

(ii) $\max\{\widetilde{o}(G_i) + \deg_\rho(h_i) : h_i \neq 0\} = \widetilde{d}(F)$.

Let $\pi_p : B_p \to \widetilde{B}_p \subset \widetilde{K}'$ denote a residue epimorphism (of B-modules), and write $\widetilde{K} = \widetilde{B}_p \oplus V$ for some $\widetilde{B}$-vector space V. Then

$$\widetilde{T}_{m+n} = \widetilde{K}[\xi,\rho] = \widetilde{B}_p[\xi,\rho] \oplus V[\xi,\rho] \tag{3.3.2}$$

as $\widetilde{B}[\xi,\rho]$ modules. Since $\|F - h\| < \|F\|$,

$$\pi_p(F) \in (\iota'_\varepsilon(M)\cdot T_{m+n})^\sim.$$

Since $T_{m,n}(\varepsilon)$ is isometrically isomorphic to T_{m+n}, by Theorem 3.2.3 and Lemma 3.1.4, $\{\widetilde{G}_1, \ldots, \widetilde{G}_r\}$ generates $(\iota'_\varepsilon(M)\cdot T_{m+n})^\sim$. Thus there are $\widetilde{h}_i \in \widetilde{K}[\xi,\rho]$ such that

$$\pi_p(F) = \sum_{i=1}^r \widetilde{h}_i\widetilde{G}_i. \tag{3.3.3}$$

By (3.3.2) we may assume that $\widetilde{h}_1, \ldots, \widetilde{h}_r \in \widetilde{B}_p[\xi,\rho]$. Furthermore, since each component of each $\widetilde{G}_i$ is either 0 or a sum of monomials of total ρ-degree equal to $\widetilde{o}(\widetilde{G}_i)$ we may assume that

$$\max\{\widetilde{o}(G_i) + \widetilde{d}(\widetilde{h}_i) : \widetilde{h}_i \neq 0\} = \widetilde{d}(F).$$

Find $h_1, \ldots, h_r \in B_p[\xi,\rho]$ with

$$\max\{\widetilde{o}(G_i) + \deg_\rho(h_i) : h_i \neq 0\} = \widetilde{d}(F)$$

and $\pi_p(h_i) = \widetilde{h}_i$, $1 \le i \le r$. Now by (3.3.3),

$$\pi_p\Big(F - \sum_{i=1}^{r} h_i G_i\Big) = 0.$$

This proves the claim.

By (3.3.1) and Claim A, there are polynomials $h_{i0} \in B[\xi, \rho]$ such that

$$\max_{1\le i\le r} \|h_{i0}\| = \|\iota'_\varepsilon(f)\|,$$

$$\Big\|\iota'_\varepsilon(f) - \sum_{i=1}^{r} h_{i0} G_i\Big\| < \|\iota'_\varepsilon(f)\| \quad \text{and}$$

$$\max\{\widetilde{\mathrm{o}}(G_i) + \deg_\rho(h_{i0})\colon h_{i0} \ne 0\} = \widetilde{d}(\iota'_\varepsilon(f)).$$

Moreover, since $\sum_\nu c^{|\nu|}\rho^\nu$ majorizes each component of $\iota'_\varepsilon(f)$,

$$\|h_{i0}\| \le \varepsilon^{\widetilde{d}(\iota'_\varepsilon(f))} \le \varepsilon^{\widetilde{\mathrm{o}}(G_i)} \cdot \varepsilon^{\deg_\rho(h_{i0})}.$$

In the next claim, we iterate this procedure.

***Claim* (B).** — *There is a finite sequence $\{h_{ij}\} \subset B[\xi, \rho]$ such that*

(i) *for each s,* $\Big\|\iota'_\varepsilon(f) - \sum_{j=0}^{s}\sum_{i=1}^{r} h_{ij} G_i\Big\| < \Big\|\iota'_\varepsilon(f) - \sum_{j=0}^{s-1}\sum_{i=1}^{r} h_{ij} G_i\Big\|$,

(ii) *for each s,* $\max_{1\le i\le r} \|h_{is}\| = \Big\|\iota'_\varepsilon(f) - \sum_{j=0}^{s-1}\sum_{i=1}^{r} h_{ij} G_i\Big\|$,

(iii) *for each i, s,* $\sum_{j=0}^{s} h_{ij}$ *is majorized by* $c^{\widetilde{\mathrm{o}}(G_i)} \sum_\nu c^{|\nu|}\rho^\nu$, *and*

(iv) $\Big\|\iota'_\varepsilon(f) - \sum_{j\ge 0}\sum_{i=1}^{r} h_{ij} G_i\Big\| < \varepsilon^\beta$.

Note that the sum in (iv) *is a finite sum.*

Assume h_{ij}, $1 \le i \le r$, $0 \le j \le s$, have been chosen so that conditions (i), (ii) and (iii) are satisfied, as they are by $h_{10}, \ldots, h_{r0}$. Assume condition (iv) is not satisfied, and find $p \in \mathbb{N}$ so that

$$\iota'_\varepsilon(f) - \sum_{j=0}^{s}\sum_{i=1}^{r} h_{ij} G_i \in (B_p\langle\xi, \rho\rangle)^\ell \setminus (B_{p+1}\langle\xi, \rho\rangle)^\ell. \tag{3.3.4}$$

Since condition (iv) is not satisfied and since $\varepsilon^\beta > \|\iota'_\varepsilon(f)\|_{\iota'_\varepsilon(M)\cdot T_{m+n}}$, we may apply Claim A to $F := \iota'_\varepsilon(f) - \sum_{j=0}^{s}\sum_{i=1}^{r} h_{ij} G_i$. This yields polynomials $h_{is+1} \in B_p[\xi, \rho]$ such that

$$\Big\|\iota'_\varepsilon(f) - \sum_{j=0}^{s+1}\sum_{i=0}^{r} h_{ij} G_i\Big\| < \Big\|\iota'_\varepsilon(f) - \sum_{j=0}^{s}\sum_{i=1}^{r} h_{ij} G_i\Big\| \tag{3.3.5}$$

and

$$(3.3.6) \qquad \max_{1\leq i\leq r} \{\widetilde{o}(G_i) + \deg_\rho h_{is+1} : h_{is+1} \neq 0\} = d,$$

where $d := \widetilde{d}\left(\iota'_\varepsilon(f) - \sum_{j=0}^{s} \sum_{i=1}^{r} h_{ij} G_i\right)$.

By (3.3.5), condition (i) is satisfied for $s+1$. Since $h_{is+1} \in B_p[\xi,\rho]$, by (3.3.4), condition (ii) is also satisfied for $s+1$. To prove (iii) for $s+1$, it suffices to show, for each $1 \leq i \leq r$, that $\|h_{is+1}\| \leq \varepsilon^{\widetilde{o}(G_i)+\deg_\rho(h_{is+1})}$. If $h_{is+1} = 0$ we are done. Otherwise, by (3.3.6),

$$\deg_\rho(h_{is+1}) \leq d - \widetilde{o}(G_i).$$

By (iii), each component of $\iota'_\varepsilon(f) - \sum_{j=0}^{s} \sum_{i=1}^{r} h_{ij} G_i$ is majorized by $\sum_\nu c^{|\nu|}\rho^\nu$. Therefore, $\left\|\iota'_\varepsilon(f) - \sum_{j=1}^{s} \sum_{i=1}^{r} h_{ij} G_i\right\| \leq \varepsilon^d$.

Since (ii) is satisfied for $s+1$, the above yields

$$\begin{aligned} \|h_{is+1}\| &\leq \left\|\iota'_\varepsilon(f) - \sum_{j=0}^{s}\sum_{j=1}^{r} h_{ij}G_i\right\| \\ &\leq \varepsilon^d \\ &= \varepsilon^{\widetilde{o}(G_i)+(d-\widetilde{o}(G_i))} \\ &\leq \varepsilon^{\widetilde{o}(G_i)+\deg_\rho(h_{is+1})}, \end{aligned}$$

proving that (iii) is satisfied for $s+1$. The claim now follows from the fact that $|B \setminus \{0\}| \subset \mathbb{R}_+ \setminus \{0\}$ is discrete.

For $1 \leq i \leq r$, put

$$h_i := c^{-\widetilde{o}(G_i)} \sum_{j\geq 0} h_{ij}.$$

Since h_i is a polynomial (recall that the above sum is finite), there is some $h_i^* \in S_{m,n}$ so that $h_i = \iota'_\varepsilon(h_i^*)$. By Claim B (iii), $\max_{1\leq i\leq r} \|h_i^*\| \leq 1$. Write

$$\iota'_\varepsilon(f) - \sum_{j\geq 0}\sum_{i=1}^{r} h_{ij}G_i = \sum_\nu C_\nu(\xi)\rho^\nu.$$

Then

$$f - \sum_{i=1}^{r} h_i^* g_i = \sum_\nu c^{-|\nu|} C_\nu(\xi)\rho^\nu.$$

Note that

$$\left\|f - \sum_{i=1}^{r} h_i^* g_i\right\| \leq 1 = \|f\|.$$

If $\left\|f - \sum_{i=1}^r h_i^* g_i\right\| < 1$ we are done. Otherwise, $\left\|f - \sum_{i=1}^r h_i^* g_i\right\| = 1$, and we want $\widetilde{\mathrm{o}}\left(f - \sum_{i=1}^r h_i^* g_i\right) > \beta$. Put $\gamma := \widetilde{\mathrm{o}}\left(f - \sum_{i=1}^r h_i^* g_i\right)$. Then

$$\max_{|\nu|=\gamma} \|c^{-\gamma} C_\nu\| = 1;$$

i.e., $\varepsilon^\gamma = \max_{|\nu|=\gamma} \|C_\nu\| \leq \left\|\iota'_\varepsilon(f) - \sum_{j\geq 0} \sum_{i=1}^r h_{ij} G_i\right\| < \varepsilon^\beta$. Therefore, $\gamma > \beta$.

Finally, in the case that $\alpha = \infty$, we must show that $v_M(f) = (0,0)$. By Theorem 3.1.3, we may assume that $v(f) = v_M(f)$ and hence $\|f\| = \|f\|_M$. By the above, we have

$$v(f) < (\|f\|, 2^{-\beta})$$

for all $\beta \in \mathbb{N}$. Hence $f = 0$; i.e., $v_M(f) = (0,0)$. □

Corollary 3.3.2. — *Let M be a submodule of $(S_{m,n})^\ell$, $n \geq 1$, and let $\varepsilon \in \sqrt{|K \setminus \{0\}|}$ with $1 > \varepsilon > \sigma(M)$. Then $M = \iota_\varepsilon^{-1}(\iota_\varepsilon(M) \cdot T_{m,n}(\varepsilon))$.*

Proof. — Let $f \in \iota_\varepsilon^{-1}(\iota_\varepsilon(M) \cdot T_{m,n}(\varepsilon))$. Since $\iota_\varepsilon(f) \in \iota_\varepsilon(M) \cdot T_{m,n}(\varepsilon)$, Theorem 3.3.1 with $\alpha = \infty$ yields $v_M(f) = (0,0)$. Hence by Theorem 3.1.3, $f \in M$. □

Corollary 3.3.3. — *Let M be a submodule of $(S_{m,n})^\ell$, $n \geq 1$ and let $f \in (S_{m,n})^\ell$. Then*

$$\|f\|_M = \lim_{\substack{\varepsilon \to 1^- \\ \varepsilon \in \sqrt{|K|}}} \|\iota_\varepsilon(f)\|_{\iota_\varepsilon(M)\cdot T_{m,n}(\varepsilon)}.$$

Indeed, find $h \in M$ so that $v_M(f) = v(f-h)$, and let $F := f - h$. Then for every $\varepsilon \in \sqrt{|K|}$, if $1 > \varepsilon > \sigma(M)$, we have

$$\|f\|_M = \|F\| \geq \|\iota_\varepsilon(f)\|_{\iota_\varepsilon(M)\cdot T_{m,n}(\varepsilon)} \geq \varepsilon^{\widetilde{\mathrm{o}}(F)} \|F\|. \tag{3.3.7}$$

Moreover, when in addition $\varepsilon > \sigma(F)$, equality holds in the rightmost part of (3.3.7).

Proof. — The only assertion that needs proof is

$$\|\iota_\varepsilon(f)\|_{\iota_\varepsilon(M)\cdot T_{m,n}(\varepsilon)} \geq \varepsilon^{\widetilde{\mathrm{o}}(F)} \|F\|. \tag{3.3.8}$$

Let $\alpha \in \mathbb{N} \cup \{\infty\}$ be the least element such that

$$\varepsilon^\alpha \|F\| < \|\iota_\varepsilon(F)\|_{\iota_\varepsilon(M)\cdot T_{m,n}(\varepsilon)} = \|\iota_\varepsilon(f)\|_{\iota_\varepsilon(M)\cdot T_{m,n}(\varepsilon)}.$$

If (3.3.8) does not hold, $\alpha \geq \widetilde{\mathrm{o}}(F) + 1$. So by Theorem 3.3.1,

$$v_M(f) = v(F) = (\|F\|, 2^{-\widetilde{\mathrm{o}}(F)}) \leq (\|F\|, 2^{-\widetilde{\mathrm{o}}(F)-1}).$$

If $F \neq 0$, this is a contradiction. The additional assertion in the case that $\varepsilon > \sigma(F)$ follows from $\|\iota_\varepsilon(f)\|_{\iota_\varepsilon(M)\cdot T_{m,n}(\varepsilon)} \leq \|\iota_\varepsilon(F)\|_{\sup} = \varepsilon^{\widetilde{\mathrm{o}}(F)} \cdot \|F\|$. □

Corollary 3.3.4. — *Let I be an ideal of $S_{m,n}$ and M a submodule of $(S_{m,n}/I)^\ell$. Let $\varphi : (S_{m,n})^\ell \to (S_{m,n}/I)^\ell$ denote the canonical projection and put $N := \varphi^{-1}(M)$. Let $\varepsilon \in \sqrt{|K \setminus \{0\}|}$ with $1 > \varepsilon > \sigma(N)$, and let $f \in (S_{m,n}/I)^\ell$. Then $v_M(f) \leq (\|f\|_{I\cdot(S_{m,n})^\ell}, 2^{-\alpha})$ where $\alpha \in \mathbb{N} \cup \{\infty\}$ is the least element such that*

$$\varepsilon^\alpha \|f\|_{I\cdot(S_{m,n})^\ell} \leq \|\iota_\varepsilon(f)\|_{\iota_\varepsilon(M)\cdot(T_{m,n}(\varepsilon)/\iota_\varepsilon(I)\cdot T_{m,n}(\varepsilon))}.$$

In particular, if $\alpha = \infty$ then $v_M(f) = 0$.

Proof. — By Lemma 3.1.4, there is some $F \in (S_{m,n})^\ell$ such that $\varphi(F) = f$ and $\|F\| = \|f\|_{I\cdot(S_{m,n})^\ell}$. Since

$$\|\iota_\varepsilon(f)\|_{\iota_\varepsilon(M)\cdot(T_{m,n}(\varepsilon)/\iota_\varepsilon(I)\cdot T_{m,n}(\varepsilon))} = \|\iota_\varepsilon(F)\|_{\iota_\varepsilon(N)\cdot T_{m,n}(\varepsilon)}$$

and

$$v_M(f) = v_N(F),$$

the conclusion follows from Theorem 3.3.1. □

3.4. Restrictions to Open Polydiscs. — In previous subsections, we studied properties of the restriction maps

$$\iota_\varepsilon : S_{m,n} \longrightarrow T_{m,n}(\varepsilon)$$

to the closed polydiscs $\operatorname{Max} T_{m,n}(\varepsilon)$. As in [**6**, Section 9.3], the collection

$$\{\operatorname{Max} T_{m,n}(\varepsilon) \colon \varepsilon \in \sqrt{|K \setminus \{0\}|}\}$$

is an admissible open cover of $\cup_\varepsilon \operatorname{Max} T_{m,n}(\varepsilon)$. In fact, as we will see in Subsection 4.1, $\cup_\varepsilon \operatorname{Max} T_{m,n}(\varepsilon) = \operatorname{Max} S_{m,n}$. Properties of the restriction maps ι_ε gave us information about residue norms v_M.

In this subsection, we study properties of restrictions from $\operatorname{Max} S_{m,n}$ to finite unions of disjoint open polydiscs. When the polydiscs have K-rational centers, these restriction maps take the form $\varphi : S_{m,n} \to \oplus_{j=1}^r S_{0,m+n}$. Such restrictions are not related in any natural way to admissible covers of $\operatorname{Max} S_{m,n}$. Nonetheless, as we show in Theorems 3.4.3 and 3.4.6, such restrictions are isometries in the residue norms derived from $\|\cdot\|$ and, respectively, I and $\varphi(I)$, provided that the finite collection of open polydiscs is chosen appropriately.

In Subsection 5.5, we prove that for certain reduced quotients $S_{m,n}/I$, the norms $\|\cdot\|_I$ and $\|\cdot\|_{\sup}$ are equivalent. In that subsection we use Theorems 3.4.3 and 3.4.6 to reduce this to the much simpler case of reduced quotients $S_{0,m+n}/I$.

We first treat the case of a restriction to a finite union of disjoint open polydiscs with K-rational centers. The extension to the case of non-K-rational centers is explained in Definition 3.4.4, Lemma 3.4.5 and Theorem 3.4.6.

Definition 3.4.1. — Let $c_1, \ldots, c_r \in (K^\circ)^m$ with $|c_i - c_j| = 1$, $1 \le i < j \le r$. For $j = 1, \ldots, r$, consider the ideal I_j of $S_{m,n+m}$ given by

$$I_j := (\xi_1 - c_{j1} - \rho_{n+1}, \ldots, \xi_m - c_{jm} - \rho_{n+m}) \cdot S_{m,n+m}.$$

Put $I := \cap_{j=1}^r I_j$ and define

$$D_{m,n}(c) := S_{m,n+m}/I.$$

Let

$$\omega_c : S_{m,n} \longrightarrow D_{m,n}(c)$$

be the K-algebra homomorphism induced by the natural inclusion $S_{m,n} \hookrightarrow S_{m,n+m}$.

For $c_1, \ldots, c_r$ as above, consider the open polydiscs

$$\Delta_{m,n}(c_j) := \{(a,b) \in (K')^{m+n} \colon |a - c_j| < 1 \text{ and } |b| < 1\},$$

where $K' \supset K$ is complete and algebraically closed. Put

$$\Delta_{m,n}(c) := \bigcup_{j=1}^r \Delta_{m,n}(c_j).$$

It is a consequence of the results in Subsection 5.3 that $D_{m,n}(c)$ is the ring of K-quasi-affinoid functions corresponding to the quasi-rational domain $\Delta_{m,n}(c)$, and that ω_c is an inclusion. This justifies regarding ω_c as a restriction to $\Delta_{m,n}(c)$. However, we make no use of the results of Subsection 5.3 here.

It is also a consequence of the results of Subsection 5.3 that $D_{m,n}(c)$ is isomorphic to $\oplus_{j=1}^r S_{0,n+m}$. The next lemma gives a proof of a sharper result.

It is easily checked that the assignments

$$\begin{aligned} \rho_i &\longmapsto (\rho_i, \ldots, \rho_i), && 1 \le i \le n+m, \\ \xi_i &\longmapsto (\rho_{n+i} + c_{1i}, \ldots, \rho_{n+i} + c_{ri}), && 1 \le i \le m, \end{aligned}$$

induce a K-algebra homomorphism

$$\chi_c : D_{m,n}(c) \longrightarrow \bigoplus_{j=1}^r S_{0,n+m}.$$

Lemma 3.4.2. — *χ_c is an isometric isomorphism; in particular,*

$$\|\chi_c(f)\| = \|f\|_I$$

for every $f \in D_{m,n}(c)$.

Proof. — Note, by the Weierstrass Division Theorem, Theorem 2.3.2, that

$$S_{m,n+m}/I_j = S_{0,n+m}, \quad 1 \le j \le r.$$

The fact that χ_c is an isomorphism is now a consequence of [**25**, Theorem 1.4], and the fact that the ideals $I_1, \ldots, I_r$ are coprime in pairs.

Since the map $D_{m,n}(c) \to D_{m,n}(c)/I_j \cdot D_{m,n}(c)$ is a contraction, $1 \le j \le r$, it follows that χ_c is a contraction. Thus we may define a $\widetilde{K}$-algebra homomorphism

$$\widetilde{\chi}_c \colon \widetilde{D}_{m,n}(c) \longrightarrow \bigoplus_{j=1}^{r} \widetilde{S}_{0,n+m},$$

as in the paragraph preceding Lemma 3.1.10. To show that χ_c is an isometry, it suffices to show that $\widetilde{\chi}_c$ is injective.

By Lemma 3.1.4,

$$\widetilde{D}_{m,n}(c) = \widetilde{S}_{m,n+m}/\widetilde{I}.$$

It is not hard to see that

$$\widetilde{I}_j = (\xi_1 - \widetilde{c}_{j1} - \rho_{n+1}, \ldots, \xi_m - \widetilde{c}_{jm} - \rho_{n+m}) \cdot \widetilde{S}_{m,n+m},$$

$1 \le j \le r$. (Indeed, there is a linear isometric change of variables under which the image of each ideal I_j is generated by $\xi_1, \ldots, \xi_m$.) Because $|c_i - c_j| = 1$, $1 \le i < j \le r$, the ideals $\widetilde{I}_1, \ldots, \widetilde{I}_r$ are coprime in pairs. Hence by [**25**, Theorem 1.3],

$$\bigcap_{j=1}^{r} \widetilde{I}_j = \prod_{j=1}^{r} \widetilde{I}_j.$$

We have:

$$\widetilde{I} = \left(\bigcap_{j=1}^{r} I_j\right)^{\sim} \subset \bigcap_{j=1}^{r} \widetilde{I}_j = \prod_{j=1}^{r} \widetilde{I}_j \subset \left(\prod_{j=1}^{r} I_j\right)^{\sim} \subset \left(\bigcap_{j=1}^{r} I_j\right)^{\sim}.$$

Thus $\widetilde{I} = \cap_{j=1}^{r} \widetilde{I}_j$. By [**25**, Theorem 1.4], $\widetilde{\chi}_c$ is an isomorphism. □

From now on, we will also denote by ω_c the map

$$\omega_c : S_{m,n} \to D_{m,n}(c) \xrightarrow{\chi_c} \bigoplus_{j=1}^{r} S_{0,n+m}.$$

Observe that

$$\omega_c(f(\xi, \rho)) = \bigoplus_{j=1}^{r} f(\rho_{n+1} + c_{j1}, \ldots, \rho_{n+m} + c_{jm}, \rho_1, \ldots, \rho_n).$$

Theorem 3.4.3. — *Let M be a submodule of $(S_{m,n})^{\ell}$. Suppose there are $c_1, \ldots, c_r \in (K^\circ)^m$ with $|c_i - c_j| = 1$, $1 \le i < j \le r$, such that for every $\mathfrak{p} \in \operatorname{Ass}((\widetilde{S}_{m,n})^{\ell}/\widetilde{M})$, there is an i, $1 \le i \le r$, with*

$$\mathfrak{m}_i := (\xi - \widetilde{c}_i, \rho) \supset \mathfrak{p},$$

(e.g., suppose K is algebraically closed). Consider the $S_{m,n}$-module homomorphism

$$\varphi : (S_{m,n})^{\ell} \to \left(\bigoplus_{j=1}^{r} S_{0,n+m}\right)^{\ell}$$

induced by ω_c. *Put* $N := \varphi(M) \cdot (\oplus_{j=1}^r S_{0,n+m})$. *Then:*

(i) *If* $\{g_1, \ldots, g_s\}$ *is a* $\|\cdot\|$*-strict generating system of* M, *then* $\{\varphi(g_1), \ldots, \varphi(g_s)\}$ *is a* $\|\cdot\|$*-strict generating system of* N.

(ii) $\|f\|_M = \|\varphi(f)\|_N$ *for every* $f \in (S_{m,n})^\ell$.

(iii) $\varphi^{-1}(N) = M$.

In particular, under the above assumptions on K, *given an ideal* I *of* $S_{m,n}$, *there is an isometric embedding* $\varphi : S_{m,n}/I \to A$, *where* A *is a finite extension of* $S_{0,d}$ *and* $d = \dim S_{m,n}/I$.

Proof

(i) This follows from Lemma 3.1.10 (i) once we show that $\widetilde{\omega}_c$ is flat. Applying [**25**, Theorem 7.1], to each of the r maximal ideals of $\oplus_{j=1}^r \widetilde{S}_{0,n+m}$, we are reduced to proving that each map

$$(\widetilde{S}_{m,n})_{\mathfrak{m}_j} \to \widetilde{S}_{0,n+m} : f(\xi, \rho) \mapsto f(\rho_{n+1} + \widetilde{c}_{j1}, \ldots, \rho_{n+m} + \widetilde{c}_{jm}, \rho_1, \ldots, \rho_n)$$

is flat, $1 \leq j \leq r$. The flatness of these maps is a consequence of the Local Flatness Criterion ([**25**, Theorem 22.3]), because

$$\widetilde{S}_{m,n}/\mathfrak{m}_j^\ell \cong \widetilde{S}_{0,n+m}/(\rho_1, \ldots, \rho_{n+m})^\ell = \widetilde{K}[\rho]/(\rho)^\ell$$

and $\mathfrak{m}_j$ is mapped into $\operatorname{rad}(\widetilde{S}_{0,n+m})$.

(ii) Let $f \in (S_{m,n})^\ell$. By Lemma 3.1.4, we may assume that

$$\|f\| = \|f\|_M = 1,$$

and we must prove that

$$\|\varphi(f)\|_N = 1.$$

In other words, we may assume that $\widetilde{f} \notin \widetilde{M}$ and we must prove that $\widetilde{\varphi}(\widetilde{f}) \notin \widetilde{N}$. By part (i) and Lemma 3.1.4, it suffices to show that

$$\widetilde{\varphi}(\widetilde{f}) \notin \widetilde{\varphi}(\widetilde{M}) \cdot \left(\bigoplus_{j=1}^r \widetilde{S}_{0,n+m} \right).$$

Put

$$P := (\widetilde{S}_{m,n})^\ell / \widetilde{M},$$

$$A := \widetilde{S}_{m,n}, \quad B := \bigoplus_{j=1}^r (\widetilde{S}_{m,n})_{\mathfrak{m}_j}, \quad C := \bigoplus_{j=1}^r \widetilde{S}_{0,n+m}.$$

Consider the sequence

$$P \longrightarrow P \otimes_A B \longrightarrow (P \otimes_A B) \otimes_B C.$$

We wish to show that the composition is injective. The injectivity of $P \otimes_A B \to (P \otimes_A B) \otimes_B C$ is a consequence of [**25**, Theorem 7.5], because C is a faithfully flat B-algebra (see proof of part (i)). It remains to show that the map

$$P \longrightarrow \bigoplus_{j=1}^{r} P_{\mathfrak{m}_j} = P \otimes_A B$$

is injective.

Let $x \in P \setminus \{0\}$. We must show for some j, $1 \le j \le r$, that

$$\mathrm{Ann}(x) := \{a \in \widetilde{S}_{m,n} \colon ax = 0\} \subset \mathfrak{m}_j.$$

By [**25**, Theorem 6.1], there is some associated prime ideal $\mathfrak{q} \in \mathrm{Ass}(P)$ such that $\mathrm{Ann}(x) \subset \mathfrak{q}$. But we have assumed that $\mathfrak{q} \subset \mathfrak{m}_j$ for some j, $1 \le j \le r$. This completes the proof of part (ii).

(iii) This is an immediate consequence of part (ii), above.

The last assertion is now a consequence of Remark 2.3.6 and the observation that $\oplus_{j=1}^{r} S_{0,n+m}$ is a finite $S_{0,n+m}$-algebra. □

In what follows, we treat the case that the centers c may be non-K-rational. Notice that even in the rational case, because K is non-Archimedean, discs do not have uniquely determined centers (indeed, every point of the disc is a center). Hence the rational "centers" actually correspond to points of $\widetilde{K}^m \times \{0\}^n$. In the non-$K$-rational case, they correspond to maximal ideals of $\widetilde{S}_{m,n}$. In other words, for c, $c' \in (K_{\mathrm{alg}}^{\circ})^m$, the rings of K-quasi-affinoid functions on the open unit polydiscs $\Delta_{m,n}(c)$ and $\Delta_{m,n}(c')$ coincide precisely when there is an element γ of the Galois group of K_{alg} over K such that $|c - \gamma(c')| < 1$. This occurs if, and only if, $\mathfrak{m}_{\widetilde{c}} = \mathfrak{m}_{\widetilde{c}'}$, where $\mathfrak{m}_{\widetilde{c}}$ is the maximal ideal of elements of $\widetilde{S}_{m,n}$ vanishing at $(\widetilde{c}, 0)$. (The reader may wish to refer to Subsections 4.1 and 5.3.) This motivates the following definition.

Definition 3.4.4. — Let $c_1, \ldots, c_r \in (K_{\mathrm{alg}}^{\circ})^m$ satisfy

$$\mathfrak{m}_{\widetilde{c}_i} \neq \mathfrak{m}_{\widetilde{c}_j},\ 1 \le i < j \le r, \quad \text{and} \quad [K(c) : K] = [\widetilde{K}(\widetilde{c}) : \widetilde{K}].$$

For $j = 1, \ldots, r$, write $c_j = (c_{j1}, \ldots, c_{jm})$ and let $f_{j\ell}(\xi_1, \ldots, \xi_\ell)$ be the polynomial monic and of least degree in ξ_ℓ such that $f_{j\ell}(c_{j1}, \ldots, c_{j\ell}) = 0$. We may choose $f_{j\ell} \in K^{\circ}[\xi_1, \ldots, \xi_\ell]$.

Consider the ideal I_j of $S_{m,n+m}$ given by

$$I_j := (f_{j1}(\xi_1) - \rho_{n+1}, \ldots, f_{jm}(\xi_1, \ldots, \xi_m) - \rho_{n+m}) \cdot S_{m,n+m}.$$

Put $I := \cap_{j=1}^{r} I_j$ and define

$$D_{m,n}(c) := S_{m,n+m}/I.$$

Let

$$\omega_c : S_{m,n} \longrightarrow D_{m,n}(c)$$

be the K-algebra homomorphism induced by the natural inclusion $S_{m,n} \hookrightarrow S_{m,n+m}$.

As we remarked above, $D_{m,n}(c)$ is again the ring of K-quasi-affinoid functions on $\Delta_{m,n}(c)$. When c is non-K-rational, the structure of $D_{m,n}(c)$ is only slightly more complicated.

For $i \neq j$, $\mathfrak{m}_{\widetilde{c}_i} \neq \mathfrak{m}_{\widetilde{c}_j}$. It follows from the Nullstellensatz for $\widetilde{K}[T]$ that $\mathfrak{m}_{\widetilde{c}_i} + \mathfrak{m}_{\widetilde{c}_j} = (1)$. Since $\widetilde{I}_i + \widetilde{I}_j + (\rho) \supset \mathfrak{m}_{\widetilde{c}_i} + \mathfrak{m}_{\widetilde{c}_j}$, $\widetilde{I}_i + \widetilde{I}_j$ contains a unit of the form

$$1 + f, \qquad f \in (\rho)\widetilde{S}_{m,n+m}.$$

This implies that the ideals I_j are coprime in pairs. By [**25**, Theorem 1.4], the induced map

$$\chi_c : D_{m,n}(c) \longrightarrow \bigoplus_{j=1}^{r} S_{m,n+m}/I_j$$

is a K-algebra isomorphism.

Since $S_{m,n+m}/I_j = D_{m,n}(c)/I_j$, the map χ_c is a contraction. To see that it is an isometry, we show that the induced map

$$\widetilde{\chi}_c : \widetilde{D}_{m,n}(c) \longrightarrow \bigoplus_{j=1}^{r} \widetilde{S}_{m,n+m}/\widetilde{I}_j$$

is an isomorphism. This is a consequence of the above-noted fact that the ideals $\widetilde{I}_j$ are coprime in pairs.

Each element $f_{j\ell}(\xi_1, \ldots, \xi_\ell) - \rho_{n+\ell}$ is regular in ξ_ℓ in the sense of Definition 2.3.1. Therefore, by the Weierstrass Division Theorem 2.3.2, each $S_{m,n+m}/I_j$ is a finite, free $S_{0,n+m}$-module.

We have established the following generalization of Lemma 3.4.2.

Lemma 3.4.5. — *With the above notation, χ_c is an isometric isomorphism; in particular,*

$$\|\chi_c(f)\| := \max_{1 \leq j \leq r} \|f\|_{I_j} = \|f\|_I$$

for every $f \in D_{m,n}(c)$. Furthermore, there is a finite, torsion-free monomorphism $S_{0,n+m} \to D_{m,n}(c)$.

The generalization of Theorem 3.4.3 is

Theorem 3.4.6. — *Let M be a submodule of $(S_{m,n})^\ell$. Choose $c_1, \ldots, c_r \in (K_{\text{alg}}^\circ)^m$ with $\mathfrak{m}_{\widetilde{c}_i} \neq \mathfrak{m}_{\widetilde{c}_j}$, $1 \leq i < j \leq r$, such that for every $\mathfrak{p} \in \operatorname{Ass}((\widetilde{S}_{m,n})^\ell/\widetilde{M})$ there is an i, $1 \leq i \leq r$, with*

$$\mathfrak{m}_{\widetilde{c}_i} \supset \mathfrak{p},$$

where $\mathfrak{m}_{\widetilde{c}_i}$ is the maximal ideal of elements of $\widetilde{S}_{m,n}$ that vanish at $(\widetilde{c}_i, 0)$.

Consider the $S_{m,n}$-module homomorphism

$$\varphi : (S_{m,n})^\ell \longrightarrow \left(\bigoplus_{j=1}^{r} S_{m,n+m}/I_j\right)^\ell$$

induced by $\chi_c \circ \omega_c$. Put $N := \varphi(M) \cdot (\oplus_{j=1}^r S_{m,n+m}/I_j)$. Then:

(i) *If $\{g_1, \ldots, g_s\}$ is a $\|\cdot\|$-strict generating system of M, then $\{\varphi(g_1), \ldots, \varphi(g_s)\}$ is a $\|\cdot\|_I$-strict generating system of N.*

(ii) *$\|f\|_M = \|\varphi(f)\|_N$ for every $f \in (S_{m,n})^\ell$.*

(iii) *$\varphi^{-1}(N) = M$.*

In particular, for any quasi-affinoid algebra $B = S_{m,n}/I$, there is an isometric embedding $\varphi : B \to A$, where A is a finite extension of $S_{0,d}$ and $d = \dim B$.

Proof. — The proof is nearly identical to that of Theorem 3.4.3. Note that each

$$\widetilde{S}_{m,n+m}/\widetilde{I}_j \cong S_{0,n+m}(E, K(c_j))^\sim$$

by the Cohen Structure Theorem [**25**, Theorem 28.3]. □

Remark 3.4.7. — By Corollary 5.1.10, the K-algebra homomorphisms φ of Theorems 3.4.3 and 3.4.6 are isometries in $\|\cdot\|_{\sup}$.

4. The Commutative Algebra of $S_{m,n}$

In this Section, we establish several key algebraic properties of the rings of separated power series. The rings $S_{m,n}$ satisfy a Nullstellensatz (Theorem 4.1.1), they are regular rings of dimension $m+n$ (Corollary 4.2.2), they are excellent when the characteristic of K is zero (Proposition 4.2.3), and sometimes when the characteristic of K is not zero (Example 4.2.4 and Proposition 4.2.5), and they are UFDs (Theorem 4.2.7).

4.1. The Nullstellensatz. — Let A be a K-algebra. We make the following definitions (see [**6**, Definition 3.8.1.2]). Let $\operatorname{Max} A$ denote the collection of all maximal ideals of A, and put

$$\operatorname{Max}_K A := \left\{\mathfrak{m} \in \operatorname{Max} A : A/\mathfrak{m} \text{ is algebraic over } K\right\}.$$

For $\mathfrak{m} \in \operatorname{Max}_K A$ and $f \in A$, denote by $f(\mathfrak{m})$ the image of f under the canonical residue epimorphism $\pi_\mathfrak{m} : A \to A/\mathfrak{m}$. Since $A/\mathfrak{m}$ is an algebraic field extension of K and since K is complete in $|\cdot|$, there is a unique extension of $|\cdot|$ to an absolute value on $A/\mathfrak{m}$, which we also denote by $|\cdot|$. Now define the function $\|\cdot\|_{\sup} : A \to \mathbb{R}_+ \cup \{\infty\}$ by

$$\|f\|_{\sup} := \begin{cases} 0 & \text{if } \operatorname{Max}_K A = \varnothing, \\ \sup\limits_{\mathfrak{m} \in \operatorname{Max}_K A} |f(\mathfrak{m})| & \text{if } \operatorname{Max}_K A \neq \varnothing,\ f(\operatorname{Max}_K A) \text{ bounded}, \\ \infty & \text{otherwise.} \end{cases}$$

If $f(\mathrm{Max}_K A)$ is bounded for all $f \in A$, then $\|\cdot\|_{\sup}$ is a K-algebra seminorm on A, called the *supremum seminorm* ([**6**, Lemma 3.8.1.3]). We denote the *nilradical* of an ideal I by $\mathfrak{N}(I) := \{f : f^n \in I \text{ for some } n \in \mathbb{N}\}$.

Theorem 4.1.1 **(Nullstellensatz)**

(i) *Let I be any proper ideal of $S_{m,n}$, then* $\mathfrak{N}(I) = \bigcap\{\mathfrak{m} \in \mathrm{Max}_K S_{m,n} : \mathfrak{m} \supset I\}$.

(ii) $\mathrm{Max}\, S_{m,n} = \mathrm{Max}_K S_{m,n}$.

(iii) *Put*

$$U := \{\mathfrak{m} \in \mathrm{Max}\, K[\xi, \rho] : \max_{1\leq i\leq m} |\xi_i(\mathfrak{m})| \leq 1, \max_{1\leq j\leq n} |\rho_j(\mathfrak{m})| < 1\}.$$

Then the map $\mathfrak{m} \mapsto \mathfrak{m} \cdot S_{m,n}$ *is a bijective correspondence between* U *and* $\mathrm{Max}\, S_{m,n}$.

Proof. — Since $S_{m,0} = T_m$, if $n = 0$ we are done by [**6**, Theorem 7.1.2.3, Proposition 7.1.1.1 and Lemma 7.1.1.2]. Assume $n \geq 1$.

(i) Let $I \subset S_{m,n}$ be a proper ideal and let $\varepsilon \in \sqrt{|K \setminus \{0\}|}$ with $\varepsilon > \sigma(I)$. By Corollary 3.3.2, $f^\ell \in I$ if, and only if, $\iota_\varepsilon(f)^\ell \in \iota_\varepsilon(I) \cdot T_{m,n}(\varepsilon)$. Hence $\mathfrak{N}(I) = S_{m,n} \cap \mathfrak{N}(\iota_\varepsilon(I) \cdot T_{m,n}(\varepsilon))$. Therefore (i) follows from the Nullstellensatz for $T_{m,n}(\varepsilon)$ ([**6**, Theorem 7.1.2.3]).

(ii) This is an immediate consequence of (i).

(iii) In case K is algebraically closed this follows immediately from (ii). Otherwise, it follows from (ii) by Faithfully Flat Base Change (Lemma 3.1.11(iii)). Alternatively, (iii) follows immediately from (ii) and the Weierstrass Preparation and Division Theorems as follows.

Let $\mathfrak{m} \in U$. Since $K[\xi, \rho]/\mathfrak{m}$ is algebraic over K, there are polynomials $f_i(\zeta_i)$ and $g_j(\rho_j) \in \mathfrak{m}$, $1 \leq i \leq m$, $1 \leq j \leq n$. By [**6**, Proposition 3.8.1.7], we may assume that each f_i is regular in ξ_i and each g_j is regular in ρ_j in the senses of Definition 2.3.1. Applying the Weierstrass Division Theorems (Theorem 2.3.2) yields

$$K[\xi, \rho]/\mathfrak{m} = S_{m,n}/\mathfrak{m} \cdot S_{m,n};$$

hence $\mathfrak{m} \cdot S_{m,n} \in \mathrm{Max}\, S_{m,n}$.

Conversely, let $\mathfrak{m} \in \mathrm{Max}\, S_{m,n}$. By (ii), $\mathfrak{m} \in \mathrm{Max}_K\, S_{m,n}$. Since $S_{m,n}/\mathfrak{m}$ is algebraic over K, we obtain polynomials $f_i(\xi_i)$, $g_j(\rho_j) \in \mathfrak{m}$, $1 \leq i \leq m$, $1 \leq j \leq n$. By the Weierstrass Preparation Theorem (Corollary 2.3.3) we may assume that all $f_i(\xi_i)$ and $g_j(\rho_j)$ are monic polynomials, regular in the senses of Definition 2.3.1. Euclidean Division in $K[\xi, \rho]$ and Weierstrass Division in $S_{m,n}$ yield

$$K[\xi, \rho]/(\mathfrak{m} \cap K[\xi, \rho]) = S_{m,n}/\mathfrak{m}.$$

The fact that $\mathfrak{m} \cap K[\xi, \rho] \in U$ follows from the facts that no f_i nor g_j is a unit. □

Since $\|\cdot\|_{\sup}$ coincides with $\|\cdot\|_\varepsilon$ on $T_{m,n}(\varepsilon)$ ([**6**, Corollary 5.1.4.6]), it follows immediately from Theorem 4.1.1 that $\|\cdot\|_{\sup}$ coincides with $\|\cdot\|$ on $S_{m,n}$. A K-algebra A is called a *Banach function algebra* iff $\|\cdot\|_{\sup}$ is a complete norm on A. Hence when $S_{m,n}$ is complete in $\|\cdot\|$ (*cf.* Theorem 2.1.3), it is a Banach function algebra. In Subsection 5.5, we show that in many cases, reduced quotients of the $S_{m,n}$ are also Banach function algebras.

Proposition 4.1.2. — *Let $A = S_{m,n}/I$ and $\mathfrak{m} \in \operatorname{Max} A$. Consider the field $K' := A/\mathfrak{m}$, which is complete since it is a finite K-algebra. Then for each representative $f = \sum a_{\mu\nu}\xi^\mu\rho^\nu \in S_{m,n}$ of an element of A:*

(i) *$f(\mathfrak{m}) := f + \mathfrak{m} = \sum a_{\mu\nu}\overline{\xi}^\mu\overline{\rho}^\nu \in K'$, where $\overline{\xi} := \xi + \mathfrak{m}$, $\overline{\rho} := \rho + \mathfrak{m}$.*

(ii) *$|f(\mathfrak{m})| \le \|f\|_I$. Indeed*

$$|f(\mathfrak{m})| \le \|f^\ell\|_I^{1/\ell} \text{ for } \ell = 1, 2, \ldots.$$

(iii) *If $f = (f_1 + I) + (f_2 + I)$ where $f_1, f_2 \in S_{m,n}$, $\|f_1\| < 1$, $\|f_2\| \le 1$ and $f_2 \in (\rho)S^\circ_{m,n}$, then $|f(\mathfrak{m})| < 1$.*

Proof. — (ii) and (iii) follow immediately from (i) and Theorem 4.1.1(iii). (i) is immediate if $K' = K$, since $f(\xi,\rho) - f(\overline{\xi},\overline{\rho})$ belongs to the maximal ideal

$$\{g \in S_{m,n} : g(\overline{\xi},\overline{\rho}) = 0\},$$

which must contain the polynomial generators of $\mathfrak{m}$. Now note that there is a natural inclusion $S_{m,n}(E,K) \hookrightarrow S_{m,n}(E,K')$. □

In the affinoid case, the supremum seminorm behaves well with respect to extension of the ground field. This follows from the Noether Normalization Theorem for affinoid algebras [**6**, Corollary 6.1.2.2], from [**6**, Proposition 6.2.2.4], from [**6**, Lemma 6.2.2.3], and from the fact that $\|f\|_{\sup}$ cannot decrease after extension of the ground field (ground field extensions of affinoid algebras are faithfully flat: see Lemma 3.1.11 (iii)). The supremum seminorms on quotient rings of the $S_{m,n}$ also behave well with respect to ground field extensions, even though, unlike in the affinoid case, the supremum need not be attained.

Proposition 4.1.3. — *Let K' be a complete, valued field extension of K, let $E' \subset (K')^\circ$ be a complete, quasi-Noetherian ring (in characteristic p, let E' be a complete DVR) and put $S_{m,n} := S_{m,n}(E,K)$, $S'_{m,n} := S_{m,n}(E',K')$. Assume $S'_{m,n} \supset S_{m,n}$. Let I be an ideal of $S_{m,n}$ and put $I' := I \cdot S'_{m,n}$. Then for any $f \in S_{m,n}/I$,*

$$\sup\{|f(x)| : x \in \operatorname{Max} S_{m,n}/I\} = \sup\{|f(x)| : x \in \operatorname{Max} S'_{m,n}/I'\}.$$

Indeed, for any $f \in S_{m,n}/I$ and for any $c \in \mathbb{R}$, if $|f(x)| < c$ for all $x \in \operatorname{Max} S_{m,n}/I$ then also $|f(x)| < c$ for all $x \in \operatorname{Max} S'_{m,n}/I'$.

Proof. — Assume $|f(x)| < c$ for all $x \in \operatorname{Max} S_{m,n}/I$ and let $x_0 \in \operatorname{Max} S'_{m,n}/I'$. Let $\varepsilon \in \sqrt{|K \setminus \{0\}|}$ be such that $1 > \varepsilon > \max\{\sigma(I), \sigma(I'), \sigma(x_0)\}$. By the Maximum Modulus Principle [**6**, Proposition 6.2.1.4], we have: $\|\iota_\varepsilon(f)\|_{\sup} < c$, where the supremum is taken over the affinoid variety $\operatorname{Max}(T_{m,n}(\varepsilon)/\iota_\varepsilon(I) \cdot T_{m,n}(\varepsilon))$. By the above observation, it follows that $||\iota_\varepsilon(f)||_{\sup} < c$, where this time, the supremum is taken over $\operatorname{Max} T'_{m,n}(\varepsilon)/I' \cdot T'_{m,n}(\varepsilon)$. Thus $|f(x_0)| < c$. □

Remark 4.1.4. — The Maximum Modulus Principle holds for quotients of $T_m = S_{m,0}$ (see [**6**, Proposition 6.2.1.4]), but not, in general, for quotients of $S_{m,n}$, $n > 0$. Nevertheless, for $f \in S_{m,n}/I$,

$$||f||_{\sup} \in \sqrt{|K|}.$$

This is a consequence of the quantifier elimination (*cf.* [**17**, Corollary 7.3.3]), and Proposition 4.1.3. It also follows from the results of this paper (see Corollary 5.1.11).

The following weak form of the Minimum Modulus Principle is an immediate consequence of the Nullstellensatz (Theorem 4.1.1). Let $A = S_{m,n}/I$ and let $f \in A$. If $\inf\{|f(x)| : x \in \operatorname{Max} A\} = 0$ then there is an $x \in \operatorname{Max} A$ such that $f(x) = 0$.

Remark 4.1.5. — Here we give a second proof that $\operatorname{Max} S_{m,n} = \operatorname{Max}_K S_{m,n}$.

We begin by defining an additive valuation w on $S_{m,n}$. Consider $\mathbb{R} \times \mathbb{N}^n$ as an ordered group with coordinatewise addition and lexicographic order. We define a map $w : S_{m,n} \to \mathbb{R} \times \mathbb{N}^n \cup \{\infty\}$ by putting $w(0) := \infty$ and, for $f \in S_{m,n} \setminus \{0\}$, $w(f) := (\alpha, \nu_0)$, where $\alpha \in \mathbb{R}$ and $\nu_0 \in \mathbb{N}^n$ are determined as follows. Write $f = \sum_{\mu,\nu} a_{\mu,\nu}\xi^\mu\rho^\nu = \sum_\nu f_\nu(\xi)\rho^\nu$. Then put $\alpha := \min_{\mu,\nu} \operatorname{ord} a_{\mu\nu}$ (where $\operatorname{ord} : K \to \mathbb{R}$ is the additive valuation corresponding to the absolute value $|\cdot| : K \to \mathbb{R}_+$) and let $\nu_0 \in \mathbb{N}^n$ be the element uniquely determined by the conditions

$$||f_{\nu_0}|| = ||f||, \text{ and}$$
$$||f_\nu|| < ||f|| \text{ for all } \nu < \nu_0 \text{ lexicographically.}$$

We call the multi-index ν_0 the *total residue order* of f, and we call the coefficient $f_{\nu_0}(\xi)$ the *leading coefficient* of f. It is not difficult to show that w is an additive valuation on $S_{m,n}$.

Proposition. — *Each ideal of $S_{m,n}$ is strictly closed in w.*

Proof. — This is proved analogously to Theorem 3.1.3 using the facts that

$$||B\langle\xi\rangle[\![\rho]\!] \setminus \{0\}||$$

is discrete and that $\mathbb{N}^n$ with the lexicographic order is well-ordered. We leave the details to the reader. (See also [**17**, Section 2.6].) □

Note that if I is an ideal of $S_{m,n}$ and if $\infty \neq w(f) \geq w(f-h)$ for each $h \in I$, then there is no element h of I with the same total residue order ν_0 as f and such that $||h_{\nu_0}|| = ||f_{\nu_0}|| > ||f_{\nu_0} - h_{\nu_0}||$.

Theorem. — $\operatorname{Max} S_{m,n} = \operatorname{Max}_K S_{m,n}$.

Proof. — If there is some $f \in \mathfrak{m}$ which is preregular (in the sense of Definition 2.3.4) in ξ (or ρ) then, after a change of variables among the ξ's (or ρ's), we may assume that f is regular in ξ_m (or in ρ_n). If f is regular in ξ_m (the case that f is regular in ρ_n is similar), then by Weierstrass Division, the map $S_{m-1,n} \to S_{m,n}/\mathfrak{m}$ is finite. Thus $\mathfrak{m}' := \mathfrak{m} \cap S_{m-1,n}$ is maximal, and we are done by induction on the number of variables. We henceforth assume that $\mathfrak{m}$ contains no element which is preregular in any variables.

For each $\nu \in \mathbb{N}^n$, let $\mathfrak{m}_\nu$ be the set in $S_{m,0}$ of leading coefficients of those elements of $\mathfrak{m}$ with total residue order ν. If $\mu_1 \leq \nu_1, \ldots, \mu_n \leq \nu_n$ then $\mathfrak{m}_\mu \subset \mathfrak{m}_\nu$. Let $\widetilde{\mathfrak{m}}_\nu = (\mathfrak{m}_\nu \cap S^{\circ}_{m,0})/(\mathfrak{m}_\nu \cap S^{\circ\circ}_{m,0})$, if $\mathfrak{m}_\nu \neq \varnothing$ and $\widetilde{\mathfrak{m}}_\nu = (0)$ otherwise. Then $\widetilde{\mathfrak{m}}_\nu$ is an ideal of $\widetilde{S}_{m,0}$. Note that none of the ideals $\widetilde{\mathfrak{m}}_\nu$ can be the unit ideal since then there would be an element of $\mathfrak{m}$ which is preregular in ρ. Since $\mathfrak{m} \neq (0)$, at least one $\widetilde{\mathfrak{m}}_\nu \neq (0)$. Moreover, if A is any Noetherian ring and $\{I_\nu\}_{\nu \in \mathbb{N}^n}$ is a family of ideals of A such that $I_\mu \subset I_\nu$ whenever $\mu_1 \leq \nu_1, \ldots, \mu_n \leq \nu_n$, then the family $\{I_\nu\}_{\nu \in \mathbb{N}^n}$ is finite (induct on n).

We can therefore find some $a(\xi) \in S_{m,0}$ with $\|a\| = 1$ such that $\tilde{a} \in \widetilde{\mathfrak{m}}_\nu$ for each $\widetilde{\mathfrak{m}}_\nu \neq (0)$. Put

$$c := a + 1. \tag{4.1.1}$$

Since $\|a\| = 1$ and a is not a unit of $S_{m,0}$, it follows that $\|c\| = 1$ and that c is not a unit. Furthermore, $c \notin \mathfrak{m}$ since clearly c is preregular in ξ. Thus there is some $f \in S_{m,n}$ such that $cf - 1 \in \mathfrak{m}$. By the above Proposition, we may assume that for each $h \in \mathfrak{m}$

$$w(f) \geq w(f - h). \tag{4.1.2}$$

Write $f = \sum f_\nu(\xi)\rho^\nu$, and let f_{ν_0} be the leading coefficient of f. By (4.1.2), there is no $h \in \mathfrak{m}_{\nu_0}$ of total residue order ν_0 with $\|h\| = \|f\|$ and $\|f_{\nu_0} - h_{\nu_0}\| < \|f_{\nu_0}\|$.

Claim. — *$\|f_{\nu_0}\| > 1$ and $\nu_0 \neq 0$.*

If $\|f\| < 1$ then $cf - 1$ is a unit, contradicting the fact that $\mathfrak{m}$ is a proper ideal. Hence $\|f\| \geq 1$. If $\nu_0 = 0$, then since c is not a unit, $cf - 1$ is preregular in ξ, which is a contradiction. Hence $\|f\| \geq 1$ and $\nu_0 \neq 0$. If $\|f\| = 1$ and $\|f_0\| = 1$, then the total residue order of f is 0, a contradiction. If $\|f\| = 1$ and $\|f_0\| < 1$ then $cf - 1 \in \mathfrak{m}$ is a unit, also a contradiction. This proves the claim.

Let $\|f_{\nu_0}\| = |b|$. By the claim, $\frac{1}{b}(cf - 1)$ has total residue order ν_0 and leading coefficient $\frac{c}{b} f_{\nu_0} \in \mathfrak{m}_{\nu_0}$. But by (4.1.1), $cf_{\nu_0} \in \mathfrak{m}_{\nu_0}$ implies $(\frac{1}{b} f_{\nu_0})^\sim \in \widetilde{\mathfrak{m}}_{\nu_0}$, contradicting (4.1.2). □

4.2. Completions. — One of the main applications of the Nullstellensatz is to give us information about maximal-adic completions of the $S_{m,n}$. In this subsection, we prove the following facts: $S_{m,n}$ is a regular ring of dimension $m + n$, restriction maps to closed subpolydiscs are flat, $S_{m,n}$ is a UFD, $S_{m,n}$ is excellent in characteristic 0 and sometimes in characteristic $p>0$, and, when $S_{m,n}$ is a G-ring, radical ideals of $S_{m,n}$ stay radical when they are expanded under restriction maps to closed polydiscs.

Proposition 4.2.1. — *Let $\varepsilon \in \sqrt{|K \setminus \{0\}|}$, $1>\varepsilon>0$, let $\mathfrak{M} \in \operatorname{Max} T_{m,n}(\varepsilon)$, put $\mathfrak{m} := K[\xi,\rho] \cap \mathfrak{M}$, and $\mathfrak{N} := \iota_\varepsilon^{-1}(\mathfrak{M}) \in \operatorname{Max} S_{m,n}$. Then ι_ε induces K-algebra isomorphisms*

$$\text{(i)} \qquad S_{m,n}/\mathfrak{N}^\ell \cong T_{m,n}(\varepsilon)/\mathfrak{M}^\ell \cong K[\xi,\rho]/\mathfrak{m}^\ell$$

for every $\ell \in \mathbb{N}$.

Let I be an ideal of $S_{m,n}$. Suppose $\mathfrak{M} \in \operatorname{Max} T_{m,n}(\varepsilon)$ with $\mathfrak{M} \supset \iota_\varepsilon(I)$, and put $\mathfrak{N} := \iota_\varepsilon^{-1}(\mathfrak{M})$. Then ι_ε induces K-algebra isomorphisms

$$\text{(ii)} \qquad \big(S_{m,n}/I\big)\widehat{_{\mathfrak{N}}} \cong \big(T_{m,n}(\varepsilon)/\iota_\varepsilon(I)\cdot T_{m,n}(\varepsilon)\big)\widehat{_{\mathfrak{M}}},$$

where $\widehat{\ }$ denotes the maximal-adic completion of a local ring.

Proof

(i) is immediate from the Weierstrass Preparation and Division Theorems, and Theorem 4.1.1(ii).

(ii) By part (i), ι_ε induces a K-algebra isomorphism

$$\widehat{\iota_\varepsilon} : (S_{m,n})\widehat{_{\mathfrak{N}}} \longrightarrow (T_{m,n}(\varepsilon))\widehat{_{\mathfrak{M}}}.$$

Part (ii) now follows immediately from [**25**, Theorem 8.11]. □

Corollary 4.2.2. — *For each $\mathfrak{m} \in \operatorname{Max} S_{m,n}$, $(S_{m,n})_\mathfrak{m}$ is a regular local ring of Krull dimension $m+n$; moreover, $S_{m,n}$ is a regular ring.*

Proof. — By Hilbert's Nullstellensatz, each $\mathfrak{N} \in \operatorname{Max} K[\xi,\rho]$ can be generated by $m+n$ elements and $\dim K[\xi,\rho]\widehat{_{\mathfrak{N}}} = m+n$; in particular, $K[\xi,\rho]\widehat{_{\mathfrak{N}}}$ is a regular local ring. By Theorem 4.1.1, there is some $\varepsilon \in \sqrt{|K \setminus \{0\}|}$, $1>\varepsilon>0$, such that

$$\mathfrak{M} := \iota_\varepsilon(\mathfrak{m}) \cdot T_{m,n}(\varepsilon) \in \operatorname{Max} T_{m,n}(\varepsilon).$$

Now by Proposition 4.2.1,

$$(S_{m,n})\widehat{_\mathfrak{m}} \cong (T_{m,n}(\varepsilon))\widehat{_{\mathfrak{M}}} = (K[\xi,\rho])\widehat{_{K[\xi,\rho]\cap\mathfrak{m}}},$$

so $\dim (S_{m,n})\widehat{_\mathfrak{m}} = m+n$. It follows that $(S_{m,n})_\mathfrak{m}$ is a regular local ring of Krull dimension $m+n$. Moreover, by [**25**, Theorem 19.3], $S_{m,n}$ is a regular ring. □

Proposition 4.2.3. — *Assume* $\operatorname{Char} K = 0$. *Then $S_{m,n}$ is an excellent ring; in particular, it is a G-ring.*

Proof. — In light of Theorem 4.1.1 and Corollary 4.2.2, this follows directly from [**26**, Theorem 2.7]. □

The next example and proposition show that the situation in characteristic p is more complicated.

Example 4.2.4. — If $\operatorname{Char} K = p \neq 0$, then $S_{m,n} = S_{m,n}(K, E)$ may fail to be a G-ring. Assume, for the moment, that we have found an element $g \in K[\![\rho]\!] \setminus S_{0,1}$ such that $g^p \in S_{0,1}$ (*cf.* [**28**, Section A1, Example 6]). Put $\mathfrak{m} := (\rho) \cdot S_{0,1}$ and put $R := (S_{0,1})_{\mathfrak{m}}[g]$; if $S_{0,1}$ is a G-ring, so is R (see [**25**, Section 32, p. 260]). Since $R \subset K[\![\rho]\!]$, it is reduced. Put $\mathfrak{M} := \mathfrak{m}R$, and let $\widehat{R}$ denote the $\mathfrak{M}$-adic completion of R. Since $S_{0,1}$ is a UFD, $X^p - g^p$ is irreducible in $(S_{0,1})_{\mathfrak{m}}[X]$; hence

$$R = (S_{0,1})_{\mathfrak{m}}[X]/(X^p - g^p) \text{ and } \widehat{R} = K[X][\![\rho]\!]/(X^p - g^p) \cdot K[X][\![\rho]\!].$$

So $X - g$ is a non-zero nilpotent element of $\widehat{R}$, which is the direct sum of finitely many maximal-adic completions of R ([**25**, Theorem 8.15]). Thus, some maximal-adic completion of R is not reduced. It follows from [**25**, Theorem 32.2 (i)], that R, and hence $S_{0,1}$, cannot be a G-ring. An example of K, E and g can be constructed as follows: let $K := \mathbb{F}_p(t_1, t_2, \dots)((Z))$, $E := \mathbb{F}_p(t_1^p, t_2^p, \dots)$ and $g := \sum_{i \geq 0} t_i \rho^i$. In fact, a similar example can be constructed whenever $[E^{1/p} \cap K : E] = \infty$.

Proposition 4.2.5. — *Assume* $\operatorname{Char} K = p$. *Then:*

(i) *if $S_{m,n}$ is a finite extension of $(S_{m,n})^p$, then $S_{m,n}$ is excellent;*

(ii) *if $[K : K^p] < \infty$ and if $E \subset K^\circ$ is a complete DVR which is a finite extension of E^p (e.g., take $E = \mathbb{F}_p \subset K^\circ$), then $S_{m,n}$ is excellent;*

(iii) *if $E \subset K^\circ$ is a DVR and if K' is a complete, perfect, valued field extension of K, then there is a field E' with $E' \subset (K')^\circ$ such that $S_{m,n}(E', K')$ is an excellent and faithfully flat $S_{m,n}(E, K)$-algebra.*

Proof

(i) By [**38**, Théorème 2.1], it suffices to show that $S_{m,n}$ is universally catenary. But this is an immediate consequence of [**25**, Theorem 31.6 and Corollary 4.2.2].

(ii) Put $S_{m,n} := S_{m,n}(E, K) = S_{m,n}(E^p, K)$. Then, $S_{m,n} = K \otimes_{K^p} S_{m,n}(E^p, K^p)$ is finite over $S_{m,n}(E^p, K^p)$ and by the Weierstrass Division Theorem 2.3.2, $S_{m,n}$ is finite over $(S_{m,n})^p$. Now apply part (i).

(iii) Lift $\tilde{K}'$ to $(K')^\circ$ by extending the lifting of $\tilde{E}$ given by E (see Remark 2.1.4 (iv)). By part (ii), $S_{m,n}(E', K')$ is excellent, and by Lemma 3.1.11 (i), it is faithfully flat over $S_{m,n}(E, K)$. □

A useful property of reduced G-rings is that they are analytically unramified in the sense of [**28**]. The next proposition shows that reduced quotients of $S_{m,n}$ are analytically unramified in a different sense, when $S_{m,n}$ is a G-ring. Example 4.2.4 shows what goes wrong if $S_{m,n}$ is a not a G-ring.

Proposition 4.2.6. — *Let I be an ideal of $S_{m,n}$, $n \geq 1$, and let $\varepsilon \in \sqrt{|K \setminus \{0\}|}$, $1 > \varepsilon > 0$. If $\varepsilon > \sigma(I)$ and $T_{m,n}(\varepsilon)/\iota_\varepsilon(I) \cdot T_{m,n}(\varepsilon)$ is reduced then $S_{m,n}/I$ is reduced. Suppose $S_{m,n}$ is a G-ring (e.g., use Proposition 4.2.3 or Proposition 4.2.5 (ii)). If $S_{m,n}/I$ is reduced then $T_{m,n}(\varepsilon)/\iota_\varepsilon(I) \cdot T_{m,n}(\varepsilon)$ is reduced.*

Proof. — Suppose $T_{m,n}(\varepsilon)/\iota_\varepsilon(I)\cdot T_{m,n}(\varepsilon)$ is reduced and suppose $f^r\in I$ for some $f\in S_{m,n}$; then $\iota_\varepsilon(f)\in\iota_\varepsilon(I)\cdot T_{m,n}(\varepsilon)$. Hence by Corollary 3.3.2, $f\in I$. Therefore, $S_{m,n}/I$ is reduced.

Suppose $S_{m,n}/I$ is reduced and that $S_{m,n}$ is a G-ring; we must prove that

$$T_{m,n}(\varepsilon)/\iota_\varepsilon(I)\cdot T_{m,n}(\varepsilon)$$

is reduced. For this, it suffices to prove that $\left(T_{m,n}(\varepsilon)/\iota_\varepsilon(I)\cdot T_{m,n}(\varepsilon)\right)_{\mathfrak{m}}$ is reduced for every $\mathfrak{m}\in\operatorname{Max}(T_{m,n}(\varepsilon)/\iota_\varepsilon(I)\cdot T_{m,n}(\varepsilon))$. Indeed, let A be a ring such that $A_{\mathfrak{m}}$ is reduced for every $\mathfrak{m}\in\operatorname{Max}A$, and suppose $f^r=0$. Then $f\in\operatorname{Ker}(A\to A_{\mathfrak{m}})$ for every $\mathfrak{m}\in\operatorname{Max}A$. Consider the ideal $\mathfrak{a}:=\{a\in A : af=0\}$. If $\mathfrak{a}=(1)$, then $f=0$, and we are done; otherwise, $\mathfrak{a}\subset\mathfrak{m}$ for some $\mathfrak{m}\in\operatorname{Max}A$. Hence $f\notin\operatorname{Ker}(A\to A_{\mathfrak{m}})$, a contradiction. Furthermore, by the Krull Intersection Theorem ([**25**, Theorem 8.10]), $\operatorname{Ker}(A\to\widehat{A})=(0)$ for any Noetherian local ring A. Hence it suffices to prove that $\left(T_{m,n}(\varepsilon)/\iota_\varepsilon(I)\cdot T_{m,n}(\varepsilon)\right)\widehat{_{\mathfrak{m}}}$ is reduced for every $\mathfrak{m}\in\operatorname{Max}(T_{m,n}(\varepsilon)/\iota_\varepsilon(I)\cdot T_{m,n}(\varepsilon))$.

Let $\mathfrak{m}\in\operatorname{Max}(T_{m,n}(\varepsilon)/\iota_\varepsilon(I)\cdot T_{m,n}(\varepsilon))$, and put $\mathfrak{N}:=S_{m,n}\cap\mathfrak{m}\in\operatorname{Max}S_{m,n}/I$. Since $S_{m,n}/I$ is reduced, so is $(S_{m,n}/I)_{\mathfrak{N}}$. Indeed, let A be a reduced ring and let $\mathfrak{m}\in\operatorname{Max}A$. If $f^r\in\operatorname{Ker}(A\to A_{\mathfrak{m}})$ then for some $a\in A\setminus\mathfrak{m}$, $af^r=0$; whence $(af)^r=0$. But A is reduced, so $af=0$; i.e., $f\in\operatorname{Ker}(A\to A_{\mathfrak{m}})$. Now any quotient or localization of a G-ring is again a G-ring, so $(S_{m,n}/I)_{\mathfrak{N}}$ is a reduced G-ring. Thus

$$(S_{m,n}/I)_{\mathfrak{N}}\longrightarrow(S_{m,n}/I)\widehat{_{\mathfrak{N}}}$$

is regular; in particular, it is faithfully flat. By [**25**, Theorem 32.2], $(S_{m,n}/I)\widehat{_{\mathfrak{N}}}$ is reduced. Then $(T_{m,n}(\varepsilon)/\iota_\varepsilon(I)\cdot T_{m,n}(\varepsilon))\widehat{_{\mathfrak{m}}}$ is reduced by Proposition 4.2.1. Since this holds for every $\mathfrak{m}\in\operatorname{Max}(T_{m,n}(\varepsilon)/\iota_\varepsilon(I)\cdot T_{m,n}(\varepsilon))$, we have proved that $T_{m,n}(\varepsilon)/\iota_\varepsilon(I)\cdot T_{m,n}(\varepsilon)$ is reduced. □

Theorem 4.2.7. — *$S_{m,n}$ is a UFD.*

Proof. — A Noetherian integral domain is a UFD if, and only if, every height 1 prime is principal ([**25**, Theorem 20.1]). Let P be a height 1 prime ideal of $S_{m,n}$; we must prove that P is principal. By Lemma 3.2.6, it suffices to prove that the uniform residue ideal $\Lambda(P)$ is principal. Let K' be a finite algebraic extension of K such that $\widetilde{K}'=\widetilde{K}$, let $S'_{m,n}:=S_{m,n}(E,K')$ and let $P':=P\cdot S'_{m,n}$. By Lemma 3.1.11, $\widetilde{P}'=\widetilde{P}\cdot\widetilde{S}'_{m,n}=\widetilde{P}$; hence $\Lambda(P')=\Lambda(P)$. It suffices to prove that $\Lambda(P')$ is principal.

Fix a finite algebraic extension K' of K such that for some $\varepsilon\in|K'|$, $1>\varepsilon>\sigma(P)$, and $\widetilde{K}'=\widetilde{K}$.

Claim. — *For every $\mathfrak{n}'\in\operatorname{Max}S'_{m,n}$, $P'\cdot(S'_{m,n})\widehat{_{\mathfrak{n}'}}$ is a principal ideal.*

Let $\mathfrak{n}'\in\operatorname{Max}S'_{m,n}$ and put $\mathfrak{n}:=\mathfrak{n}'\cap S_{m,n}$. Since $S'_{m,n}$ is finite over $S_{m,n}$, $\mathfrak{n}\in\operatorname{Max}S_{m,n}$. By Corollary 4.2.2, $S_{m,n}$ is a regular ring. Hence by [**25**, Theorem 20.3], $(S_{m,n})_{\mathfrak{n}}$ is a UFD. If $\mathfrak{n}\supset P$ then $\operatorname{ht}P\cdot(S_{m,n})_{\mathfrak{n}}=1$, and if $\mathfrak{n}\not\supset P$ then $P\cdot(S_{m,n})_{\mathfrak{n}}=(1)$.

Thus, the ideals $P \cdot (S_{m,n})_{\mathfrak{n}}$, $P' \cdot (S'_{m,n})_{\mathfrak{n}'}$ and $P' \cdot (S'_{m,n})\widehat{_{\mathfrak{n}'}}$ are all principal. This proves the claim.

Let $T'_{m,n}(\varepsilon) := T_{m,n}(\varepsilon, K')$. By the Claim and by Proposition 4.2.1, $\iota_\varepsilon(P') \cdot (T'_{m,n}(\varepsilon))\widehat{_{\mathfrak{m}}}$ is a principal ideal of $(T'_{m,n}(\varepsilon))\widehat{_{\mathfrak{m}}}$ for every $\mathfrak{m} \in \operatorname{Max} T'_{m,n}(\varepsilon)$. By [**25**, Exercise 8.3], $\iota_\varepsilon(P') \cdot (T'_{m,n}(\varepsilon))_{\mathfrak{m}}$ is a principal ideal, hence a free $(T'_{m,n}(\varepsilon))_{\mathfrak{m}}$-module for every $\mathfrak{m} \in \operatorname{Max} T'_{m,n}(\varepsilon)$. By [**25**, Theorem 7.12], $\iota_\varepsilon(P) \cdot T'_{m,n}(\varepsilon)$ is a projective ideal. But $T'_{m,n}(\varepsilon)$ is isomorphic to $T_{m+n}(K')$, which by [**6**, Theorem 5.2.6.1], is a UFD. Hence by [**25**, Theorem 20.7], $\iota_\varepsilon(P) \cdot T'_{m,n}(\varepsilon)$ is principal. By Lemma 3.2.5, this implies that $\Lambda(P')$ is principal, as desired. □

In the next lemma we collect together some facts on flatness.

Lemma 4.2.8. — *Let $\varepsilon \in \sqrt{|K \setminus \{0\}|}$ with $1 > \varepsilon > 0$. Let K' be a complete, valued field extension of K, let $E' \subset (K')^\circ$ be a complete, quasi-Noetherian ring, and put $S_{m,n} := S_{m,n}(E, K)$, $S'_{m,n} := S_{m,n}(E', K')$. Assume $S'_{m,n} \supset S_{m,n}$; e.g., take $E' \supset E$.*

(i) *The inclusion $\iota_\varepsilon : S_{m,n} \to T_{m,n}(\varepsilon)$ is flat*

The following inclusions are faithfully flat:

(ii) $S_{m,n}(E, K)^\circ \to S_{m,n}(E', K')^\circ$
(iii) $S_{m,n}(E, K) \to S_{m,n}(E', K')$
(iv) $S_{m,n}(E, K)^\sim \to S_{m,n}(E', K')^\sim$
(v) $T_{m,n}(\varepsilon) \to T'_{m,n}(\varepsilon)$

Proof

(i) Consider the map $\iota_\varepsilon : S_{m,n} \to T_{m,n}(\varepsilon)$. Let $\mathfrak{M}$ be a maximal ideal of $T_{m,n}(\varepsilon)$, put $\mathfrak{m} := \iota_\varepsilon^{-1}(\mathfrak{M})$, $A := (S_{m,n})_{\mathfrak{m}}$ and $B := (T_{m,n}(\varepsilon))_{\mathfrak{M}}$. By [**25**, Theorem 7.1], it suffices to show that the induced map $\iota_\varepsilon : A \to B$ is flat. Let $\widehat{A}$, $\widehat{B}$ be the maximal-adic completions, respectively, of the local rings A, B. By Proposition 4.2.1 (ii), $\widehat{A} \cong \widehat{B}$, and by [**25**, Theorem 8.14], $A \to \widehat{A} \cong \widehat{B}$ and $B \to \widehat{B}$ are faithfully flat. Part (i) now follows by descent.

(ii), (iii) and (iv) are Lemma 3.1.11 (iv), (iii) and (i), respectively.

(v) For some $s \in \mathbb{N}$, $\varepsilon^s \in |K|$. Let $c \in K$ with $|c| = \varepsilon^s$, and let I be the ideal of T_{m+2n} generated by $\rho_i^s - \rho_{i+n} c$, $1 \leq i \leq n$. By [**6**, Theorem 6.1.5.4],

$$T_{m,n}(\varepsilon) = T_{m+2n}/I \text{ and } T'_{m,n}(\varepsilon) = T_{m+2n}/I \cdot T'_{m+2n}.$$

It therefore suffices to show that the inclusion $T_m \to T'_m$ is faithfully flat. But this is Lemma 3.1.11 (iii) with $n = 0$. □

Note that the inclusion $S^\circ_{m,n} \hookrightarrow T_{m,n}(\varepsilon)^\circ$ is not flat. Indeed, find $c \in K$ and $\ell \in \mathbb{N}$ such that $|c| = \varepsilon^\ell$. Let

$$\begin{aligned} M &:= \{(f, g) \in (S^\circ_{m,n})^2 : cf + \rho^\ell g = 0\}, \text{ and} \\ N &:= \{(f, g) \in (T_{m,n}(\varepsilon)^\circ)^2 : cf + \rho^\ell g = 0\}. \end{aligned}$$

If $S^\circ_{m,n} \hookrightarrow T_{m,n}(\varepsilon)^\circ$ were flat, then $N = \iota_\varepsilon(M) \cdot T_{m,n}(\varepsilon)^\circ$. But $(\frac{\rho^\ell}{c}, -1) \in N \setminus \iota_\varepsilon(M) \cdot T_{m,n}(\varepsilon)^\circ$.

5. The Supremum Semi-Norm and Open Domains

In this section, we investigate algebraic and topological relations between residue norms and the supremum seminorm on a quasi-affinoid algebra (i.e., a quotient ring $S_{m,n}/I$). The key topological concepts are power-boundedness and quasi-nilpotence (see Definition 5.1.7). The first main result is Theorem 5.1.5, which asserts that each $h \in S_{m,n}/I$ with $\|h\|_{\sup} \leq 1$ is integral over the subring of all $a \in S_{m,n}/I$ with $\|a\|_I \leq 1$. Moreover, if $|h(x)| < 1$ for all $x \in \operatorname{Max} S_{m,n}/I$, then h is integral over the set of all $a \in S_{m,n}/I$ with $v_I(a) \leq (1,1)$. It then follows (Corollary 5.1.8) for $f \in S_{m,n}/I$ that f is power bounded if, and only if, $\|f\|_{\sup} \leq 1$, and that f is quasi-nilpotent if, and only if, $|f(x)| < 1$ for all $x \in \operatorname{Max} S_{m,n}/I$. These are the quasi-affinoid analogues of well-known properties of affinoid algebras. In Subsection 5.2 we use the results of Subsection 5.1 to show that K-algebra homomorphisms are continuous (Theorem 5.2.3). Hence all residue norms on a quasi-affinoid algebra are equivalent (Corollary 5.2.4); i.e., the topology of a quasi-affinoid algebra is independent of presentation. We also prove an Extension Lemma (Theorem 5.2.6) for quasi-affinoid maps. The results of Subsection 5.1 also lead, as in the affinoid case, to a satisfactory theory of open quasi-affinoid subdomains. In particular, in Subsection 5.3 we define quasi-rational subdomains (Definition 5.3.3), and show, using the Extension Lemma (Theorem 5.2.6), that they are quasi-affinoid subdomains. Subsection 5.4 contains the definition and elementary properties of the "tensor product" in the quasi-affinoid category. In Subsection 5.5 we show when $\operatorname{Char} K = 0$ and in many cases when $\operatorname{Char} K = p$, that if $S_{m,n}/I$ is reduced then the residue norm $\|\cdot\|_I$ and the supremum norm $\|\cdot\|_{\sup}$ are equivalent. If in addition E is such that $S_{m,n}$ is complete then $S_{m,n}/I$ is a Banach function algebra.

5.1. Relations with the Supremum Seminorm. — The first step towards proving Theorem 5.1.5 is an analogue of that theorem for $T_{m,n}(\varepsilon)/\iota_\varepsilon(I) \cdot T_{m,n}(\varepsilon)$ uniformly in ε, where ε is a sufficiently large element of $\sqrt{|K \setminus \{0\}|}$.

Let A be a Noetherian ring and let $I \subset A$ be an ideal. For $r = 0, 1, \ldots$, let I_r denote the intersection of all minimal prime divisors of I of height r (if there are none, put $I_r := (1)$.) Clearly, $\mathfrak{N}(I) = \cap_{r \geq 0} I_r$, where $\mathfrak{N}(I)$ denotes the nilradical of I, and each I_r is a radical ideal. The ideals I_r are the *equidimensional components* of the ideal I.

In Lemma 5.1.1 we show that the ideals $\iota_\varepsilon(I_r) \cdot T_{m,n}(\varepsilon)$ generate the equidimensional components of the ideal $\iota_\varepsilon(I) \cdot T_{m,n}(\varepsilon)$, in the case that $S_{m,n}$ is a G-ring. This is important in applying [**6**, Proposition 6.2.2.2], in a uniform way.

Lemma 5.1.1. — *Let I be an ideal of $S_{m,n}$, $n \geq 1$, and let $\varepsilon \in \sqrt{|K \setminus \{0\}|}$, $1 > \varepsilon > 0$. Put $J := \iota_\varepsilon(I) \cdot T_{m,n}(\varepsilon)$. Then $J_r = \mathfrak{N}(\iota_\varepsilon(I_r) \cdot T_{m,n}(\varepsilon))$, $r \geq 0$. Thus, if $S_{m,n}$ is a G-ring, then $J_r = \iota_\varepsilon(I_r) \cdot T_{m,n}$, $r \geq 0$.*

Proof. — Since J_r is a radical ideal, by the Nullstellensatz (Theorem 4.1.1), it suffices to show, for each $\mathfrak{m} \in \operatorname{Max} T_{m,n}(\varepsilon)$, that $\mathfrak{m} \supset J_r$ if, and only if, $\iota_\varepsilon^{-1}(\mathfrak{m}) \supset I_r$.

Let A be any Noetherian ring, let $I \subset A$ be an ideal, and let $\mathfrak{m} \in \operatorname{Max} A$. By [**25**, Theorem 6.2], $\mathfrak{m} \supset P \supset I$ is a prime divisor of I if, and only if, $P \cdot A_\mathfrak{m}$ is a prime divisor of $I \cdot A_\mathfrak{m}$. Thus, $\mathfrak{m} \supset I_r$ if, and only if, $I \cdot A_\mathfrak{m}$ has a minimal prime divisor of height r.

Claim. — *Let $I \subset A$ be an ideal, and let $\mathfrak{m} \in \operatorname{Max} A$. Then $\mathfrak{m} \supset I_r$ if, and only if, $I \cdot \widehat{(A_\mathfrak{m})}$ has a minimal prime divisor of height r.*

By the foregoing, we may assume that A is a local ring with maximal ideal $\mathfrak{m}$, and we must show that I has a minimal prime divisor of height r if, and only if, $I \cdot \widehat{A}$ has one. (As usual, $\widehat{A}$ denotes the maximal-adic completion of A.)

Let $\mathfrak{p} \in \operatorname{Spec} A$ and let $\mathfrak{P} \in \operatorname{Spec} \widehat{A}$ be a minimal prime divisor of $\mathfrak{p} \cdot \widehat{A}$; we will show that $\operatorname{ht}\mathfrak{P} = \operatorname{ht}\mathfrak{p}$. Since $\widehat{A}$ is flat over A ([**25**, Theorem 8.8]), this follows from [**25**, Theorem 15.1 (ii)], if we can show that $\mathfrak{p} = \mathfrak{P} \cap A$. By the Going-Down Theorem ([**25**, Theorem 9.5]), there is some $\mathfrak{Q} \in \operatorname{Spec} \widehat{A}$ such that $\mathfrak{Q} \subset \mathfrak{P}$ and $\mathfrak{Q} \cap A = \mathfrak{p}$; hence $\mathfrak{P} \supset \mathfrak{Q} \supset \mathfrak{p} \cdot \widehat{A}$. Since $\mathfrak{P}$ is a minimal prime divisor of $\mathfrak{p} \cdot \widehat{A}$, $\mathfrak{Q} = \mathfrak{P}$. Therefore, $\mathfrak{p} = \mathfrak{P} \cap A$, as desired.

Suppose $\mathfrak{p} \in \operatorname{Spec} A$ is a minimal prime divisor of I of height r, and let $\mathfrak{P} \in \operatorname{Spec} \widehat{A}$ be a minimal prime divisor of $\mathfrak{p} \cdot \widehat{A}$. Then $\operatorname{ht}\mathfrak{P} = \operatorname{ht}\mathfrak{p} = r$. We will show that $\mathfrak{P}$ is a minimal prime divisor of $I \cdot \widehat{A}$. If $\mathfrak{P} \supset \mathfrak{Q} \supset I \cdot \widehat{A}$ for some $\mathfrak{Q} \in \operatorname{Spec} \widehat{A}$, then

$$\mathfrak{p} = \mathfrak{P} \cap A \supset \mathfrak{Q} \cap A \supset I.$$

Since $\mathfrak{p}$ is a minimal prime divisor of I, $\mathfrak{p} = \mathfrak{Q} \cap A$; i.e., $\mathfrak{Q} \supset \mathfrak{p} \cdot \widehat{A}$. Since $\mathfrak{P}$ is a minimal prime divisor of $\mathfrak{p} \cdot \widehat{A}$, $\mathfrak{Q} = \mathfrak{P}$. Thus $\mathfrak{P}$ is a minimal prime divisor of $I \cdot \widehat{A}$.

Suppose $\mathfrak{P} \in \operatorname{Spec} \widehat{A}$ is a minimal prime divisor of $I \cdot \widehat{A}$ of height r, and put $\mathfrak{p} := \mathfrak{P} \cap A$. Then $\mathfrak{P}$ is a minimal prime divisor of $\mathfrak{p} \cdot \widehat{A}$, so $\operatorname{ht}\mathfrak{p} = r$. We will show that $\mathfrak{p}$ is a minimal prime divisor of I. If $\mathfrak{p} \supset \mathfrak{q} \supset I$ for some $\mathfrak{q} \in \operatorname{Spec} A$, then by the Going-Down Theorem ([**25**, Theorem 9.5]), there is some $\mathfrak{Q} \in \operatorname{Spec} \widehat{A}$ with $\mathfrak{P} \supset \mathfrak{Q}$ and $\mathfrak{q} = \mathfrak{Q} \cap A$. Since $\mathfrak{P}$ is a minimal prime divisor of $I \cdot \widehat{A}$, $\mathfrak{Q} = \mathfrak{P}$, so $\mathfrak{q} = \mathfrak{p}$. Therefore, $\mathfrak{p}$ is a minimal prime divisor of I, proving the claim.

Let $\mathfrak{m} \in \operatorname{Max} T_{m,n}(\varepsilon)$ and put $\mathfrak{n} := \iota_\varepsilon^{-1}(\mathfrak{m})$. By the Claim, and by Proposition 4.2.1,

$$\begin{aligned} \mathfrak{m} \supset J_r \quad &\Longleftrightarrow \quad J \cdot \widehat{(T_{m,n}(\varepsilon))_\mathfrak{m}} \text{ has a minimal prime divisor of height } r \\ &\Longleftrightarrow \quad I \cdot \widehat{(S_{m,n})_\mathfrak{N}} \text{ has a minimal prime divisor of height } r \\ &\Longleftrightarrow \quad \mathfrak{n} \supset I_r, \end{aligned}$$

as desired. The last assertion of the lemma follows from Proposition 4.2.6. □

Let $\Lambda(I_r)$ be the uniform residue ideal of an equidimensional component I_r. The next proposition allows us to lift a Noether normalization map $\widetilde{T}_d \to \widetilde{T}_m/\Lambda(I_r)$ to affinoid algebras corresponding to the restriction of $S_{m,n}/I$ to closed polydiscs $\operatorname{Max} T_{m,n}(\varepsilon)$, uniformly in ε for ε large enough.

Proposition 5.1.2 **(*cf.*** [**4**, Satz 3.1]). — *Let $\varphi : T_d \to T_m$ be a K-algebra homomorphism, let I be an ideal of T_m, and let $\psi : T_d \to T_m/I$ be the composition of φ with the canonical projection $T_m \to T_m/I$. Now by* [**6**, Section 6.3], *φ induces a $\widetilde{K}$-algebra homomorphism $\widetilde{\varphi} : \widetilde{T}_d \to \widetilde{T}_m$. Let $\widetilde{\tau} : \widetilde{T}_d \to \widetilde{T}_m/\widetilde{I}$ be the composition of $\widetilde{\varphi}$ with the canonical projection $\widetilde{T}_m \to \widetilde{T}_m/\widetilde{I}$. Suppose that $\widetilde{\tau}$ is a finite monomorphism and that the $\widetilde{T}_d$-module $\widetilde{T}_m/\widetilde{I}$ can be generated by r elements. Then ψ is a finite monomorphism and the T_d-module T_m/I can be generated by r elements.*

Proof. — Put $J := \operatorname{Ker}\psi \subset T_d$; we will show that $J = (0)$. Let $f \in J$, $\|f\| \leq 1$. Since $f \in J$, $\varphi(f) \in I$; hence $\widetilde{\varphi}(\widetilde{f}) = \varphi(f)^\sim \in \widetilde{I}$. This implies $\widetilde{J} \subset \operatorname{Ker}\widetilde{\tau} = (0)$. Thus by Lemma 3.1.4, $J = (0)$; i.e., ψ is a monomorphism.

Find $G_1, \ldots, G_r, g_1, \ldots, g_s \in T_m^\circ$, with $g_1, \ldots, g_s \in I$, such that the images of $\widetilde{G}_1, \ldots, \widetilde{G}_r$ in $\widetilde{T}_m/\widetilde{I}$ generate the $\widetilde{T}_d$-module $\widetilde{T}_m/\widetilde{I}$, and $\{\widetilde{g}_1, \ldots, \widetilde{g}_s\}$ generates the ideal $\widetilde{I}$. We will show that the images of $G_1, \ldots, G_r$ in T_m/I generate the T_d-module T_m/I. Indeed, let $f \in T_m$; we will find $H_1, \ldots, H_r \in T_d$ and $h_1, \ldots, h_s \in T_m$ such that

$$f - \sum_{j=1}^{r} \varphi(H_j)G_j = \sum_{j=1}^{s} h_j g_j.$$

We may take $\|f\| \leq 1$. Let $B \in \mathfrak{B}$ with

$$f, \varphi(\xi_1), \ldots, \varphi(\xi_d), G_1, \ldots, G_r, g_1, \ldots, g_s \in B\langle\xi\rangle \subset T_m.$$

Let $B = B_0 \supset B_1 \supset \cdots$ be the natural filtration of B.

Claim. — *Let $F \in B_p\langle\xi\rangle \setminus B_{p+1}\langle\xi\rangle \subset T_m$. There are $H_1, \ldots, H_r \in B_p\langle\xi\rangle \subset T_d$ and $h_1, \ldots, h_s \in B_p\langle\xi\rangle \subset T_m$ such that*

$$F - \sum_{j=1}^{r} \varphi(H_j)G_j - \sum_{j=1}^{s} h_j g_j \in B_{p+1}\langle\xi\rangle \subset T_m.$$

Let $\pi_p : B_p \to \widetilde{B}_p \subset \widetilde{K}$ denote a residue epimorphism, and write $\widetilde{K} = \widetilde{B}_p \oplus V$ for some $\widetilde{B}$-vector space V. Then

$$\begin{aligned} \widetilde{T}_m &= \widetilde{K}[\xi_1, \ldots, \xi_m] = \widetilde{B}_p[\xi] \oplus V[\xi] \text{ and} \\ \widetilde{T}_d &= \widetilde{K}[\xi_1, \ldots, \xi_d] = \widetilde{B}_p[\xi] \oplus V[\xi] \end{aligned} \tag{5.1.1}$$

as $\widetilde{B}[\xi]$-modules. Furthermore, since $\widetilde{\varphi}(\xi_1),\dots,\widetilde{\varphi}(\xi_d)\in\widetilde{B}[\xi]$,

$$\text{(5.1.2)}\qquad \begin{aligned}&\widetilde{\varphi}(\widetilde{B}_p[\xi])\subset\widetilde{B}_p[\xi] \text{ and}\\ &\widetilde{\varphi}(V[\xi])\subset V[\xi].\end{aligned}$$

Since the images of $\widetilde{G}_1,\dots,\widetilde{G}_r$ in $\widetilde{T}_m/\widetilde{I}$ generate the $\widetilde{T}_d$-module $\widetilde{T}_m/\widetilde{I}$, and since $\{\widetilde{g}_1,\dots,\widetilde{g}_s\}$ generates the ideal $\widetilde{I}$ in $\widetilde{T}_m$, there are $\widetilde{H}_1,\dots,\widetilde{H}_r\in\widetilde{T}_d$ and $\widetilde{h}_1,\dots,\widetilde{h}_s\in\widetilde{T}_m$ such that

$$\text{(5.1.3)}\qquad \pi_p(F)-\sum_{j=1}^{r}\widetilde{\varphi}(\widetilde{H}_j)\widetilde{G}_j-\sum_{j=1}^{s}\widetilde{h}_j\widetilde{g}_j=0.$$

By (5.1.1) and (5.1.2), we may assume

$$\begin{aligned}&\widetilde{H}_1,\dots,\widetilde{H}_r\in\widetilde{B}_p[\xi]\subset\widetilde{T}_d \text{ and}\\ &\widetilde{h}_1,\dots,\widetilde{h}_s\in\widetilde{B}_p[\xi]\subset\widetilde{T}_m.\end{aligned}$$

Find $H_1,\dots,H_r\in B_p\langle\xi\rangle\subset T_d$ and $h_1,\dots,h_s\in B_p\langle\xi\rangle\subset T_m$ so that

$$\begin{aligned}&\pi_p(H_1)=\widetilde{H}_1,\dots,\pi_p(H_r)=\widetilde{H}_r \text{ and}\\ &\pi_p(h_1)=\widetilde{h}_1,\dots,\pi_p(h_s)=\widetilde{h}_s.\end{aligned}$$

By (5.1.3),

$$F-\sum_{j=1}^{r}\varphi(H_j)G_j-\sum_{j=1}^{s}h_jg_j\in B_{p+1}\langle\xi\rangle\subset T_m.$$

This proves the claim.

Now, $|B\setminus\{0\}|\subset\mathbb{R}_+\setminus\{0\}$ is discrete, and $B\langle\xi\rangle$ is complete. Thus since φ is continuous ([**6**, Theorem 6.1.3.1]), iterated application of the Claim yields the desired result. □

The following lemma is a key step towards proving Theorem 5.1.5.

Lemma 5.1.3. — *Assume $S_{m,n}$ is a G-ring (e.g., use Proposition 4.2.3 or Proposition 4.2.5 (ii)), and let I be an ideal of $S_{m,n}$. Then there is an $e\in\mathbb{N}$ such that for every $\varepsilon\in|K|$ with $1>|\varepsilon|>\sigma(I)$ and for every $f\in S_{m,n}/I$, $\iota'_\varepsilon(f)\in T_{m+n}/\iota'_\varepsilon(I)\cdot T_{m+n}$ satisfies an equation of the form*

$$t^e+a_1t^{e-1}+\dots+a_e=0$$

where the $a_i\in T_{m+n}/\iota'_\varepsilon(I)\cdot T_{m+n}$ satisfy $\max_{1\le i\le e}\|a_i\|^{1/i}_{\iota'_\varepsilon(I)\cdot T_{m+n}}=\|\iota'_\varepsilon(f)\|_{\sup}$.

Proof. — Let $\Lambda(I)$ be the uniform residue ideal of I as in Definition 3.2.4. By Noether Normalization, there is a $\widetilde{K}$-algebra homomorphism $\widetilde{\varphi}:\widetilde{T}_d\to\widetilde{T}_{m+n}$ such that $\widetilde{\tau}\colon\widetilde{T}_d\to\widetilde{T}_{m+n}/\Lambda(I)$ is a finite monomorphism where $\widetilde{\tau}$ is the composition of $\widetilde{\varphi}$ with the canonical projection $\widetilde{T}_{m+n}\to\widetilde{T}_{m+n}/\Lambda(I)$. Let I_0, $I_1,\dots,$ be defined as in Lemma 5.1.1. Since $I\subset I_r$ for $r\ge 0$, $\Lambda(I)\subset\Lambda(I_r)\subset\widetilde{T}_{m+n}$, $r\ge 0$. Thus by Noether

Normalization, for $r \geq 0$, there is a $\widetilde{K}$-algebra homomorphism $\widetilde{\varphi}_r : \widetilde{T}_{d_r} \to \widetilde{T}_d$ such that $\widetilde{\tau}_r : \widetilde{T}_{d_r} \to \widetilde{T}_{m+n}/\Lambda(I_r)$ is a finite monomorphism, where $\widetilde{\tau}_r$ is the composition of $\widetilde{\varphi} \circ \widetilde{\varphi}_r$ with the canonical projection $\widetilde{T}_{m+n} \to \widetilde{T}_{m+n}/\Lambda(I_r)$. Suppose the $\widetilde{T}_{d_r}$-module $\widetilde{T}_{m+n}/\Lambda(I_r)$ is generated by e_r elements, $r \geq 0$, and find $\alpha \in \mathbb{N}$ such that $\mathfrak{N}(I)^\alpha \subset I$ (where $\mathfrak{N}$ denotes the nilradical). Put

$$e := \alpha \sum_{r=0}^{m+n} e_r.$$

We will show that e is the exponent sought in the lemma. Fix $\varepsilon \in |K|$, $1 > \varepsilon > \sigma(I)$. By [**6**, Proposition 6.1.1.4], there are K-algebra homomorphisms $\varphi : T_d \to T_{m+n}$ and $\varphi_r : T_{d_r} \to T_d$, $0 \leq r \leq m+n$, that correspond modulo $K^{\circ\circ}$, respectively, to $\widetilde{\varphi} : \widetilde{T}_d \to \widetilde{T}_{m+n}$ and $\widetilde{\varphi}_r : \widetilde{T}_{d_r} \to \widetilde{T}_d$. Put $J := \iota'_\varepsilon(I) \cdot T_{m+n}$. Let $\psi : T_d \to T_{m+n}/J$ and $\psi_r : T_{d_r} \to T_{m+n}/\iota'_\varepsilon(I_r) \cdot T_{m+n}$, $0 \leq r \leq m+n$, be defined, respectively, by composing φ with the canonical projection $T_{m+n} \to T_{m+n}/J$ and by composing $\varphi \circ \varphi_r$ with the canonical projection $T_{m+n} \to T_{m+n}/\iota'_\varepsilon(I_r) \cdot T_{m+n}$. Since $\widetilde{\tau}, \widetilde{\tau}_0, \ldots, \widetilde{\tau}_{m+n}$ are finite monomorphisms, by Proposition 5.1.2, each of $\psi, \psi_0, \ldots, \psi_{m+n}$ is a finite monomorphism, moreover the T_{d_r}-module $T_{m+n}/\iota'_\varepsilon(I_r) \cdot T_{m+n}$ is generated by e_r elements, $0 \leq r \leq m+n$. By Lemma 5.1.1, $J_r = \iota'_\varepsilon(I_r) \cdot T_{m+n}$. Since each J_r is a radical ideal and since $\operatorname{ht} \mathfrak{p} = r$ for every prime divisor $\mathfrak{p}$ of J_r, each ψ_r is a finite torsion-free monomorphism.

Fix $f \in S_{m,n}/I$ with $\|f\|_{\sup} \leq 1$, and put $F := \iota'_\varepsilon(f)$. For $0 \leq r \leq m+n$, let $Q_r \in T_{d_r}[t]$ be the monic polynomial of least degree such that $Q_r(F)$ vanishes in T_{m+n}/J_r. Write

$$Q_r = t^{\ell_r} + a_{r1} t^{\ell_r - 1} + \cdots + a_{r\ell_r}.$$

Since ψ_r is a finite, torsion-free monomorphism, by [**6**, Proposition 6.2.2.2],

$$\max_{1 \leq i \leq \ell_r} \|a_{ri}\|^{1/i} = \|F\|_{\sup}.$$

Furthermore, by the Cayley-Hamilton Theorem [**25**, Theorem 2.1], $\ell_r = \deg Q_r \leq e_r$.

We may regard each Q_r as an element of $T_d[t]$ via the K-algebra homomorphism φ_r. Put

$$Q := \left(\prod_{r=0}^{m+n} Q_r \right)^\alpha = t^\ell + a_1 t^{\ell-1} + \cdots + a_\ell.$$

By [**6**, Corollary 3.2.1.6], $\max_{1 \leq i \leq \ell} \|a_i\|^{1/i} = \|F\|_{\sup}$, $\ell \leq e$, and by Proposition 4.2.6, $Q(F)$ vanishes in T_{m+n}/J. It follows that $\iota'_\varepsilon(f)$ satisfies the equation

$$t^e + a_1 t^{e-1} + \cdots + a_\ell t^{e-\ell} = 0,$$

as desired. □

In Lemma 5.1.3, we assumed that $\varepsilon \in |K|$ and that $S_{m,n}$ is a G-ring in order to make some computations. Under these assumptions we obtained monic polynomials of degree e over $T_{m,n}(\varepsilon)$ satisfied by $h \in S_{m,n}/I$. The coefficients of these polynomials, in addition, satisfy certain estimates depending on $||h||_{\sup}$. In Lemma 5.1.4 we show that the computations of Lemma 5.1.3 are not affected by ground field extensions; i.e., they remain valid for $\varepsilon \in \sqrt{|K \setminus \{0\}|}$ and whether or not $S_{m,n}$ is a G-ring. This allows us to transfer the data back to $S_{m,n}$ by examining the module M of relations among $h^e, h^{e-1}, \ldots, 1$.

Lemma 5.1.4. — *Let I be an ideal of $S_{m,n}$ and let M be a submodule of $(S_{m,n}/I)^\ell$. Let K' be a complete, valued extension field of K, let $E' \subset (K')^\circ$ be a complete, quasi-Noetherian ring with $E' \supset E$ (recall, if* Char $K = p > 0$, *we assume E' is also a DVR), and put*

$$S'_{m,n} := S_{m,n}(E', K') \supset S_{m,n},$$
$$I' := I \cdot S'_{m,n}, \text{ and}$$
$$M' := M \cdot (S'_{m,n}/I') \subset (S'_{m,n}/I')^\ell.$$

By φ denote the canonical projections

$$(S'_{m,n})^\ell \longrightarrow (S'_{m,n}/I')^\ell, \text{ and}$$
$$(S_{m,n})^\ell \longrightarrow (S_{m,n}/I)^\ell.$$

Put

$$N := \varphi^{-1}(M), \text{ and}$$
$$N' := \varphi^{-1}(M') = N \cdot S'_{m,n},$$

and let $\varepsilon \in |K'|$ with $1 > \varepsilon > \sigma(N')$. Put

$$T'_{m+n} := K'\langle \xi, \rho \rangle.$$

By π denote projection of an ℓ-tuple on the first coordinate. Suppose there is some

$$f \in \iota'_\varepsilon(M') \cdot (T'_{m+n}/\iota'_\varepsilon(I') \cdot T'_{m+n})$$

with $||f||_{\iota'_\varepsilon(I') \cdot T'_{m+n}} \leq 1$ and $\pi(f) = 1$. Then there is some $F \in M$ with $||F||_I \leq 1$ and $\pi(F) = 1$.

Proof. — It suffices to show that $\pi(\widetilde{N})$ is the unit ideal; indeed, by Lemma 3.1.11, it suffices to show that $\pi(\widetilde{N'})$ is the unit ideal. Let $\Lambda(N')$ be the uniform residue module of N' as in Definition 3.2.4. It suffices to show that $\pi(\Lambda(N'))$ is the unit ideal. Denote also by φ the canonical projection

$$(T'_{m+n})^\ell \to (T'_{m+n}/\iota'_\varepsilon(I') \cdot T'_{m+n})^\ell.$$

By Lemma 3.1.4 with $n = 0$, there is some

$$F \in \varphi^{-1}(\iota'_\varepsilon(M') \cdot (T'_{m+n}/\iota'_\varepsilon(I') \cdot T'_{m+n}))$$

with $\|F\| = \|f\|_{\iota'_\varepsilon(I')\cdot T'_{m+n}} \le 1$ and $\pi(F) = 1 + h$ for some $h \in \iota'_\varepsilon(I') \cdot T'_{m+n}$. Since $(h, 0, \ldots, 0) \in \operatorname{Ker}\varphi$, we may assume that $\pi(F) = 1$. Since

$$\varphi^{-1}(\iota'_\varepsilon(M') \cdot (T'_{m+n}/\iota'_\varepsilon(I') \cdot T'_{m+n})) = \iota'_\varepsilon(N') \cdot T'_{m+n},$$

by Lemma 3.2.5, $\widetilde{F} \in \Lambda(N')$. □

Theorem 5.1.5. — *Let I be an ideal of $S_{m,n}$. There is an $e \in \mathbb{N}$ such that each $h \in S_{m,n}/I$ with $\|h\|_{\sup} \le 1$ satisfies a polynomial equation of the form*

$$t^e + a_1 t^{e-1} + \cdots + a_e = 0,$$

where $a_1, \ldots, a_e \in S_{m,n}/I$ and each $\|a_i\|_I \le 1$. Moreover, if $|h(x)| < 1$ for all $x \in \operatorname{Max} S_{m,n}/I$ then each $v_I(a_i) < (1,1)$.

Proof. — Write $S_{m,n} := S_{m,n}(E,K)$. Let K' be the completion of the algebraic closure of K. If $\operatorname{Char} K = 0$, let $E' := E$ and if $\operatorname{Char} K = p > 0$, we use Remark 2.1.4 to find $E' \supset E$ as in Proposition 4.2.5 (iii). Hence $S'_{m,n} := S_{m,n}(E', K')$ is a G-ring by Proposition 4.2.3 or Proposition 4.2.5 (iii). Let $I' := I \cdot S'_{m,n}$. By Proposition 4.1.3, $\|h\|_{\sup} \le 1$, where the supremum is computed in $\operatorname{Max} S'_{m,n}/I'$.

Applying Lemma 5.1.3 to $S'_{m,n}/I'$ yields an integer e. Put

$$\begin{aligned}
M &:= \left\{ (a_0, \ldots, a_e) \in (S_{m,n}/I)^{e+1} : \sum_{i=0}^{e} a_i h^{e-i} = 0 \right\}, \\
M' &:= \left\{ (a_0, \ldots, a_e) \in (S'_{m,n}/I')^{e+1} : \sum_{i=0}^{e} a_i h^{e-i} = 0 \right\}, \\
M_0 &:= \{(a_0, \ldots, a_e) \in M : a_0 = 0\}, \text{ and} \\
M'_0 &:= \{(a_0, \ldots, a_e) \in M' : a_0 = 0\}.
\end{aligned}$$

Choose $\varepsilon \in |K'|$ with $1 > \varepsilon > 0$ and ε suitably large, as in Lemma 5.1.3, and put

$$\begin{aligned}
L' &:= \left\{ (b_0, \ldots, b_e) \in (T'_{m+n}/\iota'_\varepsilon(I') \cdot T'_{m+n})^{e+1} : \sum_{i=0}^{e} b_i \iota'_\varepsilon(h^{e-i}) = 0 \right\}, \\
L'_0 &:= \{(b_0, \ldots, b_e) \in L' : b_0 = 0\}.
\end{aligned}$$

Since T'_{m+n} is isometrically isomorphic to $T_{m,n}(\varepsilon, K')$, by Lemma 4.2.8 (i) and (ii), we have:

$$\begin{aligned}
M' &= M \cdot (S'_{m,n}/I'), \\
M'_0 &= M_0 \cdot (S'_{m,n}/I'), \\
L' &= \iota'_\varepsilon(M') \cdot (T'_{m+n}/\iota'_\varepsilon(I') \cdot T'_{m+n}), \text{ and} \\
L'_0 &= \iota'_\varepsilon(M'_0) \cdot (T'_{m+n}/\iota'_\varepsilon(I') \cdot T'_{m+n}).
\end{aligned}$$

Lemma 5.1.3 yields

$$b_1, \ldots, b_e \in T'_{m+n}/\iota'_\varepsilon(I') \cdot T'_{m+n}$$

such that

$$\max_{1\le i\le e}(\|b_i\|_{\iota'_\varepsilon(I')\cdot T'_{m+n}})^{1/i} = \|\iota'_\varepsilon(h)\|_{\sup} \le 1, \text{ and}$$
$$(1, b_1, \dots, b_e) \in L'.$$

Lemma 5.1.4 implies that there are $a_1, \dots, a_e \in S_{m,n}/I$ such that

$$\|a_i\|_I \le 1, \quad 1 \le i \le e, \text{ and}$$
$$(1, a_1, \dots, a_e) \in M.$$

This proves the first assertion.

Suppose now that $|h(x)| < 1$ for all $x \in \operatorname{Max} S_{m,n}/I$; then the same inequality holds for $x \in \operatorname{Max} S'_{m,n}/I'$ by Proposition 4.1.3. Hence $\|\iota'_\varepsilon(h)\|_{\sup} < 1$. Since

$$\iota'_\varepsilon((1, a_1, \dots, a_e)) - (1, b_1, \dots, b_e) \in L'_0,$$

we get

$$\|\iota'_\varepsilon((0, a_1, \dots, a_e))\|_{L'_0} \le \|(0, b_1, \dots, b_e)\|_{\iota'_\varepsilon(I')\cdot T'_{m+n}} < 1.$$

By Corollary 3.3.4, this yields

$$v_{M'_0}((0, a_1, \dots, a_e)) < (1, 1).$$

Hence by Lemma 3.1.11(ii),

$$v_{M_0}((0, a_1, \dots, a_e)) < (1, 1),$$

as desired. □

Remark 5.1.6. — Let I be an ideal of $S_{m,n}$ and define the seminorm $v_{\sup} : S_{m,n}/I \to \mathbb{R}_+ \times \mathbb{R}_+$ by

$$v_{\sup}(h) := (\|h\|_{\sup}, 2^{-\alpha}),$$

where

$$\alpha := \inf\{\beta \in \mathbb{R}_+ : \exists \varepsilon_0 \in \sqrt{|K \setminus \{0\}|}\ \forall \varepsilon \in \sqrt{|K \setminus \{0\}|} \text{ with } 1 > \varepsilon > \varepsilon_0,$$
$$\varepsilon^\beta \|h\|_{\sup} \le \|\iota_\varepsilon(h)\|_{\sup}\}.$$

In fact $\alpha \in \sqrt{|K \setminus \{0\}|}$. Indeed if $\|h\|_{\sup} \ne 0$, the function

$$\varepsilon \longmapsto \|\iota_\varepsilon(h)\|_{\sup}/\|h\|_{\sup}$$

is a definable function of ε, in the sense of [**17**] and [**23**]. By the analytic elimination theorem of [**23**, Corollary 4.3] it follows immediately that $\alpha \in \sqrt{|K \setminus \{0\}|}$ and that $\varepsilon^\alpha \|h\|_{\sup} = \|\iota_\varepsilon(h)\|_{\sup}$ for $\varepsilon < 1$ but sufficiently large.

There is an $e \in \mathbb{N}$ such that each $h \in S_{m,n}/I$ satisfies a polynomial equation of the form

$$t^e + a_1 t^{e-1} + \cdots + a_e = 0$$

where $a_1, \dots, a_e \in S_{m,n}/I$ and $\max_{1\le i\le e} v_I(a_i)^{1/i} \le v_{\sup}(h)$.

Definition 5.1.7. — Let I be an ideal of $S_{m,n}$. An element $f \in S_{m,n}/I$ is called *power-bounded* iff the set $\{\|f^\ell\|_I : \ell \in \mathbb{N}\} \subset \mathbb{R}$ is bounded. By $\mathfrak{b}(S_{m,n}/I)$ denote the set of all power-bounded elements; it is a subring of $S_{m,n}/I$. An element $f \in S_{m,n}/I$ is called *topologically nilpotent* iff $\{\|f^\ell\|_I : \ell \in \mathbb{N}\}$ is a zero sequence. By $\mathfrak{t}(S_{m,n}/I)$ denote the set of topologically nilpotent elements; it is an ideal of $\mathfrak{b}(S_{m,n}/I)$. An element $f \in S_{m,n}/I$ is called *quasi-nilpotent* iff for some $\ell \in \mathbb{N}$, $f^\ell \in \mathfrak{t} + (\rho)\mathfrak{b}$. By $\mathfrak{q}(S_{m,n}/I)$ denote the set of quasi-nilpotent elements; it is an ideal of $\mathfrak{b}(S_{m,n}/I)$.

Note that, even in the case $n = 0$, i.e., the affinoid case, the set $\{\|f^\ell\|_I : \ell \in \mathbb{N}\}$ appearing in Definition 5.1.7, while bounded, may not be bounded by 1. The element $\rho \in S_{0,1}$ is quasi-nilpotent, but not topologically nilpotent.

Corollary 5.1.8. — *Let I be an ideal of $S_{m,n}$ and let $f \in S_{m,n}/I$. Then f is power-bounded if, and only if, $\|f\|_{\sup} \le 1$, f is topologically nilpotent if, and only if, $\|f\|_{\sup} < 1$, and f is quasi-nilpotent if, and only if, $|f(x)| < 1$ for all $x \in \operatorname{Max} S_{m,n}/I$. Hence, in the notation of Theorem 5.1.5, each $a_i f^{e-i} \in \mathfrak{q}(S_{m,n}/I)$.*

Proof. — The 'only if' statements are immediate consequences of Proposition 4.1.2.

Suppose $\|f\|_{\sup} \le 1$. By Theorem 5.1.5

$$f^e = a_1 f^{e-1} + \cdots + a_e \tag{5.1.4}$$

for some $a_1, \ldots, a_e \in S_{m,n}/I$ with each $\|a_i\|_I \le 1$. Then for every $\ell \in \mathbb{N}$ there are $b_1, \ldots, b_e \in S_{m,n}/I$ with each $\|b_i\|_I \le 1$ such that

$$f^\ell = b_1 f^{e-1} + \cdots + b_e.$$

Thus $\{\|f^\ell\|_I : \ell \in \mathbb{N}\}$ is bounded by $\max\{\|f^i\|_I : 0 \le i \le e-1\}$, and f is power-bounded.

Suppose in addition that $|f(x)| < 1$ for all $x \in \operatorname{Max} S_{m,n}/I$. Then by Theorem 5.1.5, in (5.1.4) we may take each $v_I(a_i) \le (1,1)$. By Theorem 3.1.3 each $a_i \in \mathfrak{t}(S_{m,n}/I) + (\rho)\mathfrak{b}(S_{m,n}/I)$. To conclude the proof note that since each $\|f^i\|_{\sup} \le 1$, each $f^i \in \mathfrak{b}(S_{m,n}/I)$. Hence each $a_i f^{e-i} \in \mathfrak{q}(S_{m,n}/I)$. □

Remark 5.1.9. — The result of Corollary 5.1.8 is much easier to prove if one makes the strong additional assumption that $\|f\|_I \le 1$. In particular:

Lemma. — *Let I be an ideal of $S_{m,n}$. There is an $\ell \in \mathbb{N}$ such that for all $f \in S_{m,n}$ with $\|f\| \le 1$ and $|f(x)| < 1$ for all $x \in \operatorname{Max} S_{m,n}/I$, we have:*

(i) *for all $\varepsilon \in |K|$ with $1 > \varepsilon > \sigma(I)$, $\|\iota'_\varepsilon(f^\ell)\|_{\iota'_\varepsilon(I)\cdot T_{m+n}} < 1$, and*

(ii) $v_I(f^\ell) < (1,1)$.

Proof

(i) Let $\Lambda(I) \subset \widetilde{T}_{m+n}$ be the uniform residue ideal of I. Let $\mathfrak{N} := \mathfrak{N}(\Lambda(I)) \subset \widetilde{T}_{m+n}$ be the nilradical of $\Lambda(I)$. Then there is some $\ell \in \mathbb{N}$ such that $\mathfrak{N}^\ell \subset \Lambda(I)$. By $\sim : T^\circ_{m+n} \to \widetilde{T}_{m+n}$ denote the canonical residue epimorphism. It suffices to show that

$\iota'_\varepsilon(f)^\sim \in \mathfrak{N}$. Fix $\varepsilon \in |K|$ with $1 > \varepsilon > \sigma(I)$, and by F denote the image of $\iota'_\varepsilon(f)$ in $T_{m+n}/\iota'_\varepsilon(I) \cdot T_{m+n}$; then $\|F\|_{\sup} < 1$. By [**6**, Proposition 6.2.3.2], F is topologically nilpotent; i.e., $\lim_{r\to\infty} \|\iota'_\varepsilon(f)^r\|_{\iota'_\varepsilon(I)\cdot T_{m+n}} = 0$. Hence $\iota'_\varepsilon(f)^\sim \in \mathfrak{N}$.

(ii) By Proposition 4.1.3 and Lemma 3.1.11(ii) we may assume that $|K|$ is not discrete. Let ℓ be as in part (i) and put $F := f^\ell$. If $\widetilde{\mathrm{o}}(F) > 0$ or $\|F\| < 1$, we are done. Therefore, assume that $\|F\| = 1$ and $\widetilde{\mathrm{o}}(F) = 0$. Let $\{g_1, \dots, g_r\} \subset I$ be a v-strict generating system with $\|g_1\| = \cdots = \|g_r\| = 1$, and let $\varepsilon \in |K|$ satisfy $1 > \varepsilon > \max_{1\le i\le r} \sigma(g_i)$. Since $\widetilde{\mathrm{o}}(F) = 0$, it follows that $\|\iota'_\varepsilon(F)\| = 1$ and $\widetilde{d}(\iota'_\varepsilon(F)) = 0$. By the choice of ℓ, $\|\iota'_\varepsilon(F)\|_{\iota'_\varepsilon(I)\cdot T_{m+n}} < 1$. So by Claim A of the proof of Theorem 3.3.1, there are polynomials $h_1, \dots, h_r \in K^\circ[\xi]$ such that $\|\iota'_\varepsilon(F) - \sum_{i=1}^r h_i \varepsilon^{-\widetilde{\mathrm{o}}(g_i)} \iota'_\varepsilon(g_i)\| < 1$, and such that $h_i = 0$ for all i with $\widetilde{\mathrm{o}}(g_i) > 0$. This implies that $v(F - \sum_{i=1}^r h_i g_i) < (1,1)$; i.e., $v_I(F) < (1,1)$. □

Corollary 5.1.10. — *Let I be an ideal of $S_{m,n}$ and let $f \in S_{m,n}/I$. Then*

$$\|f\|_{\sup} = \inf_{\ell\in\mathbb{N}} \|f^\ell\|_I^{1/\ell} = \lim_{\ell\to\infty} \|f^\ell\|_I^{1/\ell}.$$

In particular if $\varphi : S_{m,n}/I \to S_{m',n'}/I'$ is a K-algebra homomorphism which is an isometry with respect to $\|\cdot\|_I$ and $\|\cdot\|_{I'}$, then φ is an isometry with respect to $\|\cdot\|_{\sup}$.

Proof. — The last equality is given in [**6**, Section 1.3.2]. We prove the first equality. Let $\mathfrak{m} \in \mathrm{Max}_K\, S_{m,n}/I$. By Proposition 4.1.2

$$|f(\mathfrak{m})| \le \|f^\ell\|_I^{1/\ell},$$

for $\ell \in \mathbb{N}$. Hence $\|f\|_{\sup} \le \inf_{\ell\in\mathbb{N}} \|f^\ell\|_I^{1/\ell}$. Suppose that $\|f\|_{\sup} < \inf_{\ell\in\mathbb{N}} \|f^\ell\|_I^{1/\ell}$. Then for some $N \in \mathbb{N}$, $\alpha \in K$ and all $\ell \in \mathbb{N}$

$$\|f^N\|_{\sup} < |\alpha| < \|f^{N\ell}\|_I^{1/N\ell},$$

since $\sqrt{|K|}$ is dense in $\mathbb{R}_+$. Put $F := \frac{1}{\alpha} f^N$. Then for all $\ell \in \mathbb{N}$

$$\|F\|_{\sup} < 1 < \|F^\ell\|_I^{1/\ell}.$$

This contradicts Corollary 5.1.8 since F is not topologically nilpotent though $\|F\|_{\sup} < 1$. □

Corollary 5.1.11. — *Let $f \in S_{m,n}/I$. Then $\|f\|_{\sup} \in \sqrt{|K|}$.*

Proof. — If $m = 0$, the result follows from Noether normalization for quotients of $S_{0,n}$ (Remark 2.3.6) and [**6**, Proposition 3.8.1.7]. We reduce to this case.

By Theorem 3.4.6, there are $m', n' \in \mathbb{N}$, an ideal J of $S_{m',n'}$ and a K-algebra homomorphism

$$\varphi : S_{m,n}/I \longrightarrow S_{m',n'}/J$$

such that (i) φ is an isometry with respect to $\|\cdot\|_I$ and $\|\cdot\|_J$, and (ii) $S_{m',n'}/J$ is a finite $S_{0,d}$-algebra for some $d \in \mathbb{N}$. By (i) and Corollary 5.1.10, φ is an isometry in $\|\cdot\|_{\sup}$. Now (ii) permits us to reduce to the case above. □

5.2. Continuity and Extension of Homomorphisms. — In this subsection we prove that K-algebra homomorphisms between quasi-affinoid algebras are continuous, i.e., bounded (Theorem 5.2.3). It follows that all residue norms on a quasi-affinoid algebra are equivalent (Corollary 5.2.4). We also prove an Extension Lemma (Theorem 5.2.6) for quasi-affinoid maps.

Depending on the choice of E, $S_{m,n}$ may not be complete in $\|\cdot\|$ (see Theorem 2.1.3). Hence the results of this subsection do not follow from [**6**, Theorem 3.7.5.1]. Nevertheless $S^\circ_{m,n}$ is the direct limit of rings $B\langle\xi\rangle[\![\rho]\!]$ that are complete both in $\|\cdot\|$ and (ρ)-adically. Furthermore (Corollary 2.2.6 and Theorem 2.3.2) the operations of factoring $S_{m,n}$ by an ideal and Weierstrass Division respect the decomposition of $S_{m,n}$ as the direct limit of the $B\langle\xi\rangle[\![\rho]\!]$.

We first establish the continuity of K-algebra homomorphisms from quasi-affinoid algebras to affinoid algebras.

Lemma 5.2.1. — *Let $\varphi : S_{m,n}/I \to S_{m',0}/J =: A$ be a K-algebra homomorphism. Then φ is continuous with respect to $\|\cdot\|_I$ and $\|\cdot\|_J$, and is uniquely determined by its values on $\xi_i + I$ and $\rho_j + I$, $i = 1,\ldots,m$; $j = 1,\ldots,n$.*

Proof of Continuity. — It is sufficient to consider the case $I = (0)$. Since φ is a K-algebra homomorphism it follows from [**6**, Propositions 6.2.3.1 and 6.2.3.2] that the $\varphi(\xi_i)$ are power-bounded and the $\varphi(\rho_j)$ are topologically nilpotent (i.e., the set $\|\varphi(\xi_i)^k\|_J$ is bounded and for each j, $\|\varphi(\rho_j)^k\|_J \to 0$ as $k \to \infty$). Therefore we may put

$$M := \max\{\|\varphi(\xi^\mu\rho^\nu)\|_J : \mu \in \mathbb{N}^m, \nu \in \mathbb{N}^n\}.$$

***Claim* (A).** — *Let $M' \in \mathbb{R}$, $B \in \mathfrak{B}$. If*

$$\|\varphi(f)\|_J \le M'\|f\|$$

for all $f \in B\langle\xi\rangle[\![\rho]\!]$, then in fact

$$\|\varphi(f)\|_J \le M\|f\|$$

for all $f \in B\langle\xi\rangle[\![\rho]\!]$.

Choose $\alpha \in \mathbb{N}$ so that for $|\nu| = \alpha$ we have $\|\varphi(\rho^\nu)\|_J < M/M'$. Let $f \in B\langle\xi\rangle[\![\rho]\!]$ and write

$$f = p(\xi,\rho) + f_0(\xi,\rho) + \sum_{|\nu_i|=\alpha} \rho^{\nu_i} f_i(\xi,\rho)$$

where the p, f_0, $f_i \in B\langle\xi\rangle[\![\rho]\!]$ satisfy

- p is a polynomial and $||p|| \leq ||f||$,
- $||f_0|| \leq \left(\frac{M}{M'}\right) ||f||$, and
- $||f_i|| \leq ||f||$ for all i.

(In other words choose a polynomial p such that $f - p \in (B_i + (\rho)^\alpha)B\langle\xi\rangle[\![\rho]\!]$ for some i with $|B_i| \subset [0, M/M']$.) Then

$$\varphi(f) = p(\varphi(\xi), \varphi(\rho)) + \varphi(f_0) + \sum_{|\nu_i|=\alpha} \varphi(\rho)^{\nu_i}\varphi(f_i)$$

and

$$\begin{aligned} ||\varphi(f)||_J &\leq \max\left\{M||p||, M'||f_0||, \frac{M}{M'}M'||f_i||\right\} \\ &\leq M||f||. \end{aligned}$$

Claim A is proved.

By Proposition 2.1.5 there is a complete, discretely valued subfield $F \subset K$ such that

$$S_{m,n} = \varinjlim_{F^\circ \subset B \in \mathfrak{B}} F\widehat{\otimes}_{F^\circ} B\langle\xi\rangle[\![\rho]\!].$$

Once we prove that each map

$$\varphi|_{F\widehat{\otimes}_{F^\circ}B\langle\xi\rangle[\![\rho]\!]} : F\widehat{\otimes}_{F^\circ}B\langle\xi\rangle[\![\rho]\!] \to A$$

of F-Banach Algebras is bounded, it will follow from Claim A that $\varphi : S_{m,n} \to A$ is also bounded. It remains to prove

***Claim* (B).** — *The restriction $\varphi|_{F\widehat{\otimes}_{F^\circ}B\langle\xi\rangle[\![\rho]\!]} : F\widehat{\otimes}_{F^\circ}B\langle\xi\rangle[\![\rho]\!] \to A$ is bounded.*

Since it is affinoid, A is certainly also an F-Banach Algebra. By the Closed Graph Theorem ([**6**, Section 2.8.1] or [**7**]) it is thus sufficient to prove that if the $v_n \in F\widehat{\otimes}_{F^\circ}B\langle\xi\rangle[\![\rho]\!]$ satisfy $\lim v_n = 0$ and $\lim \varphi(v_n) = w \in A$, then $w = 0$. We follow the proof of [**6**, Proposition 3.7.5.1]. Let $\mathfrak{b} = \mathfrak{m}^N$ for some maximal ideal $\mathfrak{m} \in \operatorname{Max} A$ and $N \in \mathbb{N}$. Let $\mathfrak{a} = \varphi^{-1}(\mathfrak{b}) \subset S_{m,n}$. Consider the commutative diagram

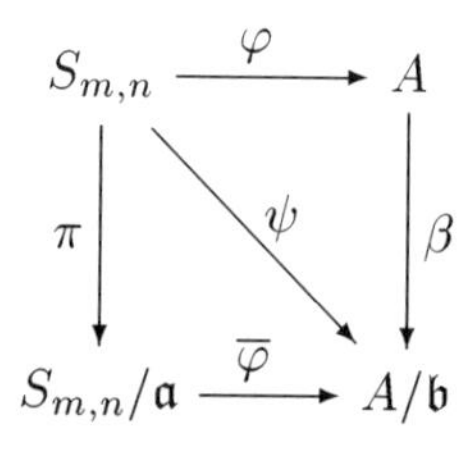

where π and β are the canonical projections, $\overline{\varphi}$ is the induced map and ψ is $\overline{\varphi} \circ \pi$. Note that π and β are contractions, and that $\overline{\varphi}$ is continuous since by Proposition 4.2.1,

$S_{m,n}/\mathfrak{a}$ and $A/\mathfrak{b}$ are finite dimensional K-algebras. Hence ψ is continuous and $\beta(w) = 0$. Since this is true for all $\mathfrak{m} \in \operatorname{Max} A$ and all $N \in \mathbb{N}$, by the Krull Intersection Theorem, $w = 0$. (Suppose $w \in \mathfrak{m}^N$ for all $\mathfrak{m} \in \operatorname{Max} A$, and let J be the ideal of all $x \in A$ such that $xw = 0$. Fix $\mathfrak{m} \in \operatorname{Max} A$. By the Krull Intersection Theorem [**25**, Theorem 8.10(i)], the image of w in the localization $A_\mathfrak{m}$ is zero. Thus, $J \not\subset \mathfrak{m}$. Since this holds for all $\mathfrak{m} \in \operatorname{Max} A$, $J = (1)$; i.e., $w = 0$.) This proves Claim B and hence φ is continuous.

Proof of Uniqueness. — This follows directly from Claim A: suppose φ and ψ agree on the $\xi_i + I$ and $\rho_j + I$. Put $\Phi := \varphi - \psi$. Now apply Claim A, with $M = 0$, to Φ. □

Next we show that there are continuous K-algebra homomorphisms

$$S_{m,n} \longrightarrow S_{m',n'}/I'$$

sending the ξ_i (respectively ρ_j) to any specified power-bounded (respectively quasi-nilpotent) elements of $S_{m',n'}/I'$.

Lemma 5.2.2. — *Let $f_i \in S_{m',n'}/I'$, $i = 1, \ldots, m$, be power-bounded and let $g_j \in S_{m',n'}/I'$, $j = 1, \ldots, n$, be quasi-nilpotent. There is a K-algebra homomorphism,*

$$\varphi : S_{m,n} \longrightarrow S_{m',n'}/I',$$

continuous in $\|\cdot\|$ and $\|\cdot\|_{I'}$, such that $\varphi(\xi_i) = f_i$ and $\varphi(\rho_j) = g_j$ for $i = 1, \ldots, m$; $j = 1, \ldots, n$.

Proof. — Since the f_i are power-bounded, by Theorem 5.1.5, there are $a_{ij} \in S_{m',n'}/I'$, $1 \le i \le m$, $1 \le j \le e$, with each $\|a_{ij}\|_{I'} \le 1$ such that

$$f_i^e + a_{i1} f_i^{e-1} + \cdots + a_{ie} = 0, \qquad 1 \le i \le m.$$

Similarly, there are $b_{ij} \in S_{m',n'}/I'$, $1 \le i \le n$, $1 \le j \le e$, with each $v_{I'}(b_{ij}) < (1,1)$ such that

$$g_i^e + b_{i1} g_i^{e-1} + \cdots + b_{ie} = 0, \qquad 1 \le i \le n.$$

By Theorem 3.1.3, there are A_{ij}, $B_{ij} \in S_{m',n'}$ such that $v(A_{ij}) = v_{I'}(a_{ij})$, $v(B_{ij}) = v_{I'}(b_{ij})$, $a_{ij} = A_{ij} + I$, and $b_{ij} = B_{ij} + I$. Put

$$\begin{aligned} P_i(\xi_{m'+i}) &:= \xi_{m'+i}^e + A_{i1}\xi_{m'+i}^{e-1} + \cdots + A_{ie}, \qquad & i = 1, \ldots, m,\\ Q_i(\rho_{n'+i}) &:= \rho_{n'+i}^e + B_{i1}\rho_{n'+i}^{e-1} + \cdots + B_{ie}, \qquad & i = 1, \ldots, n. \end{aligned}$$

Note that each P_i is regular in $\xi_{m'+i}$ of degree e and each Q_i is regular in $\rho_{n'+i}$ of degree e. Let $\psi_0 : S_{m,n} \hookrightarrow S_{m'+m,n'+n}$ be the inclusion defined by $\xi_i \mapsto \xi_{m'+i}$, $\rho_j \mapsto \rho_{n'+j}$, $i = 1, \ldots, m; j = 1, \ldots, n$. By Weierstrass Division (Theorem 2.3.2) there is a unique K-algebra homomorphism

$$\psi_1 \colon S_{m'+m,n'+n} \longrightarrow S_{m',n'}[\xi_{m'+1}, \ldots, \xi_{m'+m}, \rho_{n'+1}, \ldots, \rho_{n'+n}]/(P, Q)$$

with $\operatorname{Ker}\psi_1 = (P,Q)\cdot S_{m'+n,n'+n}$. Furthermore, by Weierstrass Division, ψ is continuous and the range of ψ_1 is a Cartesian $S_{m',n'}$-module (see [**6**, Definition 5.2.7.3]). Let

$$\psi_2 : S_{m',n'}[\xi_{m'+1},\ldots,\xi_{m'+m},\rho_{n'+1},\ldots,\rho_{n'+n}]/(P,Q) \longrightarrow S_{m',n'}/I'$$

be the unique K-algebra homomorphism that sends $S_{m',n'} \ni f \mapsto f + I'$, $\xi_{m'+i} \mapsto f_i$ and $\rho_{n'+j} \mapsto g_j$, $i = 1,\ldots,m$, $j = 1,\ldots,n$.

Since ψ_0 is an isometry in $\|\cdot\|$, ψ_1 is a contraction and

$$S_{m',n'}[\xi_{m'+1},\ldots,\xi_{m'+m},\rho_{n'+1},\ldots,\rho_{n'+n}]/(P,Q)$$

is a Cartesian $S_{m',n'}$–module, ψ_2 is continuous. Take $\varphi := \psi_2 \circ \psi_1 \circ \psi_0$. □

Theorem 5.2.3. — *Let $\varphi : S_{m,n}/I \to S_{m',n'}/I'$ be a K-algebra homomorphism. Then φ is continuous with respect to $\|\cdot\|_I$ and $\|\cdot\|_{I'}$, and is uniquely determined by the values $\varphi(\xi_i + I)$, $\varphi(\rho_j + I)$, $i = 1,\ldots,m; j = 1,\ldots,n$.*

Proof. — It is sufficient to take $I = (0)$. Let $\varphi' : S_{m,n} \to S_{m',n'}/I'$ be the continuous K-algebra homomorphism provided by Lemma 5.2.2 with $\varphi'(\xi_i) = \varphi(\xi_i)$ and $\varphi'(\rho_j) = \varphi(\rho_j)$, $i = 1,\ldots,m$; $j = 1,\ldots,n$. By Corollary 3.3.2, there is an $\varepsilon \in \sqrt{|K \setminus \{0\}|}$ such that

$$S_{m',n'}/I' \xrightarrow{\iota_\varepsilon} T_{m',n'}(\varepsilon)/\iota_\varepsilon(I')\cdot T_{m',n'}(\varepsilon)$$

is an inclusion. By Lemma 5.2.1, $\iota_\varepsilon \circ \varphi = \iota_\varepsilon \circ \varphi'$. Since ι_ε is an inclusion $\varphi = \varphi'$, and thus φ is continuous. □

In general a quasi-affinoid algebra has many representations as a quotient of an $S_{m,n}$. The residue norms corresponding to different representations may be different. However all these norms are equivalent, i.e., they induce the same topology.

Corollary 5.2.4. — *If $S_{m,n}/I \simeq S_{m',n'}/I'$ as K-algebras then the two norms $\|\cdot\|_I$ and $\|\cdot\|_{I'}$ are equivalent; i.e., they induce the same topology.*

Remark 5.2.5. — Let $c \in K^{\circ\circ}$. The $(c) + (\rho)$–adic topology on $S^\circ_{m,n}$ induces a topology on $S_{m,n}$ and on any quotient. A K–algebra homomorphism

$$\varphi : S_{m,n} \to S_{m',n'}/I'$$

is also continuous with respect to such topologies. In other words, if $f = \sum a_{\mu\nu}\xi^\mu\rho^\nu \in S^\circ_{m,n}$, then by the above arguments, $\sum a_{\mu\nu}\varphi(\xi)^\mu\varphi(\rho)^\nu$ converges to $\varphi(f)$.

***Theorem 5.2.6* (Extension Lemma, *cf.* Remark 5.2.8).** — *Let $\varphi : S_{m,n}/I \to S_{m',n'}/I'$ be a K-algebra homomorphism, let $f_1,\ldots,f_M \in S_{m',n'}/I'$ be power-bounded and let $g_1,\ldots,g_N \in S_{m',n'}/I'$ be quasi-nilpotent. Then there is a unique K-algebra homomorphism*

$$\psi : S_{m+M,n+N}/I\cdot S_{m+M,n+N} \longrightarrow S_{m',n'}/I'$$

such that $\psi(\xi_{m+i}) = f_i$, $1 \le i \le M$, $\psi(\rho_j) = g_j$, $1 \le j \le N$, *and the following diagram commutes:*

$$\begin{array}{ccc} S_{m,n}/I & \xrightarrow{\ \varphi\ } & S_{m',n'}/I' \\ \big\downarrow & \nearrow_{\psi} & \\ S_{m+M,n+N}/I \cdot S_{m+M,n+N} & & \end{array}$$

Proof. — By Lemma 5.2.2 there is a K–algebra homomorphism

$$\psi' : S_{m+M,n+N} \to S_{m',n'}/I'$$

such that

$$\begin{aligned} \psi'(\xi_i) &= \varphi(\xi_i + I), & i &= 1, \ldots, m, \\ \psi'(\rho_j) &= \varphi(\rho_j + I), & j &= 1, \ldots, n, \\ \psi'(\xi_{m+i}) &= f_i, & i &= 1, \ldots, M, \\ \psi'(\rho_{m+j}) &= g_j, & j &= 1, \ldots, N. \end{aligned}$$

By Theorem 5.2.3,

$$\psi'|_{S_{m,n}} = \varphi \circ \pi,$$

where

$$\pi : S_{m,n} \longrightarrow S_{m,n}/I$$

is the canonical projection. Hence $I \subset \operatorname{Ker} \psi'$ and ψ' gives rise to a K–algebra homomorphism

$$\psi : S_{m+M,n+N}/I \cdot S_{m+M,n+N} \longrightarrow S_{m',n'}/I'.$$

That $\psi|_{S_{m,n}/I} = \varphi$ and that ψ is unique follow immediately from Theorem 5.2.3. □

For notational convenience we make the following definition:

Definition 5.2.7. — Fix the pair (E, K) and let A be a quasi-affinoid algebra, say $A = S_{m',n'}(E, K)/I$. We define

$$A\langle \xi_1, \ldots, \xi_m \rangle [\![\rho_1, \ldots, \rho_n]\!]_s := S_{m'+m,n'+n}/I \cdot S_{m'+m,n'+n}$$

where we regard

$$S_{m',n'} = K\langle \eta_1, \ldots, \eta_{m'} \rangle [\![\tau_1, \ldots, \tau_{n'}]\!]_s$$

and

$$S_{m'+m,n'+n} = K\langle \eta_1, \ldots, \eta_{m'}, \xi_1, \ldots, \xi_m \rangle [\![\tau_1, \ldots, \tau_{n'}, \rho_1, \ldots, \rho_n]\!]_s.$$

By the Extension Lemma, Theorem 5.2.6, $A\langle \xi_1, \ldots, \xi_m \rangle [\![\rho_1, \ldots, \rho_n]\!]_s$ is independent of the presentation of A.

We will show that that

$$A\langle\xi\rangle[\![\rho]\!]_s \subset A[\![\xi,\rho]\!]$$

via the K-algebra homomorphism

$$\varphi : S_{m'+m,n'+n} \to A[\![\xi,\rho]\!] : \sum f_{\mu\nu}\xi^\mu\rho^\nu \longmapsto \sum (f_{\mu\nu}+I)\xi^\mu\rho^\nu.$$

Indeed, it suffices to verify

$$\operatorname{Ker}\varphi \subset I \cdot S_{m'+m,n'+n}.$$

Let $f = \sum f_{\mu\nu}\xi^\mu\rho^\nu \in \operatorname{Ker}\varphi$; without loss of generality $\|f\| = 1$. Hence $f \in B\langle\eta,\xi\rangle[\![\tau,\rho]\!]$ for some $B \in \mathfrak{B}$. By Lemma 3.1.6, there are $s \in \mathbb{N}$, $B \subset B' \in \mathfrak{B}$ and $h_{\mu\nu} \in B'\langle\eta,\xi\rangle[\![\tau,\rho]\!]$ such that

$$f = \sum_{|\mu|+|\nu|\le s} f_{\mu\nu}h_{\mu\nu}.$$

Since each $f_{\mu\nu} \in I$, it follows that $f \in I \cdot S_{m'+m,n'+n}$, as desired.

Let $\psi : S_{m',n'} \to A[\![\xi,\rho]\!]$ be the composition of φ with the obvious inclusion $S_{m',n'} \hookrightarrow S_{m'+m,n'+n}$. Since $\operatorname{Ker}\psi = I$, it follows that

$$A \to A\langle\xi\rangle[\![\rho]\!]_s$$

is injective.

Remark 5.2.8. — Here we rephrase the Extension Lemma (Theorem 5.2.6) in terms of the notation introduced in Definition 5.2.7.

Let $\varphi : A \to B$ be a K-algebra homomorphism of quasi-affinoid algebras A and B. Suppose $f_1,\dots,f_m \in B$ are power-bounded and $g_1,\dots,g_n \in B$ are quasi-nilpotent. Then there is a unique K-algebra homomorphism $\psi : A\langle\xi\rangle[\![\rho]\!]_s \to B$ such that $\psi(\xi_i) = f_i$ and $\psi(\rho_j) = g_j$, $1 \le i \le m$, $1 \le j \le n$, and the following diagram commutes:

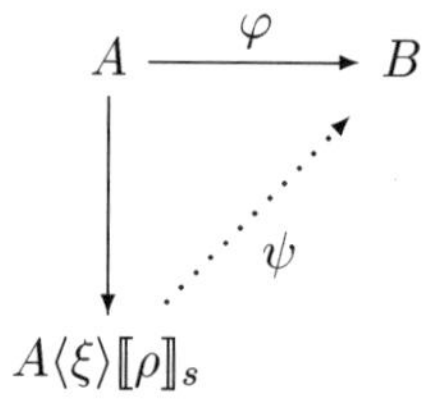

In particular, it follows that there are $m, n \in \mathbb{N}$ and a surjection of A-algebras

$$A\langle\xi_1,\dots,\xi_m\rangle[\![\rho_1,\dots,\rho_n]\!]_s \to B,$$

and hence for some ideal I,

$$B \simeq A\langle\xi_1,\dots,\xi_m\rangle[\![\rho_1,\dots,\rho_n]\!]_s/I.$$

5.3. Quasi-Rational Domains. — By analogy with [**6**, Section 6.1.4], we define generalized rings of fractions in the quasi-affinoid setting. This leads, in Definition 5.3.3, to the construction of quasi-rational domains and, by iterating, R-domains. Example 5.3.7 shows that R-domains are more general than quasi-rational domains, in contrast to the affinoid case. Nevertheless the Extension Lemma (Theorem 5.2.6) shows that generalized rings of fractions are well-defined and that the association of a generalized ring of fractions with a quasi-rational domain provides it with a canonical ring of quasi-affinoid functions. Thus quasi-rational subdomains (and by iteration, R-subdomains) are examples of quasi-affinoid subdomains (the formal generalization to the quasi-affinoid category of the notion of affinoid subdomains). This provides a foundation for a theory of quasi-affinoid varieties (see [**22**]). We end this subsection proving in Proposition 5.3.8 that a quasi-affinoid algebra is affinoid if, and only if, it satisfies the Maximum Modulus Principle.

Definition 5.3.1. — Let A be a quasi-affinoid algebra, say $A = S_{m,n}/I$, and let $f_1, \dots, f_M; g_1, \dots, g_N; h \in A$. Define the *generalized ring of fractions* $A\langle f/h\rangle[\![g/h]\!]_s$ to be the quotient ring

$$A\left\langle \frac{f}{h}\right\rangle \left[\!\left[\frac{g}{h}\right]\!\right]_s := S_{m+M,n+N}/J,$$

where J is the ideal of $S_{m+M,n+N}$ generated by the elements of I and the elements

$$H\xi_{m+i} - F_i, \quad H\rho_{n+j} - G_j, \quad 1 \le i \le M, \quad 1 \le j \le N,$$

where the F_i, G_j, $H \in S_{m,n}$ satisfy $f_i = F_i + I$, $g_j = G_j + I$, $h = H + I$, $1 \le i \le M$, $1 \le j \le N$. By Theorem 5.2.6 any isomorphism $S_{m,n}/I \to S_{m',n'}/I'$ extends to an isomorphism $S_{m+M,n+N}/I \cdot S_{m+M,n+N} \to S_{m'+M,n'+N}/I' \cdot S_{m'+M,n'+N}$ sending ξ_{m+i} to $\xi_{m'+i}$ and ρ_{n+j} to $\rho_{n'+j}$. It follows that $A\langle \frac{f}{h}\rangle[\![\frac{g}{h}]\!]_s$ is well-defined.

Let f, g, h be as in Definition 5.3.1. In general, $\operatorname{Max} A\langle \frac{f}{h}\rangle[\![\frac{g}{h}]\!]_s$ is neither open in $\operatorname{Max} A$ nor does it satisfy the Universal Property of [**6**, Section 7.2.2] (see Definition 5.3.4 below). With the additional restriction that f, g, h generate the unit ideal of A (see Definition 5.3.3, below) the following Universal Property is satisfied.

Proposition 5.3.2. — *Let A be a quasi-affinoid algebra, let $f_1, \dots, f_M; g_1, \dots, g_N; h \in A$, and put*

$$A' := A\left\langle \frac{f}{h}\right\rangle \left[\!\left[\frac{g}{h}\right]\!\right]_s .$$

Suppose $\psi : A \to B$ is a K-algebra homomorphism into a K-quasi-affinoid algebra B such that

(i) *$\psi(h)$ is a unit,*

(ii) *$\psi(f_i)/\psi(h)$ is power-bounded, $1 \le i \le M$, and*

(iii) *$\psi(g_j)/\psi(h)$ is quasi-nilpotent, $1 \le j \le N$.*

Then there is a unique K-algebra homomorphism $\psi' : A' \to B$ such that

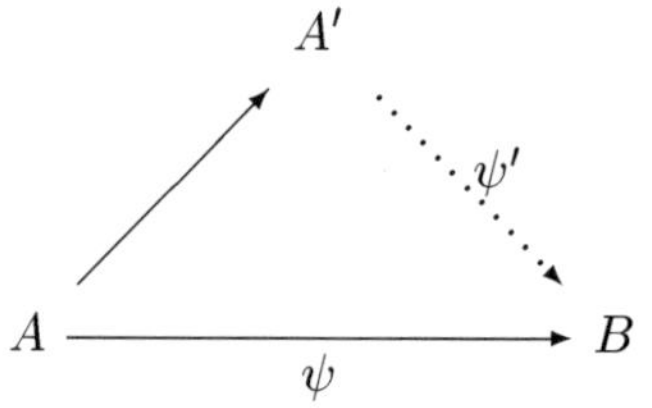

commutes. In particular, if $\{f, g, h\}$ generates the unit ideal of A and if $\operatorname{Max} B \subset \operatorname{Max} A'$ *(as subsets of* $\operatorname{Max} A$*) then by Corollary 5.1.8 and the Nullstellensatz, Theorem 4.1.1, conditions (i), (ii) and (iii) are all satisfied.*

Proof. — Immediate from Theorem 5.2.6. □

Definition 5.3.3. — Let A be a quasi-affinoid algebra and put $X := \operatorname{Max} A$. A *quasi-rational subdomain* of X is a subset $U \subset X$ of the form

$$U = \operatorname{Max}\left(A\left\langle \frac{f}{h}\right\rangle \left[\!\left[\frac{g}{h}\right]\!\right]_s\right)$$

where $f_1, \ldots, f_M;\ g_1, \ldots, g_N;\ h \in A$ generate the unit ideal. The class of *R-subdomains* of X is defined inductively as follows. Any quasi-rational subdomain of X is an R-subdomain of X. If $U \subset X$ is an R-subdomain of X and if $V \subset U$ is a quasi-rational subdomain of U, then $V \subset X$ is an R-subdomain of X.

Suppose $U = \operatorname{Max}(A\langle \frac{f}{h}\rangle [\![\frac{g}{h}]\!]_s)$ is a quasi-rational subdomain of $X = \operatorname{Max} A$. Then

$$U = \{x \in X \colon |f_i(x)| \le |h(x)|,\ |g_j(x)| < |h(x)|,\ 1 \le i \le M,\ 1 \le j \le N\}.$$

To see this, write $A = S_{m,n}/I$ and $A\langle \frac{f}{h}\rangle [\![\frac{g}{h}]\!]_s = S_{m+M,n+N}/J$, where J is generated by the elements of I together with the elements of the form

$$H\xi_{m+i} - F_i, \quad H\rho_{n+j} - G_j, \quad 1 \le i \le M, \quad 1 \le j \le N,$$

where the F_i, G_j, $H \in S_{m,n}$ satisfy $f_i = F_i + I$, $g_j = G_j$, $h = H + I$, $1 \le i \le M$, $1 \le j \le N$. The elements of U correspond naturally to the maximal ideals of $S_{m+M,n+N}$ that contain J. Let x be such a maximal ideal. By the Nullstellensatz (Theorem 4.1.1),

$$|\xi_{m+i}(x)| \le 1 \text{ and } |\rho_{n+j}(x)| < 1.$$

The description of U above then follows immediately from $h(x)\xi_{m+i}(x) - f_i(x) = 0$ and $h(x)\rho_{n+j}(x) - g_j(x) = 0$ and from the fact that $h(x) \neq 0$. The fact that $h(x) \neq 0$ for all $x \in U$ also guarantees that U is an open and closed subset of X when X is endowed with the canonical (metric) topology (see [**6**, Section 7.2.1]).

As in the affinoid case, one easily proves (*cf.* [**6**, Proposition 7.2.3.7]) that the intersection of quasi-rational domains is a quasi-rational domain. In contrast to the affinoid case, the complement of a quasi-rational domain is a finite union of quasi-rational domains. To see this, consider the quasi-rational domain

$$U = \operatorname{Max}\left(A\left\langle\frac{f}{h}\right\rangle\left[\!\left[\frac{g}{h}\right]\!\right]_s\right),$$

where the f, g, h generate the unit ideal of A. Note that h is a unit of $A\langle\frac{f}{h}\rangle[\![\frac{g}{h}]\!]_s$. Choose $1/c \in K$ with

$$\left|\frac{1}{c}\right| \geq \left\|\frac{1}{h}\right\|_{\sup}; \text{ i.e.,}$$
$$|c| \leq |h(x)|, \text{ for all } x \in U.$$

Then

$$U = \{x \in \operatorname{Max} A \colon |f_i(x)| \leq |h(x)|,\ |g_j(x)| < |h(x)|,$$
$$|c| \leq |h(x)|,\ 1 \leq i \leq M,\ 1 \leq j \leq N\}.$$

Hence

$$\begin{aligned} \operatorname{Max} A \setminus U \;=\; & \{x \in \operatorname{Max} A \colon |h(x)| < |c|\} \cup \\ & \bigcup_i \{x \in \operatorname{Max} A \colon |h(x)| < |f_i(x)|,\ |c| < |f_i(x)|\} \cup \\ & \bigcup_j \{x \in \operatorname{Max} A \colon |h(x)| \leq |g_j(x)|,\ |c| \leq |g_j(x)|\}. \end{aligned}$$

By induction, a finite intersection of R-domains is an R-domain and the complement of an R-domain is a finite union of R-domains.

Definition 5.3.4. — Let A and B be K-quasi-affinoid algebras. A *K-quasi-affinoid map*

$$(\Phi, \varphi) : (\operatorname{Max} B, B) \to (\operatorname{Max} A, A)$$

is a map $\Phi : \operatorname{Max} B \to \operatorname{Max} A$ induced by a K-algebra homomorphism $\varphi : A \to B$ via the Nullstellensatz, Theorem 4.1.1. Let U be a subset of $\operatorname{Max} A$. Following [**6**, Section 7.2.2], and suppressing mention of φ, we say that a quasi-affinoid map $\Phi : \operatorname{Max} A' \to \operatorname{Max} A$ *represents all quasi-affinoid maps into* U if $\Phi(\operatorname{Max} A') \subset U$ and if, for any quasi-affinoid map $\Psi : \operatorname{Max} B \to \operatorname{Max} A$ with $\Psi(\operatorname{Max} B) \subset U$, there exists a unique quasi-affinoid map $\Psi' : \operatorname{Max} B \to \operatorname{Max} A'$ such that $\Psi = \Phi \circ \Psi'$; i.e., such that

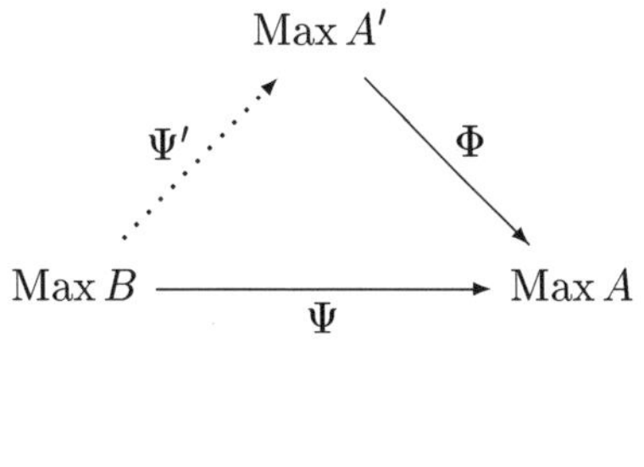

commutes. A subset $U \subset \operatorname{Max} A$ is called a *quasi-affinoid subdomain of* $\operatorname{Max} A$ if there exists a quasi-affinoid map $\varphi : \operatorname{Max} A' \to \operatorname{Max} A$ representing all quasi-affinoid maps into U.

As in [**6**, Section 7.2.2], the above universal property has useful formal consequences which are proved in Proposition 5.3.6. In addition it allows us to associate to every quasi-affinoid subdomain U of $\operatorname{Max} A$ a canonical A-algebra of quasi-affinoid functions $\mathcal{O}(U)$. Indeed if $\Phi : \operatorname{Max} A' \to \operatorname{Max} A$ represents all quasi-affinoid maps into U, then $\mathcal{O}(U) := A'$. Reversing the arrows in Proposition 5.3.2 yields many examples of quasi-affinoid subdomains.

Theorem 5.3.5. — *Let A be a quasi-affinoid algebra and let $U \subset \operatorname{Max} A$ be a quasi-rational subdomain, $U = \operatorname{Max} A\langle \frac{f}{h}\rangle[\![\frac{g}{h}]\!]_s$, where the f, g, h generate the unit ideal of A. The inclusion*

$$\operatorname{Max}\left(A\left\langle\frac{f}{h}\right\rangle\left[\!\left[\frac{g}{h}\right]\!\right]_s\right) \to \operatorname{Max} A$$

represents all quasi-affinoid maps into U. Thus every R-subdomain is a quasi-affinoid subdomain.

To every R-subdomain U of $\operatorname{Max} A$, we have thus associated the canonical A-algebra of quasi-affinoid functions $\mathcal{O}(U)$ such that $\operatorname{Max} \mathcal{O}(U) \to \operatorname{Max} A$ represents all quasi-affinoid maps into U. In particular, if $U \subset \operatorname{Max} A$ is the quasi-rational subdomain defined by

$$U = \{x \in \operatorname{Max} A : |f_i(x)| \leq |h(x)|,\ |g_j(x)| < |h(x)|,\ 1 \leq i \leq M,\ 1 \leq j \leq N\},$$

where $\{f, g, h\}$ generates the unit ideal of A, then $\mathcal{O}(U) = A\langle\frac{f}{h}\rangle[\![\frac{g}{h}]\!]_s$ is independent of the above presentation. In other words, if $U \subset \operatorname{Max} A$ is a quasi-rational subdomain, $f', g', h' \in \mathcal{O}(U)$ have no common zero and

$$|f'(x)| \leq |h'(x)|, \qquad |g'(x)| < |h'(x)|$$

for all $x \in U$, then

$$\mathcal{O}(U) = \mathcal{O}(U)\left\langle\frac{f'}{h'}\right\rangle\left[\!\left[\frac{g'}{h'}\right]\!\right]_s.$$

By induction, the same holds for R-subdomains of $\operatorname{Max} A$. This fact is a key step in developing a natural theory of quasi-affinoid varieties, as will be seen in [**22**]. A special case of this result was proved in [**18**, Theorem 3.6]. The proof of the main result of [**18**] can be simplified considerably using Theorem 5.3.5.

Proposition 5.3.6 **(*cf.*** [**6**, Proposition 7.2.2.1]). — *Let A be a quasi-affinoid algebra, let $U \subset \operatorname{Max} A$ and suppose $(\Phi, \varphi) : (\operatorname{Max} A', A') \to (\operatorname{Max} A, A)$ is a quasi-affinoid map representing all quasi-affinoid maps into U. Then*

(i) *Φ is injective and satisfies $\Phi(\operatorname{Max} A') = U$;*

(ii) *for* $x \in \operatorname{Max} A'$ *and* $n \in \mathbb{N}$, *the map* $\varphi : A \to A'$ *induces an isomorphism* $A/\Phi(x)^n \to A'/x^n$;

(iii) *for* $x \in \operatorname{Max} A'$, $x = \varphi(\Phi(x)) \cdot A'$.

Proof. — Let $y \in U$ and consider the commutative diagram

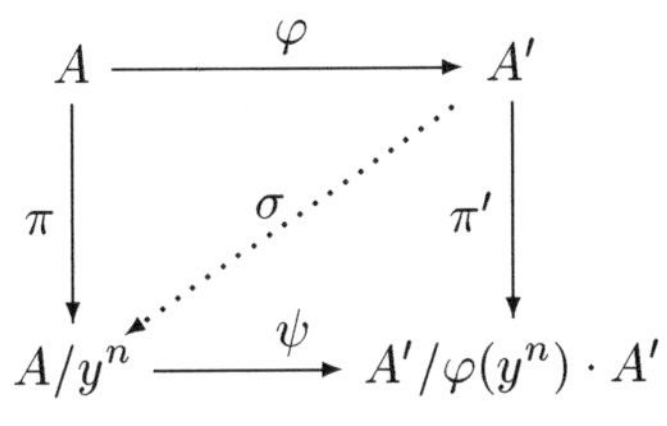

where π and π' denote the canonical projections and ψ is induced by φ. Since Φ represents all affinoid maps into U, there exists a unique homomorphism $\sigma : A' \to A/y^n$ making the upper triangle commute.

Thus both maps π' and $\psi \circ \sigma$ make

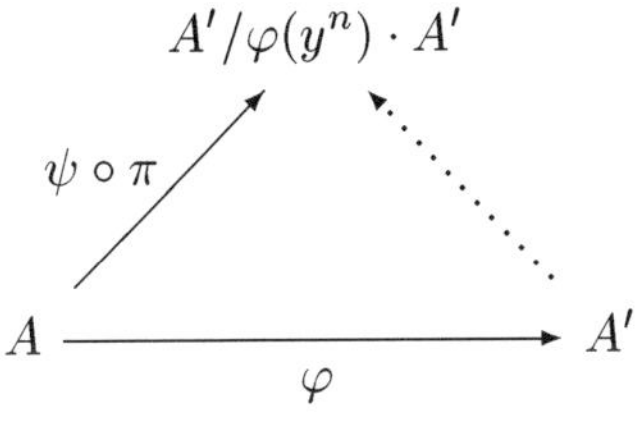

commute. Due to the universal property of φ, they must be equal; i.e., the lower triangle in the above diagram commutes.

Since π' is surjective, so is ψ. Furthermore, σ is surjective because π is. Since the upper triangle commutes, $\operatorname{Ker} \pi' = \varphi(y^n \cdot A') \subset \operatorname{Ker} \sigma$. Hence ψ must be bijective. Taking $n = 1$, we see that $\varphi(y) \cdot A'$ must be a maximal ideal of A'. Thus $\Phi^{-1}(y)$ consists precisely of one element, $\varphi(y) \cdot A'$. This proves (i) and (iii). Moreover (ii) must hold because $x^n = y^n \cdot A'$ where $y = \Phi(x)$, and because ψ is bijective. □

Example 5.3.7. — In the affinoid case, a rational subdomain V of a rational subdomain U of an affinoid variety X is itself a rational subdomain of X (see [**6**, Section 7.2.4]). This transitivity property is not in general true in the quasi-affinoid case.

First note that the quasi-rational subdomains U of the affinoid variety $\operatorname{Max} S_{m,0}$ are all of the form

$$U = \operatorname{Max} S_{m,0}\Big\langle \frac{f}{h} \Big\rangle \Big[\Big[\frac{g}{h}\Big]\Big]_s$$

where $f_1, \dots, f_M$, $g_1, \dots, g_N$, h are polynomials. That is because h is a unit of $S_{m,0}\langle \frac{f}{h}\rangle [\![\frac{g}{h}]\!]_s$ (recall that the ideal generated by f, g and h contains 1).

Let $K = \mathbb{C}_p$, the completion of the algebraic closure of the p-adic field $\mathbb{Q}_p$. Note that $\widetilde{K}$ and K°/aK° are countably infinite for every $a \in K^{\circ\circ} \setminus \{0\}$. Let $E \subset K^\circ$ be a *DVR* such that $\widetilde{E} = \widetilde{K}$, and put $S_{m,n} := S_{m,n}(E, K)$.

We will show that every quasi-rational subdomain of $\operatorname{Max} S_{2,0}$ has a property (see lemma below) that is not possessed by the set

$$U = \{(\xi, \rho) \in \operatorname{Max} S_{1,1} : |\xi - f(\rho)| < \varepsilon\},$$

for a suitable choice of $f \in S_{0,1}$ and $\varepsilon \in |K| \setminus \{0\}$. The failure of the transitivity property for quasi-rational subdomains follows, since U is a quasi-rational subdomain of $\operatorname{Max} S_{1,1}$, which is a quasi-rational subdomain of $\operatorname{Max} S_{2,0}$. By

$$\pi : \operatorname{Max} S_{2,0} \to \operatorname{Max} S_{1,0}$$

denote the map induced by the obvious inclusion $S_{1,0} \to S_{2,0}$.

Lemma. — *Let $U \subset \operatorname{Max} S_{2,0}$ be a quasi-rational subdomain such that $\pi(U)$ contains an annulus of the form*

$$\{x \in \operatorname{Max} S_{1,0} \colon \delta < |x| < 1\}, \qquad 0 < \delta < 1. \tag{5.3.1}$$

Then there is a polynomial $P \in K[\xi_1, \xi_2] \setminus \{0\}$ such that

$$\pi(U \cap \{x \in \operatorname{Max} S_{2,0} \colon P(x) = 0\})$$

contains a set of form (5.3.1).

Proof. — The set U is definable in the language of valued fields with constants in K. The statement that $\pi(U)$ contains a set of form (5.3.1) is true over any (algebraically closed) valued field extending K because the theory of algebraically closed valued fields is model complete [**40**].

In particular, it is true over the algebraic closure F of the field $K(\xi_1)$, where the valuation $|\cdot|$ on F extends that on $K \subset F$ and

$$1 - \frac{1}{n} < |\xi_1| < 1$$

for all $n \in \mathbb{N}$. Hence there is a $b \in F$ such that $(\xi_1, b) \in U$. Let $P(\xi_1, \xi_2) \in K[\xi_1, \xi_2] \subset F[\xi_2]$ be any nonzero polynomial that vanishes at b.

If

$$\pi(U \cap \{x \in \operatorname{Max} S_{2,0} : P(x) = 0\})$$

does not contain a set of form (5.3.1), then by the Quantifier Elimination Theorem for the theory of algebraically closed valued fields [**40**],

$$\pi(U \cap \{x \in \operatorname{Max} S_{2,0} : P(x) = 0\}) \subset \{x \in \operatorname{Max} S_{1,0} : |x| < \delta\}$$

for some $\delta \in |K|$, $\delta < 1$. But this is not true over F, contradicting the fact that, by model completeness, K is an elementary submodel of F. □

The following construction completes the example. For every $\varepsilon \in |K \setminus \{0\}|$, $\varepsilon < 1$, there is an $f \in S_{0,1}$ such that for every $P \in K[\xi_1, \xi_2] \setminus \{0\}$,

$$\pi\left(\{(\xi, \rho) \in \operatorname{Max} S_{1,1} : P(\xi, \rho) = 0 \text{ and } |\xi - f(\rho)| < \varepsilon\}\right)$$

contains no set of form (5.3.1).

Let P_i be an enumeration of polynomials in $K^\circ[\xi_1, \xi_2]$ such that for every $P \in K^\circ[\xi_1, \xi_2]$ there are infinitely many $i \in \mathbb{N}$ with $\|P - P_i\| < \varepsilon$. We inductively define sequences $\{n_i\} \subset \mathbb{N}$, $\{\rho_i\} \subset K^{\circ\circ}$ and $\{a_i\} \subset E$ such that $n_i \to \infty$ and $|\rho_i| \to 1$. Suppose $a_0, \ldots, a_{\ell-1}$; $n_0, \ldots, n_{\ell-1}$; $\rho_0, \ldots, \rho_{\ell-1}$ have been chosen and put

$$f_\ell := \sum_{i=0}^{\ell-1} a_i \rho^{n_i}.$$

Choose $n_\ell > n_{\ell-1}$ such that $|\rho_i^{n_\ell}| < \varepsilon$ for all $i < \ell$. Choose $\rho_\ell \in K^{\circ\circ}$ such that $|\rho_\ell^{n_\ell}| > \varepsilon$. Suppose $b_1, \ldots, b_r$ are all the roots of $P_\ell(\xi_2, \rho_\ell) = 0$. Choose $a_\ell \in E$ such that

$$\left|\sum_{i=0}^{\ell} a_i \rho_\ell^{n_i} - b_j\right| > \varepsilon$$

for $j = 1, \ldots, r$.

Put

$$f := \sum_{i \geq 0} a_i \rho^{n_i},$$

and let $P \in K^\circ[\xi_1, \xi_2] \setminus \{0\}$. There are infinitely many $i \in \mathbb{N}$ such that $\|P - P_i\| < \varepsilon$, and

$$\rho_i \notin \pi\left(\{(\xi, \rho) \in \operatorname{Max} S_{1,1} : P(\xi, \rho) = 0 \text{ and } |\xi - f(\rho)| < \varepsilon\}\right)$$

for each such i.

We include the next propositions for completeness. Proposition 5.3.8 gives conditions under which a quasi-affinoid algebra is actually affinoid (i.e., is a quotient of an $S_{m,0}$). Proposition 5.3.9 gives conditions under which a quasi-affinoid algebra is a quotient of an $S_{0,n}$.

Proposition 5.3.8. — *Let $A = S_{m,n}/I$ be a quasi-affinoid algebra. The following are equivalent:*

(i) *A is an affinoid algebra,*
(ii) *A satisfies the Maximum Modulus Principle*
(iii) *$\|\rho_i\|_{\sup}$ is attained for all $1 \leq i \leq n$,*
(iv) *$\|\rho_i\|_{\sup} < 1$ for all $1 \leq i \leq n$.*

Proof

(i)⇒(ii), (ii)⇒(iii) and (iii)⇒(iv) are immediate from [**6**, Proposition 6.2.1.4], and the Nullstellensatz, Theorem 4.1.1. To see that (iv)⇒(i) observe that if

$$||\rho_i||_{\sup} \le \varepsilon < 1 \text{ for all } 1 \le i \le n$$

and $\varepsilon \in \sqrt{|K \setminus \{0\}|}$, say $\varepsilon^r = |c|$, $c \in K^{\circ\circ}$, then by Theorem 5.3.5

$$A\left\langle \frac{\rho_1^r}{c}, \dots, \frac{\rho_n^r}{c} \right\rangle = A$$

and

$$\begin{aligned} A\left\langle \frac{\rho_1^r}{c}, \dots, \frac{\rho_n^r}{c} \right\rangle &= (S_{m,n}/I)\left\langle \frac{\rho_1^r}{c}, \dots, \frac{\rho_n^r}{c} \right\rangle \\ &= S_{m,n}\left\langle \frac{\rho_1^r}{c}, \dots, \frac{\rho_n^n}{c} \right\rangle \Big/ I \cdot S_{m,n}\left\langle \frac{\rho_1^r}{c}, \dots, \frac{\rho_n^r}{c} \right\rangle. \end{aligned}$$

By the Weierstrass Division Theorem, Theorem 2.3.2, $S_{m,n}\langle \rho_1^r/c, \dots, \rho_n^r/c\rangle$ is affinoid. □

Proposition 5.3.9. — *Assume that K is algebraically closed and let $A = S_{m,n}/I$ be a quasi-affinoid algebra. The following are equivalent:*

(i) *$A \simeq S_{0,\ell}/J$ for some ℓ, J.*

(ii) *For every $f \in A$, each set*

$$\{x \in \operatorname{Max} A \colon |f(x)| = ||f||_{\sup}\},$$
$$\{x \in \operatorname{Max} A \colon |f(x)| < ||f||_{\sup}\},$$

is Zariski-closed; hence is a union of Zariski-connected components of Max A.

(iii) *Let $\pi : S_{m,n} \to S_{m,n}/I = A$ be the canonical projection and let N be the number of Zariski-connected components of* Max A. *Then there are $c_{ij} \in K^\circ$, $1 \le i \le m$, $1 \le j \le N$, such that each*

$$\prod_{j=1}^{N} (\pi(\xi_i) - c_{ij})$$

is quasi-nilpotent. (In other words, as a subset of Max $S_{m,n}$, Max A *is contained in a finite union of open unit polydiscs, namely, those with centers $(c_{ij}, \dots, c_{mj}) \times 0$.)*

Proof

(i)⇒(ii). Let $\mathfrak{p}$ be a minimal prime ideal of A. By Remark 2.3.6, there is a finite, torsion-free monomorphism

$$\varphi : S_{0,d} \to A/\mathfrak{p}.$$

Let $f \in A$ and let $q(f)$ be the integral equation of minimal degree for f over $S_{0,d}$, where

$$q = X^s + b_1 X^{s-1} + \cdots + b_s \in S_{0,d}[X],$$

as in [**6**, Proposition 3.8.1.7]. Following the argument of [**6**, Proposition 3.8.1.7], for every $y \in \operatorname{Max} S_{0,d}$,

$$\|\overline{f}_y\|_{\sup} = \max_{\substack{\varphi(y) \subset x \\ x \in \operatorname{Max} A}} |f(x)| = \max_{1 \le i \le s} |b_i(y)|^{1/i},$$

and

$$\|f\|_{\sup} = \max_{1 \le i \le s} \|b_i\|_{\sup}^{1/i},$$

where $\overline{f}_y$ is the residue class of f in the quotient of $A/\varphi(y) \cdot A$ by its nilradical. Since each $b_i \in S_{0,d}$, either

$$|b_i(y)| < \|b_i\|_{\sup} = \|b_i\| \tag{5.3.2}$$

for all $y \in \operatorname{Max} S_{0,d}$, or

$$|b_i(y)| = \|b_i\|_{\sup} = \|b_i\| \tag{5.3.3}$$

for all $y \in \operatorname{Max} S_{0,d}$. If (5.3.2) holds for every i such that

$$\|b_i\|^{1/i} = \|f\|_{\sup},$$

then $|f(x)| < \|f\|_{\sup}$ for all $x \in \operatorname{Max} A/\mathfrak{p}$. Otherwise, there is some i_0 such that

$$\|b_{i_0}\|^{1/i_0} = \|f\|_{\sup} \quad \text{and} \quad |b_{i_0}(y)| = \|b_{i_0}\|$$

for all $y \in \operatorname{Max} S_{0,d}$. In this case, $|f(x)| = \|f\|_{\sup}$ for all $x \in \operatorname{Max} A/\mathfrak{p}$. This shows that each set

$$\{x \in \operatorname{Max} A/\mathfrak{p} \colon |f(x)| = \|f\|_{\sup}\},$$
$$\{x \in \operatorname{Max} A/\mathfrak{p} \colon |f(x)| < \|f\|_{\sup}\},$$

is Zariski-closed. Taking the union over the finitely many minimal prime ideals of A, (ii) follows.

(ii)$\Rightarrow$(iii). Let $X_1, \ldots, X_N$ be the Zariski-connected components of $\operatorname{Max} A$, choose $x_j \in X_j$, $1 \le j \le N$, and put

$$c_{ij} := \xi_i(x_j).$$

Part (iii) follows by applying part (ii) to each $\xi_i - c_{ij}$.

(iii)$\Rightarrow$(i). Put

$$g_i := \prod_{j=1}^{N} (\xi_i - c_{ij});$$

then by the Extension Lemma, Theorem 5.2.6, there is a K-algebra homomorphism $\psi : S_{0,m+n} \to A$ such that

$$\psi(\rho_i) = \pi(\rho_i), \qquad 1 \le i \le n, \text{ and}$$
$$\psi(\rho_{n+i}) = \pi(g_i), \qquad 1 \le i \le m.$$

It follows from the Weierstrass Division Theorem, Theorem 2.3.2, that ψ is finite. Thus, after a homothety, part (i) follows. □

5.4. Tensor Products. — In this subsection we prove that tensor products exist in the category of quasi-affinoid algebras with K-algebra homomorphisms. These results will be needed in **[22]** when we discuss fiber products of quasi-affinoid varieties.

Lemma 5.4.1

(i) *If A is a quasi-affinoid algebra and $\varphi : A \to B$ is a finite K-algebra homomorphism, then B is quasi-affinoid.*

(ii) *If A and B are quasi-affinoid algebras then so is the ring-theoretic direct sum $A \oplus B$.*

Proof

(i) We may take $A = S_{m,n}$. Let $b_1, \dots, b_\ell \in B$ be such that $B = \sum_{i=1}^{\ell} \varphi(S_{m,n}) b_i$. For each i, let $A_{ij} \in S_{m,n}$ be such that $b_i^{n_i} + \varphi(A_{i1}) b_i^{n_i - 1} + \cdots + \varphi(A_{in_i}) = 0$. Replacing b_i by cb_i for a suitable nonzero $c \in K^\circ$ we may assume that $\|A_{ij}\| \le 1$. Let $P_i \in S_{m+\ell,n}$ be defined by

$$P_i(\eta_i) = \eta_i^{n_i} + A_{i1}\eta_i^{n_i-1} + \cdots + A_{in_i},$$

where $S_{m+\ell,n} = K\langle \xi, \eta \rangle [\![\rho]\!]_s$. Then P_i is regular in η_i. Let

$$\pi : S_{m+\ell,n} \longrightarrow S_{m+\ell,n}/(P_1, \dots, P_\ell)$$

be the canonical projection, and consider the K-algebra homomorphism

$$\psi : S_{m,n}[\eta_1, \dots, \eta_\ell] \longrightarrow B : \Sigma f_\mu \eta^\mu \mapsto \Sigma \varphi(f_\mu) b^\mu.$$

By the Weierstrass Division Theorem (Theorem 2.3.2),

$$S_{m+\ell,n}/(P_1, \dots, P_\ell) \simeq S_{m,n}[\eta_1, \dots, \eta_\ell]/(P_1, \dots, P_\ell).$$

The K-algebra homomorphism

$$S_{m+\ell,n} \to S_{m+\ell,n}/(P_1, \dots, P_\ell) \longrightarrow S_{m,n}[\eta_1, \dots, \eta_\ell]/(P_1, \dots, P_\ell) \to B$$

is surjective, as required.

(ii) It is sufficient to consider $A = B = S_{m,n}$. The diagonal map $S_{m,n} \to S_{m,n} \oplus S_{m,n}$ is a finite K-algebra homomorphism, so the result follows from part (i). □

Definition 5.4.2. — Let A, B_1, B_2 be quasi-affinoid algebras and let B_1, B_2 be A-algebras via homomorphisms $\varphi_i : A \to B_i$, $i = 1, 2$. By Remark 5.2.8, we can write

$$B_1 = A\langle \xi_1, \dots, \xi_{m_1} \rangle [\![\rho_1, \dots, \rho_{n_1}]\!]_s / I_1 \text{ and}$$
$$B_2 = A\langle \xi_{m_1+1}, \dots, \xi_{m_1+m_2} \rangle [\![\rho_{n_1+1}, \dots, \rho_{n_1+n_2}]\!]_s / I_2.$$

We define the *separated tensor product of B_1 and B_2 over A* by

$$B_1 \otimes_A^s B_2 := A\langle \xi_1, \dots, \xi_{m_1+m_2} \rangle [\![\rho_1, \dots, \rho_{n_1+n_2}]\!]_s / (I_1 + I_2).$$

By the Extension Lemma (Theorem 5.2.6), $B_1 \otimes_A^s B_2$ is independent of the presentations of B_1 and B_2. The inclusions

$$A\langle \xi_1, \dots, \xi_{m_1} \rangle [\![\rho_1, \dots, \rho_{n_1}]\!]_s \to A\langle \xi_1, \dots, \xi_{m_1+m_2} \rangle [\![\rho_1, \dots, \rho_{n_1+n_2}]\!]_s,$$
$$\xi_i \longmapsto \xi_i, \quad \rho_j \longmapsto \rho_j, \quad i = 1, \dots, m_1, \quad j = 1, \dots, n_1;$$
$$A\langle \xi_{m_1+1}, \dots, \xi_{m_1+m_2} \rangle [\![\rho_{n_1+1}, \dots, \rho_{n_1+n_2}]\!]_s \longrightarrow$$
$$A\langle \xi_1, \dots, \xi_{m_1+m_2} \rangle [\![\rho_1, \dots, \rho_{n_1+n_2}]\!]_s,$$
$$\xi_{m_1+i} \longmapsto \xi_{m_1+i}, \quad \rho_{n_1+j} \longmapsto \rho_{n_1+j} \quad i = 1, \dots, m_2, \quad j = 1, \dots, n_2,$$

define canonical homomorphisms

$$\sigma_i : B_i \to B_1 \otimes_A^s B_2.$$

The next proposition shows that $B_1 \otimes_A^s B_2$ satisfies the universal property in the category of quasi-affinoid algebras that justifies calling it a tensor product.

Proposition 5.4.3. — *Let $\varphi_i : A \to B_i$, $i = 1, 2$, be K-algebra homomorphisms of quasi-affinoid algebras and let $\psi_i : B_i \to D$ be A-algebra homomorphisms of quasi-affinoid algebras. Then there is a unique A-algebra homomorphism $\psi : B_1 \otimes_A^s B_2 \to D$ such that*

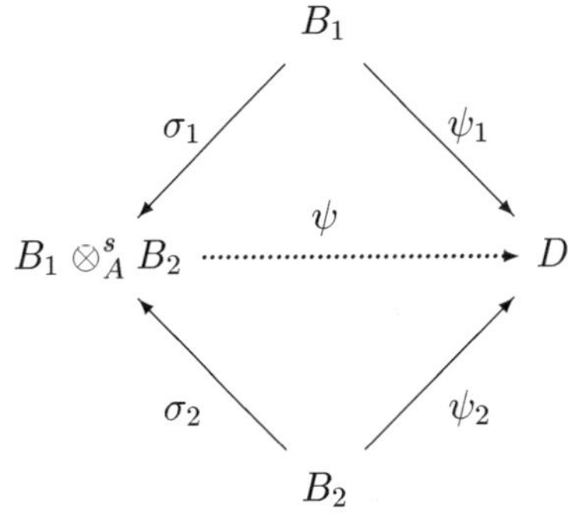

commutes, where the $\sigma_i : B_i \to B_1 \otimes_A^s B_2$ are the homomorphisms given in Definition 5.4.2.

Proof. — By the Extension Lemma (Theorem 5.2.6 or Remark 5.2.8) there is a unique $\psi' : A\langle\xi_1, \dots, \xi_{m_1+m_2}\rangle[\![\rho_1, \dots, \rho_{n_1+n_2}]\!] \to D$ that extends $\psi_1 \circ \varphi_1 = \psi_2 \circ \varphi_2$ such that

$$\begin{aligned} \psi'(\xi_i) &= \psi_1(\xi_i), & i &= 1, \dots, m_1, \\ \psi'(\rho_j) &= \psi_1(\rho_j), & j &= 1, \dots, n_1, \\ \psi'(\xi_{m_1+i}) &= \psi_2(\xi_{m_1+i}), & i &= 1, \dots, m_2, \\ \psi'(\rho_{n_1+j}) &= \psi_2(\rho_{n_1+j}), & j &= 1, \dots, n_2. \end{aligned}$$

Since $(I_1 + I_2) \subset \operatorname{Ker}(\psi')$, the result follows. □

Remark 5.4.4

(i) If A, B_1, B_2 are affinoid then it follows from the above Proposition and the universal property of the complete tensor product ([**6**, Proposition 3.1.1.2]) that

$$B_1 \otimes^s_A B_2 = B_1 \widehat{\otimes}_A B_2.$$

(ii) In general, $B_1 \otimes^s_A B_2 \neq B_1 \widehat{\otimes}_A B_2$. In the case that the $S_{m,n}(E, K)$ are complete, we have $B_1 \otimes^s_A B_2 \supset B_1 \widehat{\otimes}_A B_2$. This follows from the universal property of $\widehat{\otimes}_A$. In all cases we have $S_{0,1} \otimes^s_K S_{0,1} \not\subset S_{0,1} \widehat{\otimes}_K S_{0,1}$ since

$$\sum_i (\rho_1 \rho_2)^i \in (S_{0,1} \otimes^s_K S_{0,1}) \setminus (S_{0,1} \widehat{\otimes}_K S_{0,1}).$$

The following important examples of separated tensor products are computed directly from Definition 5.4.2.

Corollary 5.4.5. — *We have*

$$S_{m_1,n_1} \otimes^s_K S_{m_2,n_2} = S_{m_1+m_2,n_1+n_2},$$

and if A is a quasi-affinoid algebra,

$$A \otimes^s_K S_{m,n} = A\langle\xi\rangle[\![\rho]\!]_s.$$

The following two propositions are easy consequences of the definition and the universal property of the separated tensor product (*cf.* [**6**, Propositions 6.1.1.10 and 6.1.1.11]).

Proposition 5.4.6. — *Let A', A, B_1, B_2 be quasi-affinoid algebras and assume that the B_i are both A and A'-algebras via homomorphisms $A' \to A$ and $A \to B_1$, $A \to B_2$. Then the canonical homomorphism*

$$B_1 \otimes^s_{A'} B_2 \to B_1 \otimes^s_A B_2$$

is surjective.

Proposition 5.4.7. — *Let A, B_1, B_2 be quasi-affinoid algebras and assume that B_1, B_2 are A-algebras via homomorphisms $A \to B_i$, $i = 1, 2$. Let $\mathfrak{b}_i \subset B_i$, $i = 1, 2$ be ideals and denote by $(\mathfrak{b}_1, \mathfrak{b}_2)$ the ideal in $B_1 \otimes^s_A B_2$ generated by the images of $\mathfrak{b}_1$ and $\mathfrak{b}_2$. Then the canonical map $\pi : B_1 \otimes^s_A B_2 \to B_1/\mathfrak{b}_1 \otimes^s_A B_2/\mathfrak{b}_2$ is surjective and satisfies $\operatorname{Ker} \pi = (\mathfrak{b}_1, \mathfrak{b}_2)$. Hence $(B_1 \otimes^s_A B_2)/(\mathfrak{b}_1, \mathfrak{b}_2) \simeq B_1/\mathfrak{b}_1 \otimes^s_A B_2/\mathfrak{b}_2$.*

It follows from Lemma 5.4.1 and Proposition 5.4.7 that base change preserves finite (respectively surjective) morphisms.

Proposition 5.4.8. — *Let A and B be quasi-affinoid algebras. Let $\varphi : A \to B$ be a K-algebra homomorphism and let C be a quasi-affinoid A-algebra. If φ is finite (respectively surjective) then the induced map $C \to B \otimes_A^s C$ is finite (respectively surjective).*

Proof. — Suppose B is a finite A-module via φ. It follows from the right-exactness of the ordinary tensor product that $B \otimes_A C$ is a finite C-module. By Lemma 5.4.1 $B \otimes_A C$ is a quasi-affinoid algebra. It therefore follows from the universal property for tensor products that $B \otimes_A^s C = B \otimes_A C$. In particular, $C \to B \otimes_A^s C$ is finite.

If φ is surjective, then we may write $B = A/I$, where $I := \operatorname{Ker} \varphi$. Then by Proposition 5.4.7,

$$B \otimes_A^s C = A/I \otimes_A^s C/(0) \cong (A \otimes_A^s C)/(I, (0)),$$

which is a quotient of C. Therefore $C \to B \otimes_A^s C$ is surjective. □

A small extension of Definition 5.4.2 yields a ground field extension functor for quasi-affinoid algebras.

Definition 5.4.9. — Let (E, K), (E', K') be such that $S_{m,n}(E, K) \subset S_{m,n}(E', K')$ and let $A := S_{m,n}(E, K)/I$. We say that the K'-affinoid algebra

$$A' = S_{0,0}(E', K') \otimes_{S_{0,0}(E,K)}^s A := S_{m,n}(E', K')/I \cdot S_{m,n}(E', K')$$

results from A by *ground field extension* from (E, K) to (E', K').

Proposition 5.4.10. — *The canonical homomorphism*

$$A \to S_{0,0}(E', K') \otimes_{S_{0,0}(E,K)}^s A$$

is a faithfully flat norm-preserving monomorphism both in $\|\cdot\|_I$ and $\|\cdot\|_{I \cdot S_{m,n}(E',K')}$ and in $\|\cdot\|_{\sup}$.

Proof. — Immediate from Lemma 3.1.11 and Proposition 4.1.3. □

5.5. Banach Function Algebras. — Each representation of a quasi-affinoid algebra A as a quotient $S_{m,n}/I$ yields the K-algebra norm $\|\cdot\|_I$, which by Lemma 3.1.4, is complete if $S_{m,n}$ is. We saw (Corollary 5.2.4) that even though A may not be complete, all these norms are equivalent. By the Nullstellensatz, Theorem 4.1.1, if A is reduced then $\|\cdot\|_{\sup}$ is a norm on A. In this subsection we shall show when $\operatorname{Char} K = 0$ (Theorem 5.5.3) and often when $\operatorname{Char} K = p \neq 0$ (Theorem 5.5.4) that if A is reduced, $\|\cdot\|_{\sup}$ is equivalent to the residue norms $\|\cdot\|_I$. It follows that if in addition E and K are such that A is complete in $\|\cdot\|_I$ then A is complete in $\|\cdot\|_{\sup}$, i.e., it is a Banach function algebra.

The obstruction to following the argument of [**6**, Theorem 6.2.4.1], is, as usual, the lack of a suitable Noether Normalization for quasi-affinoid algebras. Theorems 3.4.3 and 3.4.6 allow us to reduce the problem to considering quotient rings of $S_{0,n+m}$, for which a Noether Normalization is available. The fact that the quotients of $S_{0,n+m}$ so obtained are reduced is guaranteed when the $S_{m,n}$ are excellent.

Lemma 5.5.1. — *Suppose K and E are such that the $S_{m,n}$ are complete and the fields of fractions of the $S_{0,n}(E,K)$ are weakly stable. Let A be a reduced quasi-affinoid algebra. If there is a finite K-algebra homomorphism $S_{0,n}/I \to A$ then A is a Banach function algebra.*

Proof. — As in the proof of [**6**, Theorem 6.2.4.1], we use Noether Normalization for quotients of $S_{0,n}$ (Remark 2.3.6) to reduce to the case that $I = (0)$ and $S_{0,n} \to A$ is a finite, torsion-free monomorphism.

Note that $S_{0,n}$ is integrally closed (for example, apply Theorem 4.2.7 or use Noether Normalization as in [**6**, Theorem 5.2.6.1]). Since, in addition, we have assumed that $Q(S_{0,n})$ is a weakly stable field ([**6**, Definition 3.5.2.1]), we may apply [**6**, Theorem 3.8.3.7]. □

Proposition 5.5.2. — *Under any of the conditions*

(i) $\operatorname{Char} K = 0$,

(ii) $\operatorname{Char} K = p \neq 0$ *and* $S_{m,n}(E,K) \simeq \oplus_{i=1}^{N} (S_{m,n}(E,K))^p$ *as normed* K^p*-algebras,*

(iii) $\operatorname{Char} K = p \neq 0$, $[K : K^p] < \infty$ *and* $[\widetilde{E} : \widetilde{E}^p] < \infty$,

the fields of fractions of the rings $S_{m,n}(E,K)$ are weakly stable.

Proof. — When $\operatorname{Char} K = 0$, this is [**6**, Proposition 3.5.1.4]. Note that condition (iii) implies condition (ii) because K is complete (use [**6**, Proposition 2.3.3.4]). Thus it remains only to verify case (ii), which follows from [**6**, Lemma 3.5.3.2]. □

Note that under any of the conditions of Proposition 5.5.2, the rings $S_{m,n}(E,K)$ are excellent (see Propositions 4.2.3 and 4.2.5).

In characteristic zero, we show in Theorem 5.5.3 that the supremum norm of a reduced quasi-affinoid algebra A is equivalent to the residue norm arising from any presentation of A as a quotient of a ring of separated power series. In some cases this is an extension of Corollary 5.2.4, which establishes the equivalence of all the residue norms (whether or not A is reduced and of characteristic zero). In characteristic p, our results are less complete (see Theorem 5.5.4). The proofs of Theorems 5.5.3 and 5.5.4 rely on restriction to finite disjoint unions of open polydiscs, for which one has a Noether Normalization. In the proof of Theorem 5.5.3, we reduce to the case of polydiscs with rational centers. The proof of Theorem 5.5.4 does not depend on the characteristic.

Theorem 5.5.3. — *Suppose that* Char $K = 0$ *and that* $A = S_{m,n}(E,K)/I$ *is a reduced quasi-affinoid algebra. Then* $\|\cdot\|_I$ *and* $\|\cdot\|_{\sup}$ *on* A *are equivalent. If in addition* A *is complete in* $\|\cdot\|_I$*, then* A *is a Banach function algebra.*

Proof. — Let $E' \supset E$ be as in Theorem 2.1.3 (ii) so that the $S_{m,n}(E',K)$ are complete. By Propositions 4.2.3 and 4.2.6, $A' = S_{m,n}(E',K)/I \cdot S_{m,n}(E',K)$ is reduced, since $T_{m,n}(\varepsilon) = T_{m,n}(\varepsilon, K)$ does not depend on E or E'. By Proposition 4.1.3 and Lemma 3.1.11 the map

$$S_{m,n}(E,K)/I \longrightarrow S_{m,n}(E',K)/I \cdot S_{m,n}(E',K)$$

is an inclusion which is an isometry in both the supremum and residue norms. Hence it is sufficient to prove the equivalence of $\|\cdot\|_I$ and $\|\cdot\|_{\sup}$ when E is such that the $S_{m,n}(E,K)$ are complete.

Let K' be a finite extension of K such that there are $c_1, \ldots, c_r \in ((K')^\circ)^m$ with $|c_i - c_j| = 1$, $1 \leq i < j \leq r$, such that for every

$$\mathfrak{p} \in \operatorname{Ass}(S_{m,n}(E, \widehat{K}_{\text{alg}})^\sim / \widetilde{I} \cdot S_{m,n}(E, \widehat{K}_{\text{alg}})^\sim)$$

there is an i, $1 \leq i \leq r$, with

$$\mathfrak{m}_{\widetilde{c}_i} = (\xi - \widetilde{c}_i, \rho) \supset \mathfrak{p},$$

where $\widehat{K}_{\text{alg}}$ is the completion of the algebraic closure of K.

Let $S'_{m,n} := S_{m,n}(E,K')$ and $I' := I \cdot S'_{m,n}$. Observe that $S'_{m,n}/I'$ is reduced. (Indeed, we may write $K' = K(\alpha)$, so every $f \in S'_{m,n}$ may be written in the form

$$f = \sum_{j=0}^{d-1} f_j \alpha^j,$$

for $f_j \in S_{m,n}$. Let $\sigma_0, \ldots, \sigma_{d-1}$ be the distinct embeddings of K' over K in an algebraic closure of K and let $\alpha_i := \sigma_i(\alpha)$, $0 \leq i \leq d-1$. Then

$$\det(\alpha_i^j) = \Pi_{i \neq j}(\alpha_i - \alpha_j) \neq 0.$$

It follows that the f_j are linear combinations of the $\sigma_i(f)$. Hence, if $f \in \sqrt{I'}$, so is each f_j. But the map $S_{m,n} \to S'_{m,n}$ is faithfully flat (Lemma 4.2.8(iii)), so each $f_j \in \sqrt{I} = I$. It follows that $f \in I'$.) Now, by Proposition 4.1.3 and Lemma 3.1.11(ii), the map $S_{m,n}/I \to S'_{m,n}/I'$ is an inclusion and an isometry in both the supremum norm and the residue norm. Since $S_{m,n}/I$ is complete in $\|\cdot\|_I$, it therefore suffices to prove the theorem for $S'_{m,n}/I'$. Note that all the $S_{m',n'}(E,K')$ are complete

By Theorem 3.4.3(ii), the map

$$\psi : S'_{m,n}/I' \longrightarrow \left(\oplus_{j=1}^r S'_{0,n+m}\right) / \omega_c(I') \cdot \left(\oplus_{j=1}^r S'_{0,n+m}\right)$$

is an isometry in the residue norms. By Proposition 4.2.3 and [**25**, Theorem 32.2],

$$\left(\oplus_{j=1}^r S'_{0,n+m}\right) / \omega_c(I') \cdot \left(\oplus_{j=1}^r S'_{0,n+m}\right)$$

is reduced. Since ψ is a contraction with respect to $\|\cdot\|_{\sup}$, it suffices to prove the theorem for this ring. That is Lemma 5.5.1. □

Theorem 5.5.4. — *Suppose that the rings $S_{m,n}(E,K)$ are excellent (see Proposition 4.2.3 or 4.2.5) and that at least one of the following two conditions is satisfied:*

(i) *K is perfect*

(ii) *There is an E', $E \subset E'$, such that the fields of fractions of the $S_{0,n}(E',K)$ are weakly stable, and the $S_{0,n}(E',K)$ are complete.*

Let $A = S_{m,n}(E,K)/I$ be reduced. Then on A the norms $\|\cdot\|_I$ and $\|\cdot\|_{\sup}$ are equivalent. If in addition A is complete in $\|\cdot\|_I$ then A is a Banach function algebra.

Proof. — We may assume (see Remark 2.1.4(i)) that E is a field. We now show that (i) implies (ii). In the case that K is perfect there is an $E' \supset E$ such that $S_{m,n}(E',K)$ is complete (see Theorem 2.1.3(ii)). Since K is perfect, we may extend further so that E' is perfect. Then, by Proposition 5.5.2 the fields of fractions of the $S_{0,n}(E',K)$ are also weakly stable.

Choose $c_1, \ldots, c_r \in (K_{\mathrm{alg}}^{\circ})^m$ with $\mathfrak{m}_{\widetilde{c}_i} \neq \mathfrak{m}_{\widetilde{c}_j}$, $1 \le i < j \le r$, such that for every $\mathfrak{p} \in \mathrm{Ass}(\widetilde{S}_{m,n}/\widetilde{I})$ there is some i, $1 \le i \le r$, with

$$\mathfrak{m}_{\widetilde{c}_i} \supset \mathfrak{p}.$$

(The $\widetilde{m}_{\widetilde{c}_i}$ are the maximal ideals of $\widetilde{S}_{m,n}$ corresponding to $\widetilde{c}_i$ as in Definition 3.4.4.)

By Theorem 3.4.6(ii), the map

$$\psi : S_{m,n}/I \longrightarrow D_{m,n}(c)/\omega_c(I)$$

is an isometry in the residue norms $\|\cdot\|_I$ and $\|\cdot\|_{\omega_c(I)}$. Since $S_{m,n}(E,K)$ is excellent, by [**25**, Theorem 32.2], $D_{m,n}(c)/\omega_c(I)$ is reduced. Since ψ is a contraction with respect to $\|\cdot\|_{\sup}$, it suffices to prove the theorem for that ring. Recall that $D_{m,n}(c) = S_{m,n+m}(E,K)/J$ for some ideal J. Let

$$D'_{m,n}(c) := S_{m,n+m}(E',K)/J \cdot S_{m,n+m}(E',K).$$

Then $D'_{m,n}(c)/\omega_c(I) \cdot D'_{m,n}(c)$ is reduced since the maximal-adic completions of all its local rings coincide with those of the reduced, excellent ring $D_{m,n}(c)/\omega_c(I)$. By Proposition 4.1.3 and Lemma 3.1.11, the map

$$D_{m,n}(c)/\omega_c(I) \longrightarrow D'_{m,n}(c)/\omega_c(I).D'_{m,n}(c)$$

is an inclusion which is an isometry in both the supremum and residue norms. Hence it suffices to prove the equivalence of the residue norm and the supremum norm on $D'_{m,n}(c)/\omega_c(I) \cdot D'_{m,n}(c)$. By Lemma 3.4.5, this ring is a finite extension of a quotient of a ring $S_{0,d}(E',K)$. Now apply Lemma 5.5.1. □

6. A Finiteness Theorem

In Subsection 6.1 we prove a finiteness theorem, which is a weak analogue of Zariski's Main Theorem, for quasi-finite maps, and in Subsection 6.2 we apply this finiteness theorem to show that every quasi-affinoid subdomain is a finite union of R-subdomains.

6.1. A Finiteness Theorem. — In applications ([**2**], [**16**], [**17**], [**18**], [**19**], [**20**], [**21**] and [**23**]), certain weaker forms of Noether Normalization have proved useful. We collect two examples here. Recall that we showed in Subsection 5.3 that we associate canonically with each R-domain $U \subset \operatorname{Max} A$, the A-algebra of quasi-affinoid functions $\mathcal{O}(U)$.

We call a quasi-affinoid map $\pi : \operatorname{Max} B \to \operatorname{Max} A$ *finite* if, and only if, B is a finite A-module via the induced map $\pi^* : A \to B$.

Proposition 6.1.1. — *Let $\pi : \operatorname{Max} B \to \operatorname{Max} A$ be a quasi-affinoid map. Suppose $U_1, \ldots, U_n$ is a cover of $\operatorname{Max} B$ by R-subdomains. If each $\pi|_{U_i} : U_i \to \operatorname{Max} A$ is finite then π is finite.*

Proof. — By Proposition 5.3.6(ii) and the Krull Intersection Theorem ([**25**, Theorem 8.10]), the natural map

$$B \to \prod_{i=0}^{n} \mathcal{O}(U_i)$$

is injective. Each $\mathcal{O}(U_i)$ is a finite A-module; hence B, being a submodule of the finite A-module $\Pi\mathcal{O}(U_i)$, is a finite A-module as well. □

Let $\pi : \operatorname{Max} B \to \operatorname{Max} A$ be a quasi-affinoid map. If $U \subset \operatorname{Max} A$ is an R-domain defined by inequalities among $f_1, \ldots, f_\ell$ then $\pi^{-1}(U) \subset \operatorname{Max} B$ is an R-domain defined by the corresponding inequalities among $f_1 \circ \pi, \ldots, f_\ell \circ \pi$.

The affinoid analog of the following is false; see Example 6.1.3.

***Theorem 6.1.2* (Finiteness Theorem)**. — *Let $\pi : \operatorname{Max} B \to \operatorname{Max} A$ be a quasi-affinoid map which is finite-to-one. There exists a finite cover of $\operatorname{Max} A$ by R-domains U_i such that each map*

$$\pi|_{\pi^{-1}(U_i)} \colon \pi^{-1}(U_i) \longrightarrow U_i$$

is finite. (Note: We do not assume that π is surjective.)

Proof. — Let $\varphi : A \to B$ be the K-algebra homomorphism corresponding to π. Since B is quasi-affinoid, there is a K-algebra epimorphism

$$S_{m,n} \longrightarrow B.$$

The images of $\xi_1, \dots, \xi_m$ (respectively, $\rho_1, \dots, \rho_n$) in B are power-bounded (respectively, quasi-nilpotent). By Remark 5.2.8, this induces a unique K-algebra homomorphism ψ such that the following diagram commutes

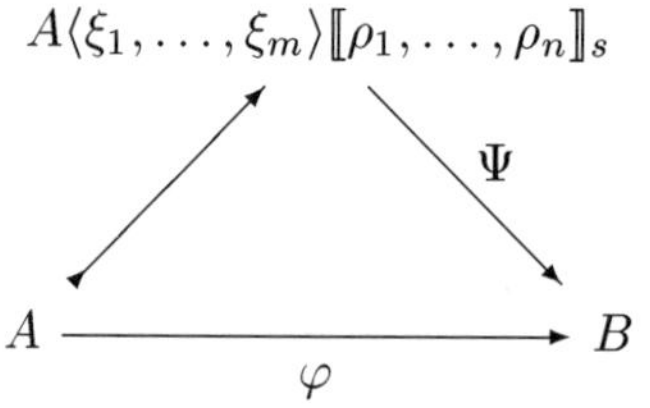

Since $S_{m,n} \to B$ is surjective, so is ψ.

Let

$$I := \operatorname{Ker} \psi;$$

then

$$B \cong A\langle \xi_1, \dots, \xi_m \rangle [\![\rho_1, \dots, \rho_n]\!]_s / I,$$

and we may therefore assume that the original map φ is of the form

$$A \xrightarrow{\varphi} A\langle \xi \rangle [\![\rho]\!]_s / I.$$

The proof proceeds by induction on (m, n), ordered lexicographically. Assume $m+n > 0$. (If $m+n = 0$, then $B = K$ and the K-algebra homomorphism φ, being surjective, is finite.)

Let $f_1, \dots, f_\ell$ generate I, and write

$$f_i = \sum a_{i\mu\nu} \xi^\mu \rho^\nu, \quad 1 \le i \le \ell,$$

where each $a_{i\mu\nu} \in A$. Since π is finite-to-one, $\{a_{i\mu\nu}\}$ generates the unit ideal of A.

Writing A as a quotient of a ring of separated power series and applying Lemma 3.1.6 to pre-images of the f_i, we obtain a finite index set $J \subset \mathbb{N}^m \times \mathbb{N}^n$ such that for each $x \in \operatorname{Max} A$ there is an i_0, $1 \le i_0 \le \ell$, and an index $(\mu_0, \nu_0) \in J$ such that

$$\begin{aligned} &|a_{i_0\mu_0\nu_0}(x)| \ge |a_{i\mu\nu}(x)| && \text{for all } i, \mu, \nu \\ &|a_{i_0\mu_0\nu_0}(x)| > |a_{i_0\mu\nu}(x)| && \text{for all } \nu < \nu_0 \text{ and all } \mu \\ &|a_{i_0\mu_0\nu_0}(x)| > |a_{i_0\mu\nu_0}(x)| && \text{for all } \mu > \mu_0. \end{aligned} \tag{6.1.1}$$

(Note, in particular, that (6.1.1) guarantees that $\{a_{i\mu\nu} : 1 \le i \le \ell, (\mu, \nu) \in J\}$ generates the unit ideal of A.)

Fix i_0, $1 \le i_0 \le \ell$, and $(\mu_0, \nu_0) \in J$. Let $U_{i_0\mu_0\nu_0}$ be the set of points $x \in \operatorname{Max} A$ such that

$$\begin{aligned} &|a_{i_0\mu_0\nu_0}(x)| \ge |a_{i\mu\nu}(x)| && \text{for all } 1 \le i \le \ell \text{ and } (\mu, \nu) \in J \\ &|a_{i_0\mu_0\nu_0}(x)| > |a_{i_0\mu\nu}(x)| && \text{for all } (\mu, \nu) \in J \text{ with } \nu < \nu_0 \\ &|a_{i_0\mu_0\nu_0}(x)| > |a_{i_0\mu\nu_0}(x)| && \text{for all } (\mu, \nu) \in J \text{ with } \mu > \mu_0. \end{aligned}$$

As in Subsection 5.3, $U_{i_0\mu_0\nu_0}$ is a quasi-rational subdomain of $\operatorname{Max} A$, which is in fact equal to the set of points $x \in \operatorname{Max} A$ where (6.1.1) holds. Furthermore, the $U_{i_0\mu_0\nu_0}$ cover $\operatorname{Max} A$.

We may now replace A by $\mathcal{O}(U_{i_0\mu_0\nu_0})$ and B by

$$\mathcal{O}(U_{i_0\mu_0\nu_0})\langle\xi\rangle[\![\rho]\!]_s / I \cdot \mathcal{O}(U_{i_0\mu_0\nu_0})\langle\xi\rangle[\![\rho]\!]_s.$$

Replacing f_{i_0} by $a_{i_0\mu_0\nu_0}^{-1} f_{i_0}$, we may assume that $a_{i_0\mu_0\nu_0} = 1$. Put

$$f_{i_0\nu_0} := \sum_{\mu} a_{i_0\mu\nu_0}\xi^{\mu};$$

then $f_{i_0\nu_0}$ is preregular in ξ (*cf.* Definition 2.3.7).

The two quasi-rational subdomains

$$V := \{y \in \operatorname{Max} B : |f_{i_0\nu_0}(y)| = 1\} \text{ and } W := \{y \in \operatorname{Max} B : |f_{i_0\nu_0}(y)| < 1\}$$

cover $\operatorname{Max} B$, and each restriction $\pi|_V$ and $\pi|_W$ is finite-to-one. By Proposition 5.3.6(ii) and the Krull Intersection Theorem ([**25**, Theorem 8.10]), the natural map

$$B \longrightarrow \mathcal{O}(V) \oplus \mathcal{O}(W)$$

is injective. Hence it suffices to treat the maps $A \to \mathcal{O}(V)$ and $A \to \mathcal{O}(W)$.

***Case* (A).** — $A \to \mathcal{O}(V)$.

Observe that

$$\mathcal{O}(V) = A\langle\xi_1, \ldots, \xi_{m+1}\rangle[\![\rho_1, \ldots, \rho_n]\!]_s / J,$$

where J is the ideal generated by I and the element

$$F := \xi_{m+1} f_{i_0\nu_0} - 1.$$

Put

$$G := \rho^{\nu_0} + \sum_{\substack{\nu\neq\nu_0 \\ \mu}} a_{i_0\mu\nu}\xi_{m+1}\xi^{\mu}\rho^{\nu} \equiv \xi_{m+1} f_{i_0} \mod J;$$

in particular, $G \in J$. By (6.1.1), after a change of variables among the ρ's, we can assume that G is regular in ρ_n (in the sense of Definition 2.3.7). Similarly, after a change of variables among the ξ's, we can assume that F is regular in ξ_{m+1}. Applying Theorem 2.3.8, first to divide by G, then by F, shows that $\mathcal{O}(V)$ is a finite extension of an A-algebra of the form

$$B' := A\langle\xi_1, \ldots, \xi_m\rangle[\![\rho_1, \ldots, \rho_{n-1}]\!]_s / I'.$$

Since $\mathcal{O}(V)$ is a finite extension of the A-algebra B', the map

$$\operatorname{Max} B' \longrightarrow \operatorname{Max} A$$

is finite-to-one. Furthermore, $(m, n-1) < (m, n)$. We are done by induction.

***Case* (B).** — $A \to \mathcal{O}(W)$.

Observe that

$$\mathcal{O}(W) = A\langle \xi_1, \dots, \xi_m \rangle [\![\rho_1, \dots, \rho_{n+1}]\!]_s / J,$$

where J is generated by I and the element

$$F := f_{i_0 \nu_0} - \rho_{n+1}.$$

By (6.1.1), after a change of variables among the ξ's, F is regular in ξ_m (in the sense of Definition 2.3.7). By Theorem 2.3.8, $\mathcal{O}(W)$ is a finite extension of an A-algebra of the form

$$B' := A\langle \xi_1, \dots, \xi_{m-1} \rangle [\![\rho_1, \dots, \rho_{n+1}]\!]_s / I'.$$

Since $\mathcal{O}(W)$ is a finite extension of the A-algebra B', the map

$$\operatorname{Max} B' \to \operatorname{Max} A$$

is finite-to-one. Furthermore, $(m-1, n+1) < (m, n)$, completing Case B.

To complete the proof, we pass to a common refinement of the covers by R-domains obtained in the above two cases, observing that the intersection of R-domains is an R-domain, and that if $\pi : \operatorname{Max} B \to \operatorname{Max} A$ is finite, so is $\pi|_{\pi^{-1}(U)} : \pi^{-1}(U) \to U$ for any R-subdomain U of $\operatorname{Max} A$. □

Example 6.1.3. — The affinoid map induced by

$$\varphi : K\langle \xi \rangle \to K\langle \xi, \eta \rangle / (\xi \eta^2 + \eta + 1)$$

is finite-to-one. But if $\operatorname{Char} \widetilde{K} \neq 2$, φ is not finite. Indeed, if it were, the polynomial $\xi \eta^2 + \eta + 1$, being prime, would have to divide a monic polynomial in $K\langle \xi \rangle [\eta]$. Since ξ is not a unit, φ cannot be finite.

Now, suppose there is a finite cover of $\operatorname{Max} K\langle \xi \rangle$ by affinoid rational subdomains U such that each induced map

$$\mathcal{O}(U) \longrightarrow \mathcal{O}(U) \widehat{\otimes}_{K\langle \xi \rangle} K\langle \xi, \eta \rangle / (\xi \eta^2 + \eta + 1)$$

is finite. Then the affinoid map induced by φ is proper by [**6**, Proposition 9.6.2.5], and [**6**, Proposition 9.6.2.3]. It then follows from [**6**, Corollary 9.6.3.6], that φ is finite, a contradiction. This shows that the analogue of Theorem 6.1.2 does not hold in the affinoid case. Indeed the covering obtained is not in general admissible in the sense of [**22**].

6.2. An Application to Quasi-Affinoid Domains. — In this subsection we apply Theorem 6.1.2 to prove that every quasi-affinoid subdomain is a finite union of R-subdomains. As a corollary we deduce that every quasi-affinoid subdomain is open.

Lemma 6.2.1. — *Let A and B be commutative rings and let $\varphi : A \to B$ be a finite homomorphism.*

(i) *Suppose that for every maximal ideal* $\mathfrak{M}$ *of* B*, the induced map*

$$A_{\mathfrak{m}} \longrightarrow B \otimes_A A_{\mathfrak{m}}$$

is surjective, where $\mathfrak{m} := A \cap \mathfrak{M}$*. Then* φ *is surjective and* $\operatorname{Spec} B$ *is a closed subset of* $\operatorname{Spec} A$*.*

(ii) *Suppose that for every maximal ideal* $\mathfrak{M}$ *of* B*, the induced map*

$$A_{\mathfrak{m}} \longrightarrow B \otimes_A A_{\mathfrak{m}}$$

is bijective, where $\mathfrak{m} := A \cap \mathfrak{M}$*. Then* $\operatorname{Spec} B$ *is an open subset of* $\operatorname{Spec} A$*.*

Proof

(i) For every $\mathfrak{m} \in \operatorname{Max} A$ the map

$$A_{\mathfrak{m}} \longrightarrow B \otimes_A A_{\mathfrak{m}}$$

is surjective. This is true by assumption when $\mathfrak{m} = A \cap \mathfrak{M}$ for some $\mathfrak{M} \in \operatorname{Max} B$. It only remains to treat the other elements of $\operatorname{Max} A$. Let $\mathfrak{m} \in \operatorname{Max} A$ be such an ideal. By [**25**, Theorem 9.3], there is an $a \in \operatorname{Ker} \varphi$ such that $a \notin \mathfrak{m}$. Since a annihilates the A-module B and the image of a in $A_{\mathfrak{m}}$ is nonzero, it follows that $B \otimes_A A_{\mathfrak{m}} = (0)$. Thus the map $A_{\mathfrak{m}} \to B \otimes_A A_{\mathfrak{m}}$ is surjective.

Now let $b \in B$ and consider the ideal

$$I := \{a \in A : ab \in \varphi(A)\}.$$

We will show that I is the unit ideal. Suppose not. Then there is an $\mathfrak{m} \in \operatorname{Max} A$ such that $I \subset \mathfrak{m}$. But $A_{\mathfrak{m}} \to B \otimes_A A_{\mathfrak{m}}$ is surjective so $IA_{\mathfrak{m}}$ is the unit ideal, a contradiction. This proves that φ is surjective. By [**25**, Theorem 9.3], $\operatorname{Spec} B \cap \operatorname{Spec} A = V(\operatorname{Ker} \varphi)$. Hence $\operatorname{Spec} B$ is a closed subset of $\operatorname{Spec} A$.

(ii) Since we are only concerned with prime ideals, it is no loss of generality to assume that A and B are both reduced, i.e. have no nonzero nilpotent elements. It suffices to show that B is a direct summand of A.

By part (i), φ is surjective, so $B = A/I$ where $I := \operatorname{Ker} \varphi$. Since B is reduced, I is the intersection of some prime ideals of A. Let J be the intersection of the unit ideal with all the minimal prime ideals of A that do not contain I. We will show that

$$A = A/I \oplus A/J.$$

This is obvious if $J = (1)$. So assume $J \neq (1)$. By [**25**, Theorem 1.4], it suffices to show that $I + J$ is the unit ideal of A. Suppose not. Then there is an $\mathfrak{m} \in \operatorname{Max} A$ such that $\mathfrak{m} \supset I + J$; in particular $\mathfrak{m} \supset J$. Since J is an intersection of minimal prime ideals of A, at least one such prime must be contained in $\mathfrak{m}$. In other words, there is a minimal prime ideal $\mathfrak{p}$ of A contained in $\mathfrak{m}$ that does not contain I. We show that $\mathfrak{p}A_{\mathfrak{m}} \not\supset IA_{\mathfrak{m}}$. Let $a \in I \setminus \mathfrak{p}$; if $\mathfrak{p}A_{\mathfrak{m}} \supset IA_{\mathfrak{m}}$, then $a = \sum_{i=1}^{r} \frac{g_i}{s}$ for some $s \in A \setminus \mathfrak{m}$ and $g_i \in \mathfrak{p}$. Thus $sa \in \mathfrak{p}$ and $s, a, \notin \mathfrak{p}$, a contradiction. So, $\mathfrak{p}A_{\mathfrak{m}}$ is a minimal prime ideal of $A_{\mathfrak{m}}$ that does not contain $IA_{\mathfrak{m}}$. But by assumption $A_{\mathfrak{m}} = A_{\mathfrak{m}}/IA_{\mathfrak{m}}$; i.e. $IA_{\mathfrak{m}} = (0)$.

In particular, since $A_{\mathfrak{m}}$ is reduced, $I \cdot A_{\mathfrak{m}}$ is the intersection of all the minimal prime ideals of $A_{\mathfrak{m}}$, a contradiction. Thus $I + J$ is the unit ideal of A. □

Recall that in Subsection 5.3 we showed that every R-subdomain is a quasi-affinoid subdomain.

Theorem 6.2.2. — *Let A be a quasi-affinoid algebra and let $U \subset \operatorname{Max} A$ be a quasi-affinoid subdomain. Then U is a finite union of R-subdomains of* $\operatorname{Max} A$.

Proof. — Let $B := \mathcal{O}(U)$, and let $\pi : \operatorname{Max} B \to \operatorname{Max} A$ be the canonical inclusion. By Theorem 6.1.2 there is a finite cover of $\operatorname{Max} A$ by R-subdomains U_i such that each map

$$\pi|_{\pi^{-1}(U_i)} : \pi^{-1}(U_i) \longrightarrow U_i$$

is finite. Thus, without loss of generality, we assume that $\pi : \operatorname{Max} B \to \operatorname{Max} A$ is finite.

We will apply Lemma 6.2.1 to show that U is a Zariski-open and -closed subset of $\operatorname{Max} A$. Let $\mathfrak{M} \in \operatorname{Max} B$, and put $\mathfrak{m} := A \cap \mathfrak{M}$. We wish to show that $A_{\mathfrak{m}} \to B \otimes_A A_{\mathfrak{m}}$ is bijective. Since $B \otimes_A A_{\mathfrak{m}}$ is a finite $A_{\mathfrak{m}}$-module, this follows from Nakayama's Lemma [**25**, Theorem 2.3], once we know that $B \otimes_A (A_{\mathfrak{m}}/\mathfrak{m}A_{\mathfrak{m}}) \cong A_{\mathfrak{m}}/\mathfrak{m}A_{\mathfrak{m}}$. Indeed,

$$B \otimes_A (A_{\mathfrak{m}}/\mathfrak{m}A_{\mathfrak{m}}) = B \otimes_A A/\mathfrak{m} = B/\mathfrak{m}B = B/\mathfrak{M} = A/\mathfrak{m} = A_{\mathfrak{m}}/\mathfrak{m}A_{\mathfrak{m}},$$

by Proposition 5.3.6 (ii) and (iii).

By Lemma 6.2.1, U is a Zariski-open and -closed subset of $\operatorname{Max} A$, thus there is some $f \in A$ such that $f|_U \equiv 0$ and $f|_{\operatorname{Max} A \setminus U} \equiv 1$. So

$$U = \{x \in \operatorname{Max} A : |f(x)| \le 1/2\}$$

is an R-subdomain of $\operatorname{Max} A$. □

Note that the covering of U given by Theorem 6.2.2 is not necessarily a quasi-affinoid covering in the sense of [**22**]; nonetheless Theorem 6.2.2 does show that quasi-affinoid subdomains are well-behaved. In particular the following openness theorem (*cf.* [**6**, Theorem 7.2.5.3]) is an immediate consequence.

***Corollary 6.2.3* (Openness Theorem).** — *Let A be a quasi-affinoid algebra. All quasi-affinoid subdomains of A are open in the canonical topology on* $\operatorname{Max} A$ *derived from the absolute value $|\cdot| : K \to \mathbb{R}_+$.*

Proof. — As we remarked in Subsection 5.3 all R-subdomains of $\operatorname{Max} A$ are open. □

References

[1] W. BARTENWERFER. — *Der allgemeine Kontinuitätssatz für k-meromorphe Funktionen im Dizylinder.* Math. Ann., 191 (1971) 196-234.

[2] W. BARTENWERFER. — *Die Beschränktheit der Stückzahl der Fasern K-analytischer Abbildungen.* J. reine angew. Math., 416 (1991) 49-70.

[3] V. BERKOVICH. — *Spectral Theory and Analytic Geometry Over Non-Archimedean Fields.* Math. Surveys and Monographs, Vol. 33, A.M.S., Providence, 1990.

[4] S. BOSCH. — *Orthonormalbasen in der nichtarchimedischen Funktionentheorie.* Manuscripta Math., 1 (1969) 35-57.

[5] S. BOSCH. — *Eine bemerkenswerte Eigenschaft der formellen Fasern affinoider Räume.* Math. Ann., 229 (1977) 25-45.

[6] S. BOSCH, U. GÜNTZER AND R. REMMERT. — *Non-Archimedean Analysis.* Springer-Verlag, 1984.

[7] N. BOURBAKI. — *Éléments de Mathématiques, XV. Espaces Vectoriels Topologiques,* Chapter 1. Hermann, 1953.

[8] N. BOURBAKI. — *Algèbre Commutative III.* Hermann, 1961.

[9] J. DENEF AND L. VAN DEN DRIES. — *p-adic and real subanalytic sets.* Ann. Math., 128, (1988) 79-138.

[10] J. FRESNEL AND M. VAN DER PUT. — *Géométrie Analytique Rigide et Applications.* Birkhäuser, 1981.

[11] J. FRESNEL AND M. VAN DER PUT. — *Localisation formelle et Groupe de Picard.* Ann. Inst. Fourier (Grenoble), 33 (1983) 19-82.

[12] T. GARDENER. — *Local flattening in rigid analytic geometry.* Preprint.

[13] T. GARDENER AND H. SCHOUTENS. — *Flattening and subanalytic sets in rigid analytic geometry.* Preprint.

[14] H. GRAUERT AND R. REMMERT. — *Über die Methode der diskret bewerteten Ringe in der nicht-Archimedischen Analysis.* Invent. Math., 2 (1966) 87-133.
Begründung

[15] H. HIRONAKA. — *Subanalytic Sets,* in *Number Theory, Algebraic Geometry and Commutative Algebra in honor of Y. Akizuki,* Kinokuniya, 1973, 453-493.

[16] L. LIPSHITZ. — *Isolated points on fibers of affinoid varieties.* J. reine angew. Math., 384 (1988) 208-220.

[17] L. LIPSHITZ. — *Rigid subanalytic sets.* Amer. J. Math., 115 (1993) 77-108.

[18] L. LIPSHITZ AND Z. ROBINSON. — *Rigid subanalytic subsets of the line and the plane.* Amer. J. Math., 118 (1996) 493-527.

[19] L. LIPSHITZ AND Z. ROBINSON. — *Rigid subanalytic subsets of curves and surfaces.* To appear in J. London Math. Soc.

[20] L. LIPSHITZ AND Z. ROBINSON. — *One-dimensional fibers of rigid subanalytic sets.* J. Symbolic Logic, 63 (1998) 83–88.

[21] L. LIPSHITZ AND Z. ROBINSON. — *Rigid subanalytic sets II.* Manuscript.

[22] L. LIPSHITZ AND Z. ROBINSON. — *Quasi-affinoid varieties.* This volume.

[23] L. LIPSHITZ AND Z. ROBINSON. — *Model completeness and subanalytic sets.* This volume.

[24] A. MACINTRYE. — *On definable subsets of p-adic fields.* J. Symbolic Logic, 41 (1976) 605-610.

[25] H. MATSUMURA. — *Commutative Ring Theory.* Cambridge University Press, 1989.

[26] H. MATSUMURA. — *Formal power series rings over polynomial rings I.* In *Number Theory, Algebraic Geometry and Commutative Algebra.* Kinokuniya, 1973, pp. 511-520. In honor of Y. Akizuki.

[27] F. MEHLMANN. — *Ein Beweis für einen Satz von Raynaud über flache Homomorphismen affinoider Algebren.* — Schr. Math. Inst. Univ. Munster, 2 (1981).

[28] M. NAGATA. — *Local Rings.* Interscience Publishers, 1962.

[29] Z. ROBINSON. — *Smooth points of p-adic subanalytic sets.* Manuscripta Math., 80 (1993) 45-71.

[30] Z. ROBINSON. — *Flatness and smooth points of p-adic subanalytic sets.* Ann. Pure Appl. Logic, 88 (1997) 217-225.

[31] Z. ROBINSON. — *A rigid analytic approximation theorem.* This volume.

[32] H. SCHOUTENS. — *Rigid subanalytic sets.* Comp. Math., 94 (1994) 269-295.

[33] H. SCHOUTENS. — *Rigid subanalytic sets in the plane.* J. Algebra, 170 (1994) 266-276.

[34] H. SCHOUTENS. — *Uniformization of rigid subanalytic sets.* Comp. Math., 94 (1994) 227-245.

[35] H. SCHOUTENS. — *Blowing up in rigid analytic geometry.* Bull. Belg. Math. Soc., 2 (1995) 399-417.

[36] H. SCHOUTENS. — *Closure of rigid semianalytic sets.* J. Algebra, 198 (1997) 120-134.

[37] H. SCHOUTENS. — *Rigid analytic flatificators.* Preprint.

[38] H. SEYDI. — *Sur une note d'Ernst Kunz.* C. R. Acad. Sci. Paris, Sér. A-B, 274 (1972) A714-A716.

[39] J. TATE. — *Rigid analytic spaces.* Invent. Math., 12, (1971) 257-289.

[40] V. WEISPFENNING. — *Quantifier Elimination and Decision Procedures for Valued Fields.* In *Models and Sets, Aachen, 1983.* Lecture Notes in Math., 1103 (1984) 419-472. Springer-Verlag.

[41] O. ZARISKI AND P. SAMUEL. — *Commutative Algebra II.* Springer-Verlag, 1975.

MODEL COMPLETENESS AND SUBANALYTIC SETS

1. Introduction

The class of real subanalytic sets was defined by Gabrielov **[2]**, where he proved that the class is closed under complementation. Real subanalytic sets have attracted extensive study; in particular, Hironaka **[7]** proved uniformization and rectilinearization theorems for real subanalytic sets. In **[1]**, Denef and van den Dries introduced the class of p-adic subanalytic sets and showed how to develop both the real and p-adic theories from a suitable analytic quantifier elimination theorem. In **[9]** an analogous quantifier elimination theorem was proved for K an algebraically closed field, complete with respect to a non-Archimedean absolute value, using the functions of $S = \cup_{m,n} S_{m,n}$. (See below.) That paper developed a theory of subanalytic sets (termed rigid subanalytic sets). This theory was developed further in **[10]**, **[11]** and **[12]**. In **[17]**–**[21]**, Schoutens developed a theory of subanalytic sets (which he termed strongly subanalytic), over such fields. This theory used a class of functions somewhat smaller than $T = \cup T_m$. (The T_m are the Tate rings of strictly convergent power series over K.)

In this paper we prove a quantifier elimination theorem (Theorem 4.2) for algebraically closed extension fields of K in language $L_{\mathcal{E}}$, the language of valued rings augmented with function symbols for the members of $\mathcal{E}$, where $\mathcal{E} = \mathcal{E}(\mathcal{H})$ is a class of analytic (partial) functions obtained from $\mathcal{H} \subset S$ by closing up with respect to "differentiation" and existential definition (see below for precise definitions). For suitable choice of $\mathcal{E} = \mathcal{E}(T)$ this gives a quantifier elimination theorem (Corollary 4.4) in $L_{\mathcal{E}(T)}$ (or a quantifier simplification theorem, Corollary 4.5, in L_T, the language of valued rings augmented with function symbols for the members of T) suitable for developing the theory of subanalytic sets based on T, which we term K-affinoid (Corollaries 5.4 and 5.5). These results have been used by Gardener and Schoutens in their proof, **[3]**, **[4]**, and **[22]**, of a quantifier elimination theorem in the language L_T^D ($= L_T$ enriched by "restricted division" (see below)). Section 2 contains precise definitions of what we mean by "closed under differentiation and existential definitions", in all characteristics. Section 3 gives the Weierstrass Preparation and Division Theorems for these classes of functions that we need for all the Elimination Theorems in Section 4. Section 5 contains the application of the Elimination Theorems to the theory of Subanalytic Sets.

We recall some of the basic definitions. K is a field complete with respect to a non-Archimedean absolute value $|\cdot| : K \to \mathbb{R}_+$. We do not assume that K is algebraically closed. $K^\circ = \{x \in K : |x| \leq 1\}$ is the valuation ring of K, and $K^{\circ\circ} = \{x \in K : |x| < 1\}$ is the maximal ideal of K°. $T_m = T_m(K)$ is the (Tate) ring of strictly convergent power series over K and $S_{m,n} = S_{m,n}(E, K)$ is a ring of separated power series over K (see [**13**, Definition 2.1.1]). Recall that $T_{m+n} \subset S_{m,n}$ and that elements of $S_{m,n}$ represent analytic functions $(K^\circ)^m \times (K^{\circ\circ})^n \to K$.

The language of multiplicatively valued rings is

$$L = (0, 1, +, \cdot, |\cdot|, \overline{0}, \overline{1}, \bar{\cdot}, \overline{<}).$$

The symbols 0, 1, $+$, $\cdot$ denote the obvious elements and operations on the field; $\overline{0}$, $\overline{1}$, $\bar{\cdot}$ denote the obvious elements and multiplication on the value group $\cup\{\overline{0}\}$; $|\cdot|$ denotes the valuation and $\overline{<}$ the order relation on the value group $\cup\{\overline{0}\}$. Section 0 of [**1**] provides all the background about first order languages that we will need.

A structure F (for a language L') has elimination of quantifiers if every subset of F^m defined by an L'-formula is in fact defined by a quantifier free L'-formula. We say that F has quantifier simplification (or is model complete) if every subset of F^m defined by an L' formula is in fact defined by an existential L'-formula.

In [**13**] we defined certain open domains in K^m which we termed R-domains ([**13**, Definition 5.3.3]) and showed that each R-domain U carries a canonical ring of functions denoted $\mathcal{O}(U)$; R-domains generalize the Rational Domains of Affinoid geometry.

2. Existentially Defined Analytic Functions

As usual K is a complete non-Archimedean valued field. Let F be a complete field extending K and let F_{alg} be its algebraic closure. In general F_{alg} will not be complete. However if $F' \subset F_{\text{alg}}$ is a finitely generated extension of F, then F' is complete and hence the power series $f \in S_{m,n}$ actually define analytic functions $(F^\circ_{\text{alg}})^m \times (F^{\circ\circ}_{\text{alg}})^n \to F_{\text{alg}}$. By the Nullstellensatz ([**13**, Theorem 4.1.1]) there is a map

$$\tau_m : (F^\circ_{\text{alg}})^m \to \operatorname{Max} T_m(F).$$

Since $T_m(K) \subset T_m(F)$ we may therefore regard any R-domain $U \subset \operatorname{Max} T_m(K)$ as a subset of $(F^\circ_{\text{alg}})^m$. In this section we set up the formalism for the quantifier elimination theorem.

The (not necessarily algebraically closed) field K will be the field over which the functions in our language are defined in the sense that these functions will all be elements of generalized rings of fractions (see below) defined over K. Formulas in the language define subsets of $(F^\circ_{\text{alg}})^m$. The Quantifier Elimination Theorem (Theorem 4.2) is uniform in the sense that if φ is defined over K then there is a quantifier-free formula φ^*, also defined over K, such that for each complete F with $K \subset F$, φ and φ^* define the same subset of $(F^\circ_{\text{alg}})^m$.

In [**1**] and [**9**] the quantifier elimination takes place in a language L_{an}^D which has symbols for all functions built up from a suitable class of analytic functions and "restricted division" D, where $D(x,y) = x/y$ if $|x| \leq |y| \neq 0$ and $D(x,y) = 0$ otherwise. In this paper the use of "restricted division" is replaced by that of generalized rings of fractions (see definition below). This is necessary for us because Theorems 3.1 and 3.3 give definitions of the Weierstrass data in terms of functions, but do not in general produce representations of the Weierstrass data by (definable) D-terms. (In the special case that $\mathcal{H} = S$, definability issues drop away and the treatment in this paper is easily seen to be equivalent to the treatment of [**9**] using restricted division. See Corollary 4.3).

Definition 2.1 ***(cf.*** [**13**, Definition 5.3.1]). — We define the *generalized rings of fractions over* T_m inductively as follows: T_m is a generalized ring of fractions, and if A is generalized ring of fractions and $f, g \in A$ then both $A\langle f/g\rangle$ and $A[\![f/g]\!]_s$ are generalized rings of fractions.

$S_{m,n} = T_{m,n}[\![\xi_{m+1},\ldots,\xi_{m+n}]\!]_s$ is a generalized ring of fractions over T_{m+n}.

Definition 2.2. — Let $\varphi : T_m \to A$ be a generalized ring of fractions and let Φ : $\operatorname{Max} A \to \operatorname{Max} T_m$ be the induced map. We define the *domain of* A, $\operatorname{Dom} A \subset \operatorname{Max} T_m$, by saying that $x \in \operatorname{Dom} A$ iff there is a quasi-rational subdomain U (see [**13**, Definition 5.3.3]) of $\operatorname{Max} T_m$ with $x \in U$, such that

$$\Phi^{-1}(U) \to U$$

is bijective.

Remark 2.3

(i) The set $\operatorname{Dom} A$ does not depend on the representation of the generalized ring of fractions A as a quasi-affinoid T_m-algebra. Suppose that $\varphi : T_m \to A$ and $\psi : T_m \to B$ are isomorphic quasi-affinoid T_m-algebras, i.e. there is a K-algebra isomorphism σ such that

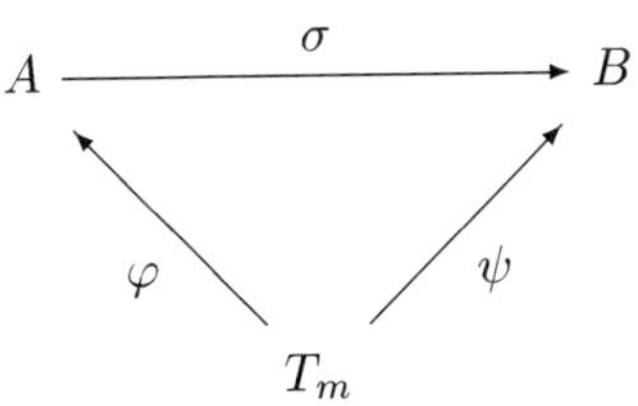

commutes. By the Nullstellensatz [**13**, Theorem 4.1.1]

$$X := \operatorname{Max} T_m \cap \operatorname{Max} A = \operatorname{Max} T_m \cap \operatorname{Max} B.$$

Let $x \in X$ and suppose there is a quasi-rational subdomain $x \in U \subset X$ such that $\Phi^{-1}(U) \to U$ is bijective, where $\Phi : \operatorname{Max} A \to \operatorname{Max} T_m$ corresponds to φ (as in Definition 2.2). Let Ψ correspond to ψ. Since σ is an isomorphism, $\Psi^{-1}(U) \to U$ is bijective. Since the argument is symmetric in A and B, this shows that $\operatorname{Dom} A$ is independent of the presentation of A as a T_m-algebra. (Note however that $\operatorname{Dom} A$ is not in general a quasi-affinoid subdomain in the sense of [**13**, Definition 5.3.4].)

(ii) Let $\varphi : T_m \to A$ be a generalized ring of fractions. It follows from the Nullstellensatz, ([**13**, Theorem 4.1.1]), that

$$\operatorname{Dom} A\langle f/g\rangle = \{x \in \operatorname{Dom} A : |f(x)| \leq |g(x)| \neq 0\}, \text{ and}$$
$$\operatorname{Dom} A[\![f/g]\!]_s = \{x \in \operatorname{Dom} A : |f(x)| < |g(s)|\}.$$

(iii) Let $\varphi : T_m \to A$ be a generalized ring of fractions. By ground field extension ([**13**, Definition 5.4.9 and Proposition 5.4.10]) $A \subset A' = S_{0,0}(E, F) \otimes^s_{S_{0,0}(E,K)} A$ and we may regard $\operatorname{Dom} A$ as a subset of $(F^\circ_{\text{alg}})^m$ and each $f \in A$ as determining an analytic function $\operatorname{Dom} A \to F_{\text{alg}}$. In fact, given $x \in \operatorname{Dom} A$, there is a unique power series $\overline{f} \in K[\![\xi]\!]$ and a rational polydisc $x \in U \subset \operatorname{Dom} A$ such that $\overline{f}(y - x)$ converges on U and $f(y) = \overline{f}(y - x)$ for all $y \in U$.

(iv) As we noted in the discussion before Definition 2.1, in this paper we work with generalized rings of fractions instead of with D-functions. Any element f of a generalized ring of fractions A over T_m defines a partial function on $\operatorname{Dom} A \subset \operatorname{Max} T_m$. We may regard f as a total function by assigning $f(x) = 0$ for $x \in \operatorname{Max} T_m \setminus \operatorname{Dom} A$. It is a consequence of (ii) above that such functions are represented by D-terms in the sense of [**9**, Section 3.2], and conversely.

We will see below that the Weierstrass data of a power series are existentially definable from f and its partial derivatives. In characteristic $p \neq 0$, "partial derivatives" must be interpreted as Hasse derivatives which we define next.

Definition 2.4. —Let $f \in R[\![\xi_1, \ldots, \xi_m]\!]$, R a commutative ring, and let $t = (t_1, \ldots, t_m)$. The *Hasse Derivatives* of f, denoted $D_\nu f \in R[\![\xi]\!]$, $\nu = (\nu_1, \ldots, \nu_m) \in \mathbb{N}^m$, are defined by the equation

$$f(\xi + t) = \sum_{\nu \in \mathbb{N}^m} (D_\nu f)(\xi) t^\nu.$$

(See [**5**] or [**6**, Section 3].)

Remark 2.5

(i) In characteristic zero the Hasse derivatives are constant multiples of the usual partial derivatives. In fact

$$\frac{\partial^{|\nu|}}{\partial \xi_1^{\nu_1} \ldots \partial \xi_m^{\nu_m}} f = \nu_1! \ldots \nu_m! D_\nu f.$$

Hence the partial derivatives of f and the Hasse derivatives of f are quantifier free definable from each other (*cf.* Definition 2.7). The following facts are not hard to prove. Proofs can be found in [**5**] or [**6**, Section 3].

(ii) In characteristic $p \neq 0$ the situation is more complicated. If

$$\nu = (0, \ldots, 0, p^n, 0 \ldots, 0)$$

with p^n in the ith position denote D_ν by D_i^n. Then the whole family of Hasse derivatives is generated by the D_i^n under composition. In particular $D_i^m D_j^n = D_j^n D_i^m$ and $D_\nu = D_1^{\nu_1} D_2^{\nu_2} \dots D_m^{\nu_m}$.

(iii) Suppose the characteristic is $p \neq 0$ and let $f \in R[\![\xi_1, \dots, \xi_m]\!]$. Fix $i, 1 \leq i \leq m$, and write

$$f = \sum_{j=0}^{p-1} f_j(\xi_1, \dots, \xi_{i-1}, \xi_i^p, \xi_{i+1}, \dots, \xi_m)\xi_i^j.$$

The power series f_j are uniquely determined by this equation, so we may define

$$\delta_{\xi_i,j}(f) := f_j.$$

If f converges on a rational polydisc $0 \in U \subset (F_{\text{alg}}^\circ)^m$, so do the $\delta_{\xi_i,j}(f)$. We call the $\delta_{\xi_i,j}(f)$ the *p-components* of f. By induction, we define the *$p^{\ell+1}$-components* of f to be the $\delta_{\xi_i,j}(g)$, where g is a p^ℓ-component of f. Thus,

$$f = \sum_{j=0}^{p^\ell-1} f_{\ell j}(\xi_1, \dots, \xi_{i-1}, \xi_i^{p^\ell}, \xi_{i+1}, \dots, \xi_m)\xi_i^j,$$

where the $f_{\ell j}$ are p^ℓ-components of f with respect to ξ_i.

It is not hard to show that the D_ν are existentially definable from the $\delta_{\xi_i,j}$ and conversely. Indeed the D_ν are linear combinations of compositions of the $\delta_{\xi_i,j}$ with polynomial coefficients, and conversely.

(iv) The following properties of the D_ν follow easily from the definition

(a) $D_{\underline{0}} = id$
(b) $D_\nu c = 0$ for $c \in R$, $\nu \neq \underline{0}$
(c) $D_\nu(f + g) = D_\nu f + D_\nu g$
(d) $D_\mu \circ D_\nu = \binom{\mu+\nu}{\mu} D_{\mu+\nu}$, where $\binom{\mu+\nu}{\mu} = \prod_i \binom{\mu_i+\nu_i}{\nu_i}$
(e) $D_\nu(f \cdot g) = \sum_{\mu+\mu'=\nu} (D_\mu f)(D_{\mu'} g)$.
(f) a chain rule (see [**5**]).

Definition 2.6. — Let $\varphi : T_m \to A$ be a generalized ring of fractions and let $f \in A$. Using Remark 2.3 we define $\Delta(f)$ to be the collection of functions $\operatorname{Dom} A \to F_{\text{alg}}$ determined by the $D_\nu f$, $\nu \in \mathbb{N}^m$. In other words $\Delta(f)$ is the smallest collection of functions $\operatorname{Dom} A \to F_{\text{alg}}$ containing f and closed under the Hasse derivatives.

Definition 2.7. — Let $\mathcal{H} \subset \cup_{m,n} S_{m,n}$ be any collection such that $\Delta(\mathcal{H}) \subset \mathcal{H}$. (In the most important application $\mathcal{H} = T = \cup_m T_m$; another possibility is $\mathcal{H} = \Delta(f_1, \dots, f_n)$.) Let

$$L_{\mathcal{H}} := L(0, 1, +, \cdot, \{f\}_{f \in \mathcal{H}}; |\cdot|, \overline{0}, \overline{1}, \bar{\cdot}, \overline{<})$$

be the first-order language of multiplicatively valued rings, augmented by symbols for the functions of $\mathcal{H}$. A subset $X \subset (F_{\text{alg}}^\circ)^m$ is said to be *definable* (respectively, *existentially definable, quantifier-free definable*) in $L_{\mathcal{H}}$ iff there is an $L_{\mathcal{H}}$-formula (respectively, an existential $L_{\mathcal{H}}$-formula, quantifier-free $L_{\mathcal{H}}$-formula) $\varphi(\xi_1, \ldots, \xi_m)$ such that

$$(a_1, \ldots, a_m) \in X \Longleftrightarrow \varphi(a_1, \ldots, a_m) \text{ is true.}$$

A partial function $f : X \to F_{\mathrm{alg}}$ is said to be definable (respectively, existentially definable, quantifier-free definable) in $L_{\mathcal{H}}$ iff its graph (and domain) are. The $\mathcal{H}$-subanalytic sets discussed in Section 5 are exactly the sets existentially definable in $L_{\mathcal{H}}$. A function f is quantifier free (respectively, existentially) definable from functions $g_1, \ldots, g_\ell$ if there is a quantifier-free (respectively, existential) formula φ in the language L of multiplicatively valued rings, such that

$$y = f(x) \Leftrightarrow \varphi(x, y, g_1(x), \ldots, g_\ell(x)).$$

We next define the class of functions $\mathcal{E}(\mathcal{H})$ all of whose "derivatives" are existentially definable from $\mathcal{H}$. The Quantifier Elimination Theorem (Theorem 4.2) applies to the language $L_{\mathcal{E}(\mathcal{H})}$ where $\mathcal{H} = \Delta(\mathcal{H})$. Since all functions of $\mathcal{E}(\mathcal{H})$ are existentially definable in $L_{\mathcal{H}}$ a corresponding quantifier simplification theorem for the language $L_{\mathcal{H}}$ follows.

Definition 2.8. — The collection $\mathcal{E}(\mathcal{H})$ consists of all functions $f : X \to F_{\mathrm{alg}}$ such that $f \in A$ and $X = \operatorname{Dom} A$ for some generalized ring of fractions $\varphi : T_m \to A$, and such that the members of $\Delta(f)$ are all existentially definable in $L_{\mathcal{H}}$. We define the language $L_{\mathcal{E}}$ in analogy to Definition 2.7, i.e., $L_{\mathcal{E}}$ is the language of multiplicatively valued rings augmented by symbols for the functions of $\mathcal{E}(\mathcal{H})$.

The languages $L_{\mathcal{H}}$ (or $L_{\mathcal{E}(\mathcal{H})}$) are three-sorted languages. The three sorts are F°, $F^{\circ\circ}$ and $|F^\circ|$. (See [**9**, Sections 3.1–3.7].)

We shall use the following in Section 3.

Remark 2.9

(i) Let $\operatorname{Char} K = p \neq 0$, let $f(y)$ be a convergent power series in y, let $\overline{y} \in K$ sufficiently near 0, and let $\ell \in \mathbb{N}$. There is a polynomial $\overline{f}(y)$ such that

$$\overline{f}(y) \equiv f(y) \mod (y - \overline{y})^{p^\ell}$$

and $\overline{f}$ is existentially definable from the p^ℓ-components of f with respect to y. To see this write

$$f = \sum_{j=0}^{p^\ell - 1} f_{\ell j}(y^{p^\ell}) y^j$$

and let $\overline{f} = \sum_{j=0}^{p^\ell-1} f_{\ell j}(\overline{y}^{p^\ell}) y^j$. By Remark 2.5(iii), $\overline{f}$ is existentially definable from Δf.

(ii) If $f(x, y) \in \mathcal{E}(\mathcal{H})$ and $f = \sum f_i(x) y^i$ then each $f_i \in \mathcal{E}(\mathcal{H})$.

3. Existential Definability of Weierstrass Data

Let A be a generalized ring of fractions over T and let $f, g \in A\langle\xi\rangle[\![\rho]\!]_s$ with f regular of degree s in y (where y is either ξ_m or ρ_n). By the Weierstrass Division and Preparation Theorems ([**13**, Theorem 2.3.8 and Corollary 2.3.9]) we can write

$$f = uP \quad \text{and} \quad g = qf + r$$

where u, P, q and r are as described in those theorems.

In this section we show that all the members of $\Delta(u)$ and $\Delta(P)$ are existentially definable from $\Delta(f)$ and all the members of $\Delta(q)$ and $\Delta(r)$ are existentially definable from $\Delta(f)$ and $\Delta(g)$. These results are needed for the Elimination Theorem (Theorem 4.2).

Analogous questions in the real case are considered in [**23**]. For completeness, we include proofs below not only in characteristic p but also in characteristic zero.

Theorem 3.1 **(Weierstrass Preparation for $\mathcal{E}$).** — *Let $\varphi : T_m \to A$ be a generalized ring of fractions and let $f \in A\langle\xi\rangle[\![\rho]\!]_s$. Suppose f is regular of degree s in ξ_M (respectively, in ρ_N) in the sense of* [**13**, Definition 2.3.7]. *By* [**13**, Corollary 2.3.9], *there exist a uniquely determined polynomial $P \in A\langle\xi'\rangle[\![\rho]\!]_s[\xi_M]$ (respectively, $P \in A\langle\xi\rangle[\![\rho']\!]_s[\rho_N]$) monic and regular of degree s and a unit $u \in A\langle\xi\rangle[\![\rho]\!]_s$ such that*

$$f = u \cdot P.$$

(Here $\xi' := (\xi_1, \ldots, \xi_{M-1})$ and $\rho' := (\rho_1, \ldots, \rho_{N-1})$.) Each member of $\Delta(u)$ and $\Delta(P)$ is existentially definable in $L_{\Delta(f)}$. Hence if $f \in \mathcal{E}(\mathcal{H})$, then $u, P \in \mathcal{E}(\mathcal{H})$.

Proof. — Let y denote the variable (either ξ_M or ρ_N) in which f is regular and let x denote the other variables. With this notation the above equation becomes

$$f(x, y) = u(x, y)[y^s + a_{s-1}(x)y^{s-1} + \cdots + a_0(x)].$$

We must show that each member of $\Delta(u)$ and $\Delta(a_j)$ $j = 0, \ldots, s-1$ is existentially definable in $L_{\Delta(f)}$, i.e. from $\Delta(f)$.

For each $x \in \operatorname{Dom} A\langle\xi'\rangle[\![\rho]\!]_s$ (respectively $\operatorname{Dom} A\langle\xi\rangle[\![\rho']\!]_s$), let $\overline{y}_1(x), \ldots, \overline{y}_s(x)$ be the s roots of the equation $f(x, y) = 0$ with $|y| \leq 1$ (respectively < 1). Then the $a_j(x)$ are symmetric functions of the $\overline{y}_i(x)$, say $a_j(x) = \sigma_j(\overline{y}_1(x), \ldots, \overline{y}_s(x))$.

We consider the cases $\operatorname{Char} K = 0$ and $\operatorname{Char} K = p \neq 0$ separately.

***Case* (A).** — Characteristic $K = 0$.

By Remark 2.5(i) we may work with the usual partial derivatives instead of the Hasse derivatives.

For each partition $\mathcal{P} : s = s_1 + s_2 + \cdots + s_m$, with the $s_i \geq 1$, let $\varphi_{\mathcal{P}}$ be the formula

$$\left(\bigwedge_{i=1}^{s} |y_i| \Box 1\right) \wedge (y_1 = y_2 = \cdots = y_{s_1}) \wedge (y_{s_1+1} = \cdots = y_{s_1+s_2}) \wedge \ldots$$

$$\cdots \wedge (y_{s_1+\cdots+s_{m-1}+1} = \cdots = y_s) \wedge \bigwedge_{j=0}^{s_1-1} \frac{\partial^j f}{\partial y^j}(y_1) = 0 \wedge \ldots$$

$$\cdots \wedge \bigwedge_{j=0}^{s_m-1} \frac{\partial^j f}{\partial y^j}(y_{s_1+\cdots+s_{m-1}+1}) = 0 \wedge \bigwedge_{i \neq j} (y_{s_1+\cdots+s_i} \neq y_{s_1+\cdots+s_j}),$$

where $\Box$ is $<$ or $\leq$ depending on whether y is a ξ_M or ρ_N. Hence $\varphi_{\mathcal{P}}$ expresses the fact that y_1 is a root of $f = 0$ of multiplicity s_1, y_{s_1+1} is a root of multiplicity s_2, etc. For each $j = 0, \ldots, s-1$, let $\varphi_j(x, w_j)$ be the formula

$$\exists y_1 \ldots \exists y_s \big[\bigvee_{\mathcal{P}} \varphi_P \wedge w_j = \sigma_j(y_1, \ldots, y_s)\big].$$

Then φ_j is an existential definition of $a_j(x)$. We must further show that u and the derivatives of the $a_j(x)$ are existentially definable. Notice that the $\overline{y}_i(x)$ may not be differentiable even at points where the $a_j(x)$ are analytic. Let $P(x, y) = y^s + a_{s-1}(x) y^{s-1} + \cdots + a_0(x)$. Then

$$f(x, y) = u(x, y) P(x, y). \tag{3.1}$$

Next we show that $u(x, y)$ is existentially definable. This is obvious from (3.1) except perhaps when $y = \overline{y}_i(x)$ for some i (i.e. when $P(x, y) = 0$). Note that

$$P, \ \frac{\partial P}{\partial y}, \ \frac{\partial^2 P}{\partial y^2}, \ldots, \ \frac{\partial^s P}{\partial y^s} = s! \neq 0$$

are all existentially definable. It is now easy to see that if $\overline{y}$ is an s_i-fold root of $f(x, y) = 0$ then $u(x, \overline{y})$ is defined by

$$\frac{\partial^{s_i} f}{\partial y^{s_i}}(x, \overline{y}) = u(x, \overline{y}) \frac{\partial^{s_i} P}{\partial y^{s_i}}(x, \overline{y}).$$

Iterating, we see that $\dfrac{\partial u}{\partial y}, \dfrac{\partial^2 u}{\partial y^2}, \ldots$ are all existentially definable from $\Delta(f)$.

Differentiating (3.1) with respect to x_1 we get

$$\frac{\partial f}{\partial x_1} = \frac{\partial u}{\partial x_1} P + u \frac{\partial P}{\partial x_1} = \frac{\partial u}{\partial x_1} P + u \left[\frac{\partial a_{s-1}}{\partial x_1} y^{s-1} + \cdots + \frac{\partial a_0}{\partial x_1}\right].$$

So, if $\overline{y}_1, \ldots, \overline{y}_s$ satisfy $P(x, y) = 0$, then

$$u^{-1}(x, \overline{y}_i) \frac{\partial f}{\partial x_1}(x, \overline{y}_i) = a'_{s-1} \overline{y}_i^{s-1} + \cdots + a'_0, \tag{3.2}$$

where we write a'_j for $\dfrac{\partial a_j}{\partial x_1}$. If the roots $\overline{y}_1, \ldots, \overline{y}_s$ of $P = 0$ are distinct then the equations (3.2) uniquely determine the a'_j. (The coefficient matrix of the system of linear equations (3.2) is the Vandermonde matrix with determinant $\prod_{i<j}(\overline{y}_i - \overline{y}_j) \neq 0$).

If $\overline{y}_i$ is a root of $P = 0$ of multiplicity s_i we replace the s_i identical equations in (3.2) by the subsystem

$$\begin{aligned}
u^{-1}(x,\overline{y}_i)\frac{\partial f}{\partial x_1}(x,\overline{y}_i) &= \frac{\partial P}{\partial x_1}(x,\overline{y}_i),\\
u^{-1}(x,\overline{y}_i)\frac{\partial^2 f}{\partial y \partial x_1}(x,\overline{y}_i) &= \frac{\partial^2 P}{\partial y\partial x_1}(x,\overline{y}_i) + u^{-1}(x,\overline{y}_i)\frac{\partial u}{\partial y}(x,\overline{y}_i)\frac{\partial P}{\partial x_1}(x,\overline{y}_i),\\
&\cdots\\
u^{-1}(x,\overline{y}_i)\frac{\partial^{s_i} f}{\partial y^{s_i-1}\partial x_1}(x,\overline{y}_i) &= \frac{\partial^{s_i} P}{\partial y^{s_i-1}\partial x_1}(x,\overline{y}_i) + \dots .
\end{aligned}$$

to obtain a system of equations that we denote $(3.2)'$. The coefficient matrix of the resulting system of equations is nonsingular (see Remark 3.2 below) and hence the new system of equations defines the $\dfrac{\partial a_j}{\partial x_1}$. Existential definitions of $\dfrac{\partial u}{\partial x_1}$ and the higher derivatives of the a_j and u are obtained by iterating.

***Case* (B).** — Characteristic $K = p \neq 0$.

We follow the same general outline as in Case A and indicate the necessary changes. In characteristic zero we used the derivatives $\dfrac{\partial^k f}{\partial y^k}(\overline{y})$ to detect the multiplicity of a root $\overline{y}$ of $f = 0$. In Characteristic p we use the device of Remark 2.9(i). If we choose $p^\ell > s$ then the multiplicity of $\overline{y}$ as a root of $f = 0$ is the same as the multiplicity of $\overline{y}$ as a root of $\overline{f}(y) = 0$, and since $\overline{f}$ is a polynomial in y, the multiplicity of y as a zero of $\overline{f}$ is existentially definable from the coefficients of $\overline{f}$, which are by Remark 2.9(i) existentially definable from the p^ℓ components of f. Hence P is existentially definable from the p^ℓ-components of f with respect to y and hence from the Hasse derivatives $D_\nu f$ for $\nu = (0,\dots,0,i)$, $i = 0,\dots,p^\ell - 1$.

Next we must show that u and all its Hasse derivatives with respect to y are existentially definable. From the equation

$$f = uP,$$

u is existentially definable, except when $P = 0$, i.e. except when $y = \overline{y}_i$ for some i. If $\overline{y}$ is a zero of P of order $\alpha \leq s$ then $u(\overline{y})$ is (existentially) defined using

$$\overline{f}(y) \equiv u(\overline{y})P \mod (y - \overline{y})^{\alpha+1}$$

where $\overline{f}$ is the polynomial as in Remark 2.9(i) and $p^\ell > s$. In fact, for any $\beta \in \mathbb{N}$ we can existentially define a polynomial $\overline{u}$ such that $\overline{u} \equiv u \mod (y - \overline{y})^\beta$ by considering the congruence $\overline{f} \equiv uP \mod (y - \overline{y})^{\beta+\alpha}$.

Let D_y^i denote $D_{(0,\ldots,0,i)}$. Then

$$D_y^i f = \sum_{j+k=i} D_y^j u D_y^k P$$

(see Remark 2.5(iv)(e)). Since P is a polynomial in y the $D_y^i P$ are all quantifier free definable. We proceed inductively

$$D_y^1 f = (D_y^1 u)P + uD_y^1 P.$$

This defines $(D_y^1 u)$ except when $y = \overline{y}$ is a zero of P. But for such $\overline{y}$ we consider a congruence of the form

$$D_y^1 f \equiv (D_y^1 u)P + uD_y^1 P \mod (y-\overline{y})^\beta.$$

By Remark 2.9(i), for any $\beta \in \mathbb{N}$ we can existentially define a polynomial congruent to $D_y^1 f \mod (y-\overline{y})^\beta$. We saw above that we can existentially define a polynomial $\overline{u}(y) \equiv u(y) \mod (y-\overline{y})^\beta$. Hence we can existentially define $D_y^1 u$ modulo $(y-\overline{y})^\beta$ for any β. From this, for β large enough, an existential definition of $(D_y^1 u)(\overline{y})$ follows. Next we use

$$D_y^2 f = (D_y^2 u)P + (D_y^1 u)(D_y^1 P) + u(D_y^2 P)$$

and the same argument to see that we can existentially define $D_y^2 u \mod (y-\overline{y})^\beta$ for any β. The same devices allow us to obtain existential definition of the other Hasse derivative of u and P. We do an example that will convince the reader, and show that $D_{x_1}^2 D_y^1 u$ and $D_{x_1}^2 D_y^1 P$ are existentially definable. (Here $D_{x_1}^i = D_{(i,0,\ldots,0)}$. Observe also that $D_{x_1}^i D_y^j = D_{(i,0,\ldots,0,j)}$.) We again start with the equation

$$f = uP.$$

Thus

$$D_{x_1}^1 f = (D_{x_1}^1 u)P + u(D_{x_1}^1 P). \tag{3.3}$$

Let the distinct zeros of P be $\overline{y}_1, \ldots, \overline{y}_d$ and let $\overline{y}_i$ have multiplicity α_i. Then $D_{x_1}^1 P$, which is a polynomial in y of degree $\leq s-1$ is determined by the congruences

$$D_{x_1}^1 f \equiv u(\overline{y}_i)(D_{x_1}^1 P) \mod (y-\overline{y}_i)^{\alpha_i}, \quad i = 1, \ldots, d.$$

$D_{x_1}^1 u$ is determined by equation (3.3), except where $y = \overline{y}_i$ for some i. But as above $D_{x_1}^1 u \mod (y-\overline{y}_i)^\beta$ can be existentially defined by looking at (3.3) $\mod (y-\overline{y}_i)^{p^\ell}$ for large enough ℓ and using the fact that $D_{x_1}^1 f \mod (y-\overline{y}_i)^{p^\ell}$ and $u \mod (y-\overline{y})^{p^\ell}$ are existentially definable from the $D_y^j D_{x_1}^1 f$ and $D_y^j f$. To obtain the "second derivative" with respect to x_1 we apply $D_{x_1}^2$ to the equation $f = uP$:

$$D_{x_1}^2 f = (D_{x_1}^2 u)P + (D_{x_1}^1 u)(D_{x_1}^1 P) + u(D_{x_1}^2 P). \tag{3.4}$$

Looking at this equation modulo the $(y-\overline{y}_i)^{\alpha_i}$ and using the facts that $P \equiv 0 \mod (y-\overline{y}_i)^{\alpha_i}$ and that we have existentially defined polynomials congruent to $(D_{x_1}^1 u)$ and u modulo $(y-\overline{y}_i)^{\alpha_i}$, gives an existential definition of (the polynomial in y)

$D^2_{x_1}P$. Then $D^2_{x_1}u$ is determined when y is different from all the $\overline{y}_i$ by (3.4) and $D^2_{x_1}u$ mod $(y-\overline{y}_i)^\beta$ (for any β) is determined by looking at (3.4) modulo a high enough power of $y-\overline{y}_i$ and using the facts that we have existentially defined polynomials congruent to $D^1_{x_1}u$ and u modulo any specified power of $y-\overline{y}_i$. Next apply D^1_y to (3.3):

$$D^1_yD^1_{x_1}f = (D^1_yD^1_{x_1}u)P + (D^1_{x_1}u)(D^1_yP) + (D^1_yu)(D^1_{x_1}P) + u(D^1_yD^1_{x_1}P). \tag{3.5}$$

As above, first determine $D^1_yD^1_{x_1}P$ by looking at this equation $\mod (y-\overline{y}_i)^{\alpha_i}$ and then determine $D^1_yD^1_{x_1}u$ for $y\neq\overline{y}_i$, $i=1,\dots,d$ and $D^1_yD^1_{x_1}u \mod (y-\overline{y}_i)^\beta$ for any β. Finally apply D^1_y to (3.4) to obtain

$$\begin{aligned}D^1_yD^2_{x_1}f = (D^1_yD^2_{x_1}u)P &+ (D^2_{x_1}u)(D^1_yP) + (D^1_yD^1_{x_1}u)(D^1_{x_1}P)\\ &+ (D^1_{x_1}u)(D^1_yD^1_{x_1}P) + (D^1_yu)(D^2_{x_1}P) + u(D^1_yD^2_{x_1}P).\end{aligned}$$

Exactly as above, first determine $D^1_yD^2_{x_1}P$ and then $D^1_yD^2_{x_1}u$ for $y\neq\overline{y}_i$, $i=1,\dots,d$, and finally $D^1_yD^2_{x_1}u \mod (y-\overline{y}_i)^\beta$ for any β. □

Remark 3.2. — Assume the characteristic of K is zero. Let $s_1+s_2+\cdots+s_m=s$ and let the Y_{ij} be variables $i=1,\dots,m$; $j=1,\dots,s_i$.

$$\det\begin{bmatrix} Y_{11}^{s-1} & Y_{11}^{s-2} & \dots & Y_{11} & 1\\ \vdots & \vdots & \ddots & \vdots & \vdots\\ Y_{1s_1}^{s-1} & Y_{1s_1}^{s-2} & \dots & Y_{1s_1} & 1\\ \vdots & \vdots & \ddots & \vdots & \vdots\\ \vdots & \vdots & \ddots & \vdots & \vdots\\ Y_{ms_m}^{s-1} & Y_{ms_m}^{s-2} & \dots & Y_{ms_m} & 1\end{bmatrix} = \prod_{(i,j)<(s,t)} (Y_{ij}-Y_{st})$$

where $<$ is the lexicographic ordering.

For each i and j, differentiate $j-1$ times with respect to Y_{ij}. Then set all the $Y_{ij}=Y_i$ (a new variable) for each $i=1,\dots,m$. The resulting determinant is a nonzero constant times a product of powers of (Y_i-Y_j), $i\neq j$. Call this function $\overline{V}(Y_1,\dots,Y_m)$.

Then the determinant of the coefficient matrix of the system of equations $(3.2)'$ occurring in the proof of Theorem 3.1 is $\overline{V}(\overline{y}_1,\dots,\overline{y}_m)\neq 0$ where $\overline{y}_1,\dots,\overline{y}_m$ are the distinct roots of $f(x,y)=0$, and $\overline{y}_i$ is a root of multiplicity s_i.

***Theorem 3.3* (Weierstrass Division for $\mathcal{E}$).** — *Let $\varphi: T_m\to A$ be a generalized ring of fractions and let $f,g\in A\langle\xi\rangle[\![\rho]\!]_s$. Suppose f is regular of degree s in ξ_M (respectively, ρ_N) in the sense of* [**13**, Definition 2.3.7]. *Then by* [**13**, Theorem 2.3.8] *there exist unique elements*

$$r\in A\langle\xi'\rangle[\![\rho]\!]_s[\xi_M]$$

(respectively, $r \in A\langle\xi\rangle[\![\rho']\!]_s[\rho_N]$) of degree $s-1$ and $q \in A\langle\xi\rangle[\![\rho]\!]_s$ such that

$$g = qf + r.$$

(Here $\xi' := (\xi_1, \ldots, \xi_{M-1})$ and $\rho' := (\rho_1, \ldots, \rho_{N-1})$.) Furthermore, each member of $\Delta(q)$ and $\Delta(r)$ is existentially definable in $L_{\Delta(f)\cup\Delta(g)}$. Hence if $f, g \in \mathcal{E}(\mathcal{H})$ then $q, r \in \mathcal{E}(\mathcal{H})$.

Proof. — We follow the same notational convention as in the proof of Theorem 3.1 — i.e. we let y denote ξ_M (respectively ρ_N) and let x denote the other variables. Let $r = \sum_{i=1}^{s-1} r_i(x)y^i$, and let $\overline{y}_1(x), \ldots, \overline{y}_s(x)$ be the roots of $f(x,y) = 0$. Then

$$g(x, \overline{y}_i) = \sum_{j=0}^{s-1} r_j(x)\overline{y}_i^j. \tag{3.6}$$

***Case* (A).** — Characteristic $K = 0$.

Again in this case we may consider the usual derivatives. If the $\overline{y}_i$ are all distinct then (3.6) has coefficient matrix the Vandermonde matrix and (3.6) determines the $r_j(x)$. If $\overline{y}_i$ is a root of $f = 0$ of multiplicity s_i, replace the corresponding s_i identical equations in (3.6) by the equations

$$\frac{\partial^\ell g}{\partial y^\ell}(x, \overline{y}_i) = \frac{\partial^\ell r}{\partial y^\ell}(x, \overline{y}_i), \qquad \ell = 0, \ldots, s_i - 1.$$

The resulting system again has nonsingular coefficient matrix (see Remark 3.2) and hence determines the $r_j(x)$.

Existential definitions of the derivatives of the r_j are obtained in a way similar to that employed in the proof of Theorem 3.1 to obtain those for the derivative of the a_j. The same arguments also give existential definitions of q and its derivatives from $\Delta(f) \cup \Delta(g)$.

***Case* (B).** — Characteristic $K = p \neq 0$.

We proceed in a way entirely analogous to the characteristic p case of the proof of Theorem 3.1. □

4. The Elimination Theorem

We prove an elimination theorem that both generalizes that of **[9]** and provides a basis for the theory of affinoid subanalytic sets (i.e., the images of affinoid maps) as the elimination theorem of **[9]** provided a basis for the theory of quasi-affinoid subanalytic sets. We follow the strategy of **[1]**, first using parameterized Weierstrass Preparation (and Division) to reduce to the case that some variable occurs polynomially and then using an algebraic elimination theorem. Where **[1]** used Macintyre's elimination theorem **[16]** we use the elimination theorem of **[24]**.

To obtain parametrized Weierstrass division from the usual one, [**1**] used restricted division by coefficients (with parameters). The fact that functions are not canonically represented by terms in a first order language leads to difficulties in our situation, since we have extra definability conditions to satisfy. It turns out that the generalized rings of fractions (see Definition 2.1) allow us to carry out the necessary divisions while retaining definability properties in a natural way. Furthermore, [**1**] works over discretely valued fields K, where multiplication by a uniformizing parameter for the maximal ideal of K° can be used to witness strict inequalities. As in [**9**], we use variables ranging over $F_{\mathrm{alg}}^{\circ\circ}$ to witness strict inequalities: our fields F_{alg} are never discretely valued, being algebraically closed. As we remarked in [**13**, Example 2.3.5], the class of Weierstrass automorphism for the resulting rings of analytic functions is not large enough to transform every nonzero function to one that is regular. Thus we employ Weierstrass Preparation and Division and the double induction of [**9**] to reduce to an application of the algebraic elimination theorem for algebraically closed valued fields of [**24**].

Let A be a quasi-affinoid algebra. Recall that we showed in [**13**, Section 5.2] that $A\langle\xi\rangle[\![\rho]\!]_s \subset A[\![\xi,\rho]\!]$, so we may write

$$f = \sum f_{\mu\nu}\xi^\mu\rho^\nu, \quad f_{\mu\nu} \in A,$$

for any $f \in A\langle\xi\rangle[\![\rho]\!]_s$.

Lemma 4.1. — *Let A be a generalized ring of fractions over T, and let*

$$f = \sum f_{\mu\nu}\xi^\mu\rho^\nu \in A\langle\xi\rangle[\![\rho]\!]_s.$$

Then there are: $c \in \mathbb{N}$, A-algebras $A_{\mu\nu}$, $|\mu| + |\nu| \leq c$, each a generalized ring of fractions, and elements $g_{\mu\nu} \in A_{\mu\nu}\langle\xi\rangle[\![\rho]\!]_s$ such that

(i) $f_{\mu\nu}(x)g_{\mu\nu}(x,\xi,\rho) = f(x,\xi,\rho)$ *for every* $x \in \operatorname{Dom} A_{\mu\nu}$,
(ii) *each $g_{\mu\nu}$ is preregular of degree (μ,ν) in the sense of* [**13**, Definition 2.3.7], *and*
(iii) $\operatorname{Dom} A = Z(f) \cup \bigcup_{|\mu|+|\nu|\leq c} A_{\mu\nu}$,

where $Z(f) := \{x \in \operatorname{Dom} A : f(x,\xi,\rho) \equiv 0\}$. If $f \in \mathcal{E}$, then $Z(f)$ is quantifier-free definable in $L_{\mathcal{E}}$ and each $g_{\mu\nu} \in \mathcal{E}$.

Proof. — Writing A as a quotient of a ring of separated power series and applying [**13**, Lemma 3.1.6] to a preimage of f, we obtain a $c \in \mathbb{N}$ and elements $h_{\mu\nu} \in A\langle\xi\rangle[\![\rho]\!]_s$ such that

$$f = \sum_{|\mu|+|\nu|\leq c} f_{\mu\nu}\xi^\mu\rho^\nu(1+h_{\mu\nu}) \text{ and}$$
$$|h_{\mu\nu}(y)| < 1 \text{ for all } y \in \operatorname{Max} A\langle\xi\rangle[\![\rho]\!]_s.$$

(Hence each $1 + h_{\mu\nu}$ is a unit of $A\langle\xi\rangle[\![\rho]\!]_s$.)

For each $(\mu_0, \nu_0) \in \mathbb{N}^m \times \mathbb{N}^n$ with $|\mu_0| + |\nu_0| \leq c$, we define the generalized ring of fractions $A_{\mu_0\nu_0}$ from A in the obvious way so that the inequalities

$$\begin{aligned} |f_{\mu_0\nu_0}(x)| &\geq |f_{\mu\nu}(x)| && \text{for all } |\mu| + |\nu| \leq c, \\ |f_{\mu_0\nu_0}(x)| &> |f_{\mu\nu}(x)| && \text{for all } \nu < \nu_0 \text{ and } |\mu| + |\nu| \leq c, \\ |f_{\mu_0\nu_0}(x) &> |f_{\mu\nu_0}(x)| && \text{for all } \mu > \mu_0 \text{ and } |\mu| + |\nu_0| \leq c \end{aligned}$$

hold for all $x \in \operatorname{Dom} A_{\mu_0\nu_0}$. Indeed, $A_{\mu_0\nu_0}$, so defined, has the property that $x \in \operatorname{Dom} A_{\mu_0\nu_0}$ if, and only if, $f_{\mu_0\nu_0}(x) \neq 0$ and the above inequalities hold.

Now, for $|\mu| + |\nu| \leq c$, $f_{\mu\nu}/f_{\mu_0\nu_0} \in A_{\mu_0\nu_0}$, so we may put

$$g_{\mu_0\nu_0} := \xi^{\mu_0}\rho^{\nu_0}(1 + h_{\mu_0\nu_0}) + \sum_{\substack{|\mu|+|\nu|\leq c, \\ (\mu,\nu)\neq(\mu_0,\nu_0)}} \frac{f_{\mu\nu}}{f_{\mu_0\nu_0}} \xi^{\mu}\rho^{\nu}(1 + h_{\mu\nu}), \quad |\mu_0| + |\nu_0| \leq c.$$

Finally, suppose $f \in \mathcal{E}$. Since $f_{\mu\nu}(x) \neq 0$ for $x \in \operatorname{Dom} A_{\mu\nu}$, and $f_{\mu\nu}(x) \in \mathcal{E}$ by Remark 2.9(ii), condition (i) implies that $g_{\mu\nu} \in \mathcal{E}$. To see this inductively, apply $D_{\nu'}$ to (i), use the product formula of Remark 2.5(iv)(e) and solve for $D_{\nu'}g_{\mu\nu}$. Furthermore,

$$Z(f) = \{x \in \operatorname{Dom} A : f_{\mu\nu}(x) = 0, |\mu| + |\nu| \leq c\},$$

which is a quantifier-free $L_{\mathcal{E}}$-definition. □

***Theorem 4.2* (Quantifier Elimination Theorem).** — *Let $\mathcal{H} \subset S$ with $\mathcal{H} = \Delta(\mathcal{H})$, let $\mathcal{E} := \mathcal{E}(\mathcal{H})$, and let Φ be an $L_{\mathcal{E}}$-formula. Then there is a quantifier-free $L_{\mathcal{E}}$-formula Ψ such that for every complete field F extending K, $F^{\circ}_{\text{alg}} \models \Phi \leftrightarrow \Psi$; i.e., Φ and Ψ define the same subset of $(F^{\circ}_{\text{alg}})^m$.*

Proof. — Recall that $L_{\mathcal{E}(\mathcal{H})}$ is a three-sorted language. We shall use the following convention which will greatly simplify notation. The ξ_i will denote variables of the first sort (that range over F°) and the ρ_j will denote variables of the second sort (that range over $F^{\circ\circ}$); x will denote a string of variables of sorts one and two. Observe that a quantified variable of the third sort (that ranges over $|F^{\circ}|$) can always be replaced by a quantified variable of the first sort — if v is a variable of the third sort replace it by $|\xi|$ where ξ is a variable of the first sort. Hence we need only eliminate quantified variables of sorts one and two. (Alternatively, a quantified variable of the third sort can be eliminated by a direct application of the quantifier elimination theorem of **[24]**). After routine manipulations we may assume that Φ is of the form $\exists\,\xi\rho\varphi(v, x, \xi, \rho)$, where φ is a conjunction of atomic formulas; i.e., formulas of the form

$$t_1(v)\bar{\cdot}|f(x, \xi, \rho)| \;\square\; t_2(v)\bar{\cdot}|g(x, \xi, \rho)|,$$

where $\square$ is either $<$ or $=$; $f, g \in A\langle\xi\rangle[\![\rho]\!]_s \cap \mathcal{E}$ for some fixed generalized ring of fractions over T; v denotes a string of variables of the third sort and the t_i are terms of the third sort containing no variables of sorts one or two. (Observe that the negation of such a formula is a disjunction of such formulas.)

For such formulas φ, we may define $\ell(\varphi)$ to be the number of functions in the formula that actually depend on (ξ, ρ). Writing

$$\xi = (\xi_1, \ldots, \xi_m) \quad \text{and} \quad \rho = (\rho_1, \ldots, \rho_n),$$

we induct on the triples (m, n, ℓ), ordered lexicographically.

Let $f_1, \ldots, f_\ell$ be the functions that occur in φ and depend on (ξ, ρ). Write

$$f_i = \sum f_{i\mu\nu}\xi^\mu\rho^\nu = \sum f_{i\nu}\rho^\nu \in A\langle\xi\rangle[\![\rho]\!]_s \cap \mathcal{E},$$

where $f_{i\mu\nu} \in A \cap \mathcal{E}$ and $f_{i\nu} \in A\langle\xi\rangle \cap \mathcal{E}$. Applying Lemma 4.1 to $f = f_1$ yields rings $A_{\mu\nu}$ and elements $g_{\mu\nu} \in A_{\mu\nu}\langle\xi\rangle[\![\rho]\!]_s$ preregular of degree (μ, ν).

Consider the formulas

$$\varphi_0 := x \in Z(f) \wedge \varphi \quad \text{and} \quad \varphi_{\mu\nu} := x \in \operatorname{Dom} A_{\mu\nu} \wedge \varphi.$$

By Lemma 4.1(iii), Φ is equivalent to the disjunction

$$\exists\, \xi\rho\varphi_0(\xi, \rho) \vee \bigvee \exists\, \xi\rho\varphi_{\mu\nu}(\xi, \rho).$$

Let φ_0' result from φ_0 by replacing f by 0 and let $\varphi_{\mu\nu}'$ result from $\varphi_{\mu\nu}$ by replacing f by $f_{\mu\nu} \cdot g_{\mu\nu}$. Note that $\ell(\varphi_0') < \ell(\varphi)$ and $\ell(\varphi_{\mu\nu}') = \ell(\varphi)$. By induction, we may assume that Φ is of the form $\exists\, \xi\rho\varphi_{\mu\nu}'$. Iterating this procedure reduces us to the case that Φ is of the form $\exists\, \xi\rho\varphi$, where the functions occurring in φ are $a_i(x) \cdot f_i(x, \xi, \rho)$, and each $f_i(x, \xi, \rho)$ is preregular of degree (μ_i, ν_i) with $f_{i\mu_i\nu_i} = 1$, $1 \leq i \leq \ell$.

Consider the $L_{\mathcal{E}}$-formulas

$$\varphi_0 := \varphi \wedge \bigwedge_{i=1}^{\ell} |f_{i\nu_i}(x, \xi)| = 1 \quad \text{and} \quad \varphi_i := \varphi \wedge |f_{i\nu_i}(x, \xi)| < 1.$$

Clearly, Φ is equivalent to the disjunction

$$\exists\, \xi\rho\varphi_0(\xi, \rho) \vee \bigvee \exists\, \xi\rho\varphi_i(\xi, \rho),$$

and we may consider the disjuncts separately.

***Case* (A).** — $\Phi = \exists\, \xi\rho\varphi_i(\xi, \rho)$.

We have that Φ is equivalent to

$$\exists\, \xi\rho\rho_{n+1}\varphi \wedge |f_{i\nu_i} - \rho_{n+1}| = 0.$$

Observe that $f_{i\nu_i} - \rho_{n+1}$ is preregular of degree $(\mu_i, 0)$. Hence, after a Weierstrass automorphism involving only the ξ's, we may assume that $f_{i\nu_i} - \rho_{n+1}$ is regular in ξ_m. (Recall that Weierstrass automorphisms preserve membership in $\mathcal{E}$.) After applying Weierstrass Preparation (Theorem 3.1) to $f_{i\nu_i} - \rho_{n+1}$ and Weierstrass Division (Theorem 3.3) with divisor $f_{i\nu_i} - \rho_{n+1}$ to the other functions in Φ, we may assume that all the functions occurring in Φ are polynomials in ξ_m. We may now apply the algebraic elimination theorem of **[24]** to find a formula

$$\Psi = \exists\, \xi_1 \ldots \xi_{m-1}\rho\, \rho_{n+1}\psi$$

equivalent to Φ. Since $(m-1, n+1, \ell(\psi)) < (m, n, \ell(\varphi))$, we are done by induction.

***Case* (B).** — $\Phi = \exists \xi \rho \varphi_0(\xi, \rho)$.

We have that Φ is equivalent to

$$\Psi := \exists \xi \xi_{m+1} \rho \varphi \wedge \left| \left(\prod_{i=1}^{\ell} f_{i\nu_i} \right) \xi_{m+1} - 1 \right| = 0.$$

Observe that $h = (\prod_{i=1}^{\ell} f_{i\nu_i})\xi_{m+1} - 1$ is preregular of degree $(\sum \mu_i, 1, 0)$. Hence after a Weierstrass automorphism involving only $\xi_1, \ldots, \xi_{m+1}$ we may assume that h is regular in ξ_{m+1}. Let f_i' result from f_i by multiplying by $(\prod_{j \neq i} f_{j\nu_j})\xi_{m+1}$ and replacing the coefficient $(\prod_{j=1}^{\ell} f_{j\nu_i})\xi_{m+1}$ (of ρ^{ν_i}) by 1. Then each f_i' is preregular of degree $(0, \nu_i)$. Let Ψ' result from ψ by replacing each f_i by f_i'. Then Ψ is equivalent to Ψ'. After a Weierstrass automorphism among the ρ's we may assume that each f_i' in Ψ' is regular in ρ_n. Applying Weierstrass Preparation (Theorem 3.1) to each f_i' with respect to ρ_n and to h with respect to ξ_{m+1}, and then Weierstrass Division (Theorem 3.3) with divisor h, we may assume that each function occurring in Ψ' is a polynomial in both ρ_n and ξ_{m+1}. We may now apply the algebraic elimination theorem of **[24]** to find a formula

$$\Psi'' = \exists \xi_1, \ldots, \xi_m, \rho_1, \ldots, \rho_{n-1} \psi$$

equivalent to Φ. Since $(m, n-1, \ell(\psi)) < (m, n, \ell(\varphi))$, we are done by induction. □

Taking $\mathcal{H} = S(E, K) = \cup S_{m,n}(E, K)$ we obtain the following strengthened version of the elimination theorem of **[9]**. Observe that in this case every (partial) function of $\mathcal{E}(S(E, K))$ is represented by a D-term (i.e., a function in the language L_{an}^{D} of **[9]**), and conversely, as in Remark 2.3(iv).

Corollary 4.3. — *F_{alg}° admits elimination of quantifiers in the language $L_{S(E,K)}$. The elimination is uniform in F and depends only on $S(E, K)$.*

Taking $\mathcal{H} = T(K) = \cup T_m(K)$ we obtain the following quantifier elimination theorem.

***Corollary 4.4* (Quantifier Elimination over $\mathcal{E}(T)$).** — *F_{alg}° admits elimination of quantifiers in the language $L_{\mathcal{E}(T(K))}$. The elimination is uniform in F and depends only on K.*

Observing that every member of $\mathcal{E}(T)$ is existentially definable over T gives us the following quantifier simplification (model completeness) theorem, which provides the basis of the theory of affinoid subanalytic sets discussed in Section 5.

***Corollary 4.5* (Quantifier Simplification over T)**

(i) *F_{alg}° is model complete in the language $L_{T(K)}$.*

(ii) *Every subset of* $(F_{\mathrm{alg}}^{\circ})^m$ *definable by an* $L_{T(K)}$*-formula is definable by an existential* $L_{T(K)}$*-formula.*

5. Subanalytic Sets

In this section we explain how the basic properties of subanalytic sets based on the functions in $T = \cup T_m$ (or on any set of functions $\mathcal{H} \subset S$, with $\mathcal{H} = \Delta(\mathcal{H})$) follow from Corollary 4.5.

Definition 5.1. — Let K be a complete, non-Archimedean valued field and let $\mathcal{H} \subset S = \cup_{m,n} S_{m,n}(E,K)$. Let F be a complete field extending K and let F_{alg} be its algebraic closure. A subset $X \subset (F_{\mathrm{alg}}^{\circ})^m$ is called *globally* $\mathcal{H}$*-semianalytic* iff X is defined by a quantifier-free $L_{\mathcal{H}}$-formula. A subset $X \subset (F_{\mathrm{alg}}^{\circ\circ})^m$ is called $\mathcal{H}$*-subanalytic* iff it is the projection of a globally $\mathcal{H}$-semianalytic set (or equivalently is defined by an existential $L_{\mathcal{H}}$-formula). When $\mathcal{H} = T(K)$ we use the terms K*-affinoid semianalytic* and K*-affinoid subanalytic* and when $\mathcal{H} = S(E,K)$ we use the terms (E,K)*-quasi-affinoid-semianalytic* and (E,K)*-quasi-affinoid-subanalytic.*

The following is a restatement of Theorem 4.2 (the Elimination Theorem).

Theorem 5.2. — *Let* $\mathcal{H} \subset S(E,K)$ *with* $\mathcal{H} = \Delta(\mathcal{H})$*. The* $\mathcal{H}$*-subanalytic sets are exactly the* $L_{\mathcal{H}}$*-definable sets. In particular, the class of* $\mathcal{H}$*-subanalytic sets is closed under complementation and (metric) closure.*

The following can be proved by a small modification of the arguments of [**9**, Section 5] in characteristic zero. The characteristic $p \neq 0$ case requires a larger modification. Details are given in [**14**].

Corollary 5.3. — *Every* $\mathcal{H}$*-subanalytic set is a finite disjoint union of* F_{alg}*-analytic,* $\mathcal{H}$*-subanalytic submanifolds.*

We restate the above results in the special case that $\mathcal{H} = T(K)$.

Corollary 5.4. — *The class of* K*-affinoid-subanalytic sets is closed under complementation and closure.*

Corollary 5.5. — *Each* K*-affinoid-subanalytic set is a finite disjoint union of* K*-affinoid-subanalytic sets which are also* F_{alg}*-analytic submanifolds. If* X *is such a set, this allows us to define the dimension of* X*,* $\dim X$*, to be the maximum dimension of an* F_{alg}*-analytic submanifold that occurs in a smooth subanalytic stratification, or equivalently, the maximum dimension of an* F_{alg}*-analytic submanifold of* X*.*

Remark 5.6

(i) The theory of subanalytic sets developed in [**9**] (and there termed rigid) is the special case of Theorem 5.2 with $\mathcal{H} = S$.

(ii) The Łojasiewicz inequalities proved in **[9]** for S-subanalytic sets also hold for $\mathcal{H}$-subanalytic sets. This is immediate since $\mathcal{H} \subset S$.

References

[1] J. Denef and L. van den Dries. — *p-adic and real subanalytic sets.* Ann. Math., 128, (1988) 79-138.

[2] A. M. Gabrielov. — *Projections of semi-analytic sets.* Funktsionalnyi Analiz eigo prilozheniya, 2 (1968) 18-30 (Russian). English translation: Funct. Anal. and its Appl., 2 (1968) 282-291.

[3] T. Gardener. — *Local flattening in rigid analytic geometry.* Preprint.

[4] T. Gardener and H. Schoutens. — *Flattening and subanalytic sets in rigid analytic geometry.* Preprint.

[5] H. Hasse and F. K. Schmidt. *Noch eine Begründung der Theorie der höheren Differentialquotienten in einem algebraischen, Funktionenkörper einer Unbestimmten.* J. reine agnew. Math., 177 (1937) 215-237.

[6] A. Hefez. — *Non-reflexive curves.* Compositio Math., 69 (1989) 3-35.

[7] H. Hironaka. — *Subanalytic Sets*, in *Number Theory, Algebraic Geometry and Commutative Algebra in honor of Y. Akizuki.* Kinokuniya, 1973, 453-493.

[8] L. Lipshitz. — *Isolated points on fibers of affinoid varieties.* J. reine angew. Math., 384 (1988) 208-220.

[9] L. Lipshitz. — *Rigid subanalytic sets.* Amer. J. Math., 115 (1993) 77-108.

[10] L. Lipshitz and Z. Robinson. — *Rigid subanalytic subsets of the line and the plane.* Amer. J. Math., 118 (1996) 493-527.

[11] L. Lipshitz and Z. Robinson. — *Rigid subanalytic subsets of curves and surfaces.* To appear in J. London Math. Soc.

[12] L. Lipshitz and Z. Robinson. — *One-dimensional fibers of rigid subanalytic sets.* J. Symbolic Logic, 63 (1998) 83–88.

[13] L. Lipshitz and Z. Robinson. — *Rings of separated power series.* This volume.

[14] L. Lipshitz and Z. Robinson. — *Dimension theory and smooth stratification of rigid subanalytic sets.* In *Logic Conference '98,* S. Buss, P. Hajek and P. Pudlak, eds. Springer Verlag. To appear.

[15] L. Lipshitz and Z. Robinson. — *Quasi-affinoid varieties.* This volume.

[16] A. Macintyre. — *On definable subsets of p-adic fields.* J. Symbolic Logic, 41 (1976) 605-610.

[17] H. Schoutens. — *Rigid subanalytic sets.* Comp. Math., 94 (1994) 269-295.

[18] H. Schoutens. — *Rigid subanalytic sets in the plane.* J. Algebra, 170 (1994) 266-276.

[19] H. Schoutens. — *Uniformization of rigid subanalytic sets.* Comp. Math., 94 (1994) 227-245.

[20] H. Schoutens. — *Blowing up in rigid analytic geometry.* Bull. Belg. Math. Soc., 2 (1995) 399-417.

[21] H. Schoutens. — *Closure of rigid semianalytic sets.* J. Algebra, 198 (1997) 120-134.

[22] H. Schoutens. — *Rigid analytic flatificators.* Preprint.

[23] L. van den Dries. — *On the elementary theory of restricted elementary functions.* J. Symbolic Logic. 53 (1988) 796-808.

[24] V. Weispfenning. — *Quantifier Elimination and Decision Procedures for Valued Fields.* In *Models and Sets, Aachen, 1983.* Lecture Notes in Math., 1103 (1984) 419-472. Springer-Verlag.

QUASI-AFFINOID VARIETIES

1. Introduction

In [**6**], we developed the commutative algebra of rings of separated power series and the local theory of quasi-affinoid varieties. The goal of this paper is to define the category of quasi-affinoid varieties and to treat the basic sheaf theory. The Quasi-Affinoid Acyclicity Theorem, the main result of this paper, is proved in Theorem 3.2.4. This paper uses the Nullstellensatz (Theorem 4.1.1) and results from Subsections 5.3 and 5.4 of [**6**], and the Quantifier Elimination Theorem of [**7**].

Let $X := \operatorname{Max} A$, where A is a K-quasi-affinoid algebra. Other than the canonical topology on X induced by the complete, nontrivial, ultrametric absolute value $|\cdot| : K \to \mathbb{R}_+$, there are two G-topologies we consider in this paper, the "wobbly" G-topology on X and the "rigid" G-topology on X. Both of these G-topologies are based on the same collection of admissible open sets, namely the system of R-subdomains U of X, defined in [**6**, Definition 5.3.3]. By [**6**, Theorem 5.3.5], an R-subdomain U has a canonical A-algebra of quasi-affinoid functions. In this manner X is endowed with a quasi-affinoid structure presheaf $\mathcal{O}_X$, which to each R-subdomain U of X, assigns the A-algebra $\mathcal{O}_X(U)$ of quasi-affinoid functions on U. The fact that $\mathcal{O}_X$ is a presheaf is one of the principal results of [**6**]. (See [**6**, Theorem 5.3.5 ff].)

The wobbly and rigid G-topologies on X differ, however, in the systems of admissible open coverings that they assign to X. In Subsection 2.2 we define the wobbly sheaf $\mathcal{W}_X$ to be the sheafification of $\mathcal{O}_X$ with respect to the wobbly G-topology. We show that wobbly coverings of X (finite coverings by R-domains) are $\mathcal{W}_X$-acyclic, and give a basic finiteness theorem for the wobbly sheaves based on [**6**, Theorem 6.1.2]. This finiteness theorem in various guises is a key feature that appears in many of the applications of the theory, for example the results of [**7**]. When X carries the wobbly G-topology, however, morphisms of affinoid varieties Y (carrying the usual strong affinoid G-topology) into X are not continuous (unless Y is finite), and the quasi-affinoid structure presheaf is not a sheaf.

The rigid G-topology on X, defined in subsection 2.3 assigns to X the largest collection of coverings, the quasi-affinoid coverings, such that morphisms of affinoid varieties into X are continuous. We conclude this paper, in Section 3, by proving that any quasi-affinoid covering of X is $\mathcal{O}_X$-acyclic. In particular, $\mathcal{O}_X$ is a sheaf for the rigid G-topology. Thus, the category of quasi-affinoid varieties (in the rigid G-topology) is an "extension" of the category of affinoid varieties and enjoys many similar properties from the point of view of analytic geometry and commutative algebra. It should be remarked that if X is affinoid (and infinite) then there is an R-subdomain U of X such that $\mathcal{O}_X^{\text{affinoid}}(U) \neq \mathcal{O}_X^{\text{quasi-affinoid}}(U)$ as $\mathcal{O}_X(X)$-algebras, because $\mathcal{O}_X^{\text{quasi-affinoid}}(U)$ is always a Noetherian ring.

In Subsection 2.1 we define the system of admissible open sets on a quasi-affinoid variety X, and we define the quasi-affinoid structure presheaf $\mathcal{O}_X$. In Subsection 2.2 we define the system of wobbly admissible open coverings of X to be finite coverings of X by R-domains and prove various properties of the sheafification $\mathcal{W}_X$ of the presheaf $\mathcal{O}_X$ with respect to the wobbly G-topology. In Subsection 2.3 we define the system of rigid admissible coverings of X. This is the G-topology we adopt for the category of quasi-affinoid varieties. We also give a simple characterization of rigid ("quasi-affinoid") coverings in terms of "quasi-affinoid generating systems".

In Subsection 3.1 we give an intrinsic characterization of quasi-affinoid coverings in terms of refinements by "closed" R-subdomains and we also prove some lemmas about refinements of quasi-affinoid coverings by certain closed R-subdomains that will be used in the Quasi-affinoid Acyclicity Theorem. Subsection 3.2 is devoted to the proof of this theorem.

The remainder of Section 1 is devoted to a summary, drawn from [**2**] of the definition of Čech Cohomology with coefficients in a presheaf and to statements of the basic comparison theorems.

1.1. Čech Cohomology with Coefficients in a Presheaf. — Let X be a set and let $\mathfrak{T}$ be a collection of "open" subsets of X, closed under finite intersections. A *presheaf* $\mathcal{F}$ on X is a map from $\mathfrak{T}$ to the class of abelian groups such that for all $U \subset V \subset W \in \mathfrak{T}$, there is a "restriction" homomorphism $\mathcal{F}(V) \to \mathcal{F}(U) : f \mapsto f|_U$ such that $\mathcal{F}(U) \to \mathcal{F}(U)$ is the identity and

$$\begin{array}{ccc} & \mathcal{F}(V) & \\ \nearrow & & \searrow \\ \mathcal{F}(W) & \longrightarrow & \mathcal{F}(U) \end{array}$$

commutes.

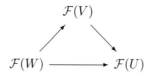

Let $\mathfrak{A} = \{U_i\}_{i \in I}$ be a covering of X by elements $U_i \in \mathfrak{T}$. For $(i_0, \dots, i_q) \in I^{q+1}$, put

$$U_{i_0 \dots i_q} := \bigcap_{j=0}^{q} U_{i_j}.$$

The $\mathbb{Z}$-module of *q-cochains* on $\mathfrak{A}$ with values in $\mathcal{F}$ is

$$\begin{aligned} C^q(\mathfrak{A}, \mathcal{F}) &:= \prod_{(i_0,\dots,i_q) \in I^{q+1}} \mathcal{F}(U_{i_0 \dots i_q}), \qquad & q \geq 0, \\ C^q(\mathfrak{A}, \mathcal{F}) &:= (0), & q < 0. \end{aligned}$$

The $(i_0, \dots, i_q)$-component of a q-cochain f is denoted $f_{i_0 \dots i_q} \in \mathcal{F}(U_{i_0 \dots i_q})$. We define the *coboundary* homomorphisms $d^q : C^q(\mathfrak{A}, \mathcal{F}) \to C^{q+1}(\mathfrak{A}, \mathcal{F})$ by $d^q := 0$ if $q < 0$, and for $q \geq 0$,

$$d^q(f)_{i_0 \dots i_{q+1}} := \sum_{j=0}^{q+1} (-1)^j f_{i_0 \dots \widehat{\imath}_j \dots i_{q+1}} \Big|_{U_{i_0 \dots i_{q+1}}},$$

where the notation $\widehat{\imath}_j$ means omit i_j. Note that $d^{q+1} \circ d^q = 0$, so $C^\bullet(\mathfrak{A}, \mathcal{F})$ is a chain complex, called the *Čech complex of cochains on* $\mathfrak{A}$ *with values in* $\mathcal{F}$. We denote the corresponding *cohomology complex* $H^\bullet(\mathfrak{A}, \mathcal{F})$, where

$$H^q(\mathfrak{A}, \mathcal{F}) := \operatorname{Ker} d^q / \operatorname{Im} d^{q-1}.$$

If $X \in \mathfrak{T}$, we define the *augmentation homomorphism*

$$\varepsilon : \mathcal{F}(X) \longrightarrow C^0(\mathfrak{A}, \mathcal{F}) : f \longmapsto (f|_{U_{i_0}})_{i_0 \in I},$$

with image contained in $\operatorname{Ker} d^0$. The covering $\mathfrak{A}$ is *$\mathcal{F}$-acyclic* iff the sequence

$$0 \to \mathcal{F}(X) \xrightarrow{\varepsilon} C^0(\mathfrak{A}, \mathcal{F}) \xrightarrow{d^0} C^1(\mathfrak{A}, \mathcal{F}) \xrightarrow{d^1} \dots$$

is exact; i.e., iff ε induces an isomorphism of $\mathcal{F}(X)$ with $C^0(\mathfrak{A}, \mathcal{F})$ and $H^q(\mathfrak{A}, \mathcal{F}) = (0)$ for $q \neq 0$. A q-cochain f is an *alternating cochain* iff for all permutations π of $\{0, \dots, q\}$,

$$f_{i_{\pi(0)} \dots i_{\pi(q)}} = (\operatorname{sgn} \pi) f_{i_0 \dots i_q}.$$

The alternating q-cochains form a submodule $C^q_{\mathrm{a}}(\mathfrak{A}, \mathcal{F})$ of $C^q(\mathfrak{A}, \mathcal{F})$. As d^q maps alternating cochains into alternating cochains, the modules $C^q_{\mathrm{a}}(\mathfrak{A}, \mathcal{F})$ constitute a subcomplex $C^\bullet_{\mathrm{a}}(\mathfrak{A}, \mathcal{F})$ of $C^\bullet(\mathfrak{A}, \mathcal{F})$ called the *Čech complex of alternating cochains on* $\mathfrak{A}$ *with values in* $\mathcal{F}$. The corresponding cohomology modules are denoted by

$$H^q_{\mathrm{a}}(\mathfrak{A}, \mathcal{F}) := H^q(C^\bullet_{\mathrm{a}}(\mathfrak{A}, \mathcal{F})).$$

There is no essential difference between the complexes $C^\bullet_{\mathrm{a}}(\mathfrak{A}, \mathcal{F})$ and $C^\bullet(\mathfrak{A}, \mathcal{F})$, since both yield the same cohomology.

Proposition 1.1.1. — *The injection* $\iota : C^\bullet(\mathfrak{A}, \mathcal{F}) \to C^\bullet_{\mathrm{a}}(\mathfrak{A}, \mathcal{F})$ *induces bijections* $H^q(\iota) : H^q_{\mathrm{a}}(\mathfrak{A}, \mathcal{F}) \xrightarrow{\sim} H^q(\mathfrak{A}, \mathcal{F})$, *for all* q.

Let $\mathfrak{A} = \{U_i\}_{i\in I}$ and $\mathfrak{B} = \{V_j\}_{j\in J}$ be $\mathfrak{T}$-coverings of X. Then $\mathfrak{B}$ is a *refinement of* $\mathfrak{A}$ iff for each $j \in J$ there is some $i \in I$ such that $V_j \subset U_i$.

Proposition 1.1.2 ([**2**, Proposition 8.1.3.4]). — *Let $\mathfrak{A}$ and $\mathfrak{B}$ be open coverings which are refinements of each other. Assume $X \in \mathfrak{T}$. Then the covering $\mathfrak{A}$ is $\mathcal{F}$-acyclic if, and only if, $\mathfrak{B}$ is $\mathcal{F}$-acyclic.*

For the next propositions, it is convenient to define some notation. Let $\mathfrak{A} = \{U_i\}_{i\in I}$ be a $\mathfrak{T}$-covering of X and let $V \in \mathfrak{T}$; then

$$\mathfrak{A}|_V := \{V \cap U_i\}_{i\in I}$$

is a $\mathfrak{T}$-covering of V which is called the *restriction of* $\mathfrak{A}$ to V. We define the presheaf $\mathcal{F}|_V$ on $(V, \mathfrak{T}|_V)$ by restricting the domain of $\mathcal{F}$ to $\mathfrak{T}|_V$.

Proposition 1.1.3 ([**2**, Theorem 8.1.4.2]). — *Assume that all coverings $\mathfrak{A}|_{V_{j_0\cdots j_q}}$ and $\mathfrak{B}|_{U_{i_0\cdots i_p}}$ are $\mathcal{F}$-acyclic. Then,*

$$H^r(\mathfrak{A}, \mathcal{F}) \cong H^r(\mathfrak{B}, \mathcal{F})$$

for all r. In particular, if $X \in \mathfrak{T}$, the covering $\mathfrak{A}$ is $\mathcal{F}$-acylic if, and only if, $\mathfrak{B}$ is $\mathcal{F}$-acyclic.

Proposition 1.1.4 ([**2**, Corollary 8.1.4.3]). — *Assume that $\mathfrak{B}$ is a refinement of $\mathfrak{A}$ and that $\mathfrak{B}|_{U_{i_0\cdots i_p}}$ is $\mathcal{F}$-acyclic for all indices $i_0, \ldots, i_p \in I$ and for all p. Then, if $X \in \mathfrak{T}$, the covering $\mathfrak{A}$ is $\mathcal{F}$-acyclic if, and only if, $\mathfrak{B}$ is $\mathcal{F}$-acyclic.*

Proposition 1.1.5 ([**2**, Corollary 8.1.4.4]). — *Assume that the covering $\mathfrak{B}|_{U_{i_0\cdots i_p}}$ is $\mathcal{F}$-acyclic for all indices $i_0, \ldots, i_p \in I$ and for all p. Then, if $X \in \mathfrak{T}$, the covering $\mathfrak{A} \times \mathfrak{B} := \{U_i \cap V_j\}_{\substack{i\in I\\ j\in J}}$ of X is $\mathcal{F}$-acyclic if, and only if, $\mathfrak{A}$ is $\mathcal{F}$-acyclic.*

We assume that the reader is familiar with the following concepts, which can be found in [**2**, Chapter 9]: G-topology ([**2**, Definition 9.1.1.1]); sheaf and stalks ([**2**, Definition 9.2.1.2 ff]); sheafification ([**2**, Definition 9.2.2.1]); and locally G-ringed space ([**2**, Section 9.3.1]).

2. G-Topologies and the Structure Presheaf

Recall that a G-topology on a set X is determined by a system $\mathfrak{T}$ of admissible open sets, and for each admissible open U, a system $\operatorname{Cov} U$ of admissible coverings of U by admissible open sets (see [**2**, Definition 9.1.1.1]). Let A be a quasi-affinoid algebra (i.e., $A = S_{m,n}/I$, see [**6**]) and put $X := \operatorname{Max} A$. In this section, we will consider two G-topologies on X, the wobbly G-topology and the rigid G-topology. The admissible open sets in both of these topologies will be the same, namely the collection of R-subdomains of X. The systems of admissible open coverings, however, will be different.

For each R-subdomain $U \subset X$, we have shown ([**6**, Subsection 5.3]) that there is a uniquely determined A-algebra $\mathcal{O}_X(U)$ that satisfies the Universal Mapping Property of [**6**, Definition 5.3.4] and such that $\operatorname{Max}\mathcal{O}_X(U) = U$. Note that $\mathcal{O}_X(X) = A$. In fact, the Universal Mapping Property for R-subdomains ([**6**, Theorem 5.3.5]) shows that $\mathcal{O}_X$, so defined, is presheaf. This is summarized in Subsection 2.1.

In Subsection 2.2, we show that $\mathcal{O}_X$ is not a sheaf with respect to the wobbly G-topology on X, and we discuss a few properties of its sheafification $\mathcal{W}_X$ with respect to the wobbly G-topology.

In Subsection 2.3, we define the class of quasi-affinoid coverings, and the rigid G-topology of a quasi-affinoid variety X. In particular, it is with respect to this G-topology that we show in Subsection 3.2 that $\mathcal{O}_X$ is indeed a sheaf. We also define the category of quasi-affinoid varieties and prove that fiber products and disjoint unions exist in this category (but the disjoint union of two quasi-affinoid subdomains is not necessarily a quasi-affinoid subdomain).

2.1. Open Sets and the Structure Presheaf.

— The notion of quasi-affinoid subdomain of a quasi-affinoid variety X was defined in [**6**, Section 5.3] by means of the following universal property.

Definition 2.1.1. — Let $X = \operatorname{Max} A$ be a quasi-affinoid variety and let $U \subset X$. Then U is a *quasi-affinoid subdomain* of X iff there is a quasi-affinoid variety Y and a quasi-affinoid map $\varphi : Y \to X$ with $\varphi(Y) \subset U$ such that φ represents all quasi-affinoid maps into U in the sense of [**6**, Definition 5.3.4].

A certain class of quasi-affinoid subdomains plays a key role in the local theory, that is the class of quasi-rational subdomains and, by iteration, R-subdomains (see [**6**, Definition 5.3.3 and Theorem 5.3.5]). Recall that if $f_1, \ldots, f_r$, $g_1, \ldots, g_s$, $h \in A$ generate the unit ideal of the quasi-affinoid algebra A, then

$$U := \{x \in \operatorname{Max} A : |f_i(x)| \leq |h(x)| \text{ and } |g_j(x)| < |h(x)|, 1 \leq i \leq r, 1 \leq j \leq s\}$$

is a quasi-rational subdomain of $X = \operatorname{Max} A$; indeed the quasi-affinoid map induced by the natural K-algebra homomorphism

$$A \to A\left\langle \frac{f}{h} \right\rangle \left[\!\left[\frac{g}{h} \right]\!\right]_s \tag{2.1.1}$$

represents all quasi-affinoid maps into U (the latter ring is defined in [**6**, Definition 5.3.1]). When $s = 0$ (i.e., when there are no g's), we will find it convenient to denote U by

$$X\left(\frac{f}{h}\right).$$

Other special types of quasi-rational subdomains are those of the form

$$X(f) := \{x \in X : |f_i(x)| \leq 1,\ 1 \leq i \leq r\},$$
$$X(f, g^{-1}) := \{x \in X : |f_i(x)| \leq 1,\ |g_j(x)| \geq 1,\ 1 \leq i \leq r,\ 1 \leq j \leq s\}.$$

Unlike the affinoid case, a quasi-rational subdomain of a quasi-rational subdomain of X, although it is by definition an R-subdomain of X, need not itself be a quasi-rational subdomain of X (see [**6**, Example 5.3.7]). In order to keep track of the complexity of R-subdomains, we define the notion of level.

Definition 2.1.2. — Let $X = \operatorname{Max} A$ be a quasi-affinoid variety. We define the class of R-subdomains of X of level $\leq \ell$ inductively as follows. Any quasi-rational subdomain of X is an *R-subdomain of X of level* ≤ 1. If U is an R-subdomain of X of level $\leq \ell$, then any quasi-rational subdomain V of U is an *R-subdomain of X of level* $\leq \ell + 1$.

The class of R-subdomains of X is closed under finite intersections.

Definition 2.1.3. — Let $X = \operatorname{Max} A$ be quasi-affinoid. By $\mathfrak{T}$, denote the system of R-subdomains of X; note that $\varnothing, X \in \mathfrak{T}$ and that $\mathfrak{T}$ is closed under finite intersection. The elements of $\mathfrak{T}$ are the *admissible open* sets. Using (2.1.1) and Definition 2.1.2, we inductively assign to each $U \in \mathfrak{T}$ a generalized ring of fractions over A, which we denote $\mathcal{O}_X(U)$. The map $U \mapsto \mathcal{O}_X(U)$ is called the *quasi-affinoid structure presheaf* on $(X, \mathfrak{T})$.

By [**6**, Theorem 5.3.5], the natural K-algebra homomorphism $A \to \mathcal{O}_X(U)$ represents all quasi-affinoid maps into U. This has the following consequence.

Theorem 2.1.4. — *$\mathcal{O}_X$ is a presheaf on $(X, \mathfrak{T})$.*

When $U \subset X$ is an affinoid R-subdomain of X (see [**6**, Proposition 5.3.8]), it follows from [**6**, Theorem 5.3.5] that $\mathcal{O}_X^{\text{affinoid}}(U) = \mathcal{O}_X^{\text{quasi}-\text{affinoid}}(U)$. But, taking $X := \operatorname{Max} K\langle\xi_1\rangle$, for example, it can easily be seen that $\mathcal{O}_X^{\text{affinoid}} \neq \mathcal{O}_X^{\text{quasi}-\text{affinoid}}$ as presheaves. Indeed, put

$$U := \{x \in X : |x| < 1\}.$$

Then $\mathcal{O}_X^{\text{quasi}-\text{affinoid}}(U) = K[\![\xi_1]\!]_s$ is a ring of separated power series, hence is Noetherian. On the other hand,

$$\mathcal{O}_X^{\text{affinoid}}(U) = \varprojlim_{\varepsilon \in \sqrt{|K^{\circ\circ} \setminus \{0\}|}} K\langle\xi_1\rangle\left\langle\frac{\xi_1}{\varepsilon}\right\rangle$$

is not Noetherian.

In [**6**, Theorem 6.2.2], we showed that a quasi-affinoid subdomain V of X is a finite union of R-subdomains $U_0, \ldots, U_p$ of X. The covering $\{U_i\}$ of V so obtained is admissible in the sense of Subsection 2.2, but it is not, in general, a"quasi-affinoid" covering in the sense of Subsection 2.3.

2.2. The Wobbly G-Topology. — Recall that the intersection of finitely many R-domains is an R-domain [**6**, Section 5.3]. This allows us to make the following definition.

Definition 2.2.1. — Let A be a quasi-affinoid algebra, $X := \operatorname{Max} A$. The *wobbly G-topology* on X is defined by taking the admissible open sets of X to be the system of R-subdomains of X. For each admissible open U, we take the admissible coverings of U to be the system of all finite coverings of U by admissible open sets.

This definition admits finite coverings of $X = \operatorname{Max} A$ by disjoint admissible open sets, for example, when $A = T_1$,

$$U_0 := \{x \in X : |\xi(x)| < 1\}, \quad U_1 := \{x \in X : |\xi(x)| = 1\}$$

is such a covering. Moreover, the complement of any R-subdomain of X is a finite disjoint union of R-subdomains of X by an easy extension of [**6**, Section 5.3]. It follows that any wobbly admissible cover of X has a wobbly admissible refinement by finitely many pairwise disjoint R-subdomains.

Definition 2.2.2. — Let A be a quasi-affinoid algebra, $X := \operatorname{Max} A$. Define $\mathcal{W}_X$, the *wobbly sheaf* on X, to be the sheafification (see [**2**, Section 9.2.2)], with respect to the wobbly G-topology on X, of the presheaf $\mathcal{O}_X$. For each admissible open U, we have

$$\mathcal{W}_X(U) = \varinjlim \mathcal{O}(U_0) \oplus \cdots \oplus \mathcal{O}(U_p),$$

where the direct limit runs over the directed system of all (wobbly) admissible open coverings of $\{U_0, \ldots, U_p\} \subset \operatorname{Cov} U$.

By the preceding remark, observe that the characteristic function of any R-subdomain of X belongs to the ring $\mathcal{W}_X(X)$; hence $\mathcal{W}_X(X) \neq \mathcal{O}_X(X)$ when X is infinite. In particular this shows that $\mathcal{O}_X$ is not in general a sheaf with respect to the wobbly G-topology.

Proposition 2.2.3. — *Let $X = \operatorname{Max} A$, where A is a quasi-affinoid algebra, and let $\mathfrak{A}$ be a wobbly admissible covering of X, i.e., a finite covering of X by R-subdomains. Then $\mathfrak{A}$ is $\mathcal{W}_X$-acyclic.*

Proof. — Since the intersection of two R-subdomains is an R-subdomain, and since the complement of any R-subdomain is a finite disjoint union of R-subdomains, there is an admissible refinement $\mathfrak{B} = \{V_j\}_{j \in J}$ of $\mathfrak{A}$ by finitely many pairwise disjoint R-subdomains. By Proposition 1.1.4, it suffices to prove that disjoint wobbly coverings are universally $\mathcal{W}_X$-acyclic; i.e., for each R-subdomain X' of X, a disjoint wobbly covering of X' is $\mathcal{W}_X$-acyclic. To see this, observe that $C^q(\mathfrak{B}|_{X'}, \mathcal{W}_X) = (0)$ for $q \neq 0$ because the elements of $\mathfrak{B}|_{X'}$ are pairwise disjoint, and the map

$$\varepsilon : \mathcal{W}_X(X') \longrightarrow C^0(\mathfrak{B}|_{X'}, \mathcal{W}_X) : f \longmapsto (f|_{V_j})_{j \in J}$$

is a bijection, by definition of $\mathcal{W}_X$. □

Remark 2.2.4

(i) The stalks of the wobbly sheaf on X agree with those of the rigid structure presheaf: for each $x \in X$,

$$\mathcal{W}_{X,x} = \mathcal{O}_{X,x} = \varinjlim_{U \ni x} \mathcal{O}_X(U).$$

This follows from the representation in Definition 2.2.2 of $\mathcal{W}_X(U)$ as a direct limit.

(ii) There is a natural map of $\operatorname{Max} \mathcal{W}_X(X)$ onto the space $\operatorname{Cont} \mathcal{O}_X(X)$ of continuous valuations (for the definition of $\operatorname{Cont} \mathcal{O}_X(X)$ see [**4**]). This is because a point of $\operatorname{Cont} \mathcal{O}_X(X)$ is uniquely determined by the collection of quasi–rational subdomains to which it belongs. The mapping is in general not injective.

(iii) Note that if $U \subset V$ are two R-subdomains of X, then the canonical restriction $\mathcal{W}_X(V) \to \mathcal{W}_X(U)$ is surjective; i.e., $\mathcal{W}_X$ is a flasque sheaf in the sense of [**3**, Exercise II.1.16].

(iv) We may reformulate [**6**, Theorem 6.1.2] in terms of the wobbly sheaf, as follows.

Theorem. — *Let $\pi : Y \to X$ be a quasi-affinoid map with finite fibers. Then the induced morphism of sheaves on X*

$$\mathcal{W}_X \longrightarrow \pi_* \mathcal{W}_Y$$

(where $\pi_* \mathcal{W}_Y$ is the direct image sheaf) is finite.

This theorem is false upon replacing $\mathcal{W}$ by the rigid structure presheaf $\mathcal{O}$ (see [**6**, Example 6.1.3]). This finiteness theorem in various guises is a key feature of the proofs of the quantifier elimination theorems of [**5**] and [**7**].

(v) Let A be an affinoid algebra of positive Krull dimension. Then the identity map

$$id : \operatorname{Sp} A \to \operatorname{Max} A$$

is not continuous if $\operatorname{Sp} A$ carries the strong affinoid G-topology of [**2**, Section 9.1.4] and $\operatorname{Max} A$ carries the wobbly G-topology induced by regarding A as a quasi-affinoid algebra (though the inverse image of an admissible open is admissible open).

2.3. Quasi-Affinoid Coverings and the Rigid G-Topology. — In this section, we define the weakest G-topology on $X = \operatorname{Max} A$, A quasi-affinoid, such that each R-subdomain of X is admissible open and such that each quasi-affinoid morphism $\varphi : Y \to X$, with Y an affinoid variety carrying the strong affinoid G-topology ([**2**, Section 9.1.4]) is continuous. Let U be an R-subdomain of X. Since $\varphi^{-1}(U)$ is admissible open in Y, specifying such a topology is equivalent to specifying an appropriate system of admissible open coverings of X. We call such coverings quasi-affinoid coverings, and we prove a simple sufficient condition for a finite covering of X by R-subdomains to be a quasi-affinoid covering.

Definition 2.3.1. — Let $X = \operatorname{Max} A$, where A is a quasi-affinoid algebra. A covering $\mathfrak{A}$ of X is said to be a *quasi-affinoid covering* iff $\mathfrak{A}$ is a finite covering by R-subdomains $U_0, \ldots, U_p$ such that for every quasi-affinoid morphism $\varphi : Y \to X$, where Y is an affinoid variety, the covering $\{\varphi^{-1}(U_0), \ldots, \varphi^{-1}(U_p)\}$ of Y has a finite refinement by rational subdomains of Y.

In other words, $\{U_0, \ldots, U_p\}$ is a quasi-affinoid covering of X iff for all $\varphi : Y \to X$ with Y affinoid, $\{\varphi^{-1}(U_0), \ldots, \varphi^{-1}(U_p)\}$ is an admissible open covering of Y, where Y is given the strong G-topology (in the sense of [**2**, Section 9.1.4]). Theorem 3.1.5 gives a more intrinsic characterization of the class of quasi-affinoid coverings.

Definition 2.3.2. — Let $X = \operatorname{Max} A$, where A is quasi-affinoid. The *rigid G-topology* on X is defined by taking the admissible open sets to be the system of R-subdomains of X. For each admissible open set U, we take the admissible coverings of U to be the system of all quasi-affinoid coverings of U.

In the rest of this section, we give a simple characterization of the rigid G-topology on a quasi-affinoid X that will be useful in Subsection 3.1, where we give a more intrinsic characterization of the rigid G-topology.

Definition 2.3.3. — Let X be quasi-affinoid. A system $\{X_i\}_{i \in I}$ of affinoid R-subdomains of X (i.e., R-subdomains of X that are, in fact, affinoid, see [**6**, Proposition 5.3.8]) is a *system of definition for the rigid G-topology of X* iff for any quasi-affinoid map $\varphi : Y \to X$, where Y is an affinoid variety, $\varphi(Y) \subset X_i$ for some i.

The different representations of a quasi-affinoid algebra A as a quotient of a ring of separated power series give (possibly different) systems of definition, as we see below.

Definition 2.3.4. — Let $A = S_{m,n}/I$ be a representation of the quasi-affinoid algebra A as a quotient of a ring of separated power series. Put $X := \operatorname{Max} A$, and for each $\varepsilon \in \sqrt{|K \setminus \{0\}|}$, $\varepsilon < 1$, put

$$X_\varepsilon := \operatorname{Max}(S_{m,n}/I)\left\langle \frac{\rho_1^\ell}{e}, \ldots, \frac{\rho_n^\ell}{e} \right\rangle = \operatorname{Max} T_{m,n}(\varepsilon)/\iota_\varepsilon(I) \cdot T_{m,n}(\varepsilon),$$

where $e \in K^\circ$ is chosen so that $\varepsilon^\ell = |e|$ for some $\ell \in \mathbb{N}$. (See [**6**, Section 3.2].) This is the intersection of X with a closed polydisc; it is an R-subdomain of X which is, in fact, affinoid. Note that X_ε depends on the representation $A = S_{m,n}/I$. (For definitions of $T_{m,n}(\varepsilon)$ and $\iota_\varepsilon(I)$ see [**6**, Section 3.2].)

We now show that $\{X_\varepsilon\}_{\varepsilon<1}$ is a system of definition for X.

Lemma 2.3.5. — *Let X and $\{X_\varepsilon\}_{\varepsilon<1}$ be as above. Then $\{X_\varepsilon\}_{\varepsilon<1}$ is a system of definition.*

Proof. — This follows from the affinoid Maximum Modulus Principle ([**2**, Proposition 6.2.1.4]) and from the fact that the X_ε are R-subdomains of X, that are affinoid.

Let $\psi^* : A \to C$ be a K-algebra homomorphism, where C is an affinoid algebra. Put $Y := \operatorname{Max} C$. By the Nullstellensatz, [**6**, Theorem 4.1.1], $|\psi^*(\overline{\rho}_i)(y)| < 1$ for all $y \in Y$, where $\overline{\rho}_i$ is the image of ρ_i in $S_{m,n}/I$, $1 \leq i \leq n$. By the Maximum Modulus Principle,

$$\max_{1 \leq i \leq n} \|\psi^*(\overline{\rho}_i)\|_{\sup} =: \varepsilon < 1.$$

Hence $\psi(Y) \subset X_\varepsilon$. □

The next proposition shows that any system of definition characterizes the quasi-affinoid coverings, hence the rigid G-topology.

Proposition 2.3.6. — *Let X be quasi-affinoid and let $\{X_i\}_{i \in I}$ be a system of definition for X. A covering $\mathfrak{A} = \{U_0, \ldots, U_p\}$ of X by R-subdomains U_i is a quasi-affinoid covering if, and only if, for each $i \in I$, the covering $\{X_i \cap U_0, \ldots, X_i \cap U_p\}$ of the affinoid variety X_i has a finite refinement by rational domains.*

Proof

($\Rightarrow$) This is immediate.

($\Leftarrow$) Let $\psi : Z \to X$ be a quasi-affinoid map, with Z affinoid. We must show that $\{\psi^{-1}(U_0), \ldots, \psi^{-1}(U_p)\}$ has a finite refinement by rational domains. For some $i \in I$, $\psi(Z) \subset X_i$, and $\{X_i \cap U_0, \ldots, X_i \cap U_p\}$ has a finite refinement by rational domains, which we pull back to Z via ψ. □

Remark 2.3.7. — Let $\{Y_i\}_{i \in I}$ be a system of definition for the rigid G-topology on X. Then by Lemma 2.3.5, $\{Y_i\}_{i \in I}$ must be a covering of X by affinoid subdomains because each $X_\varepsilon \subset Y_i$ for some i and $\{X_\varepsilon\}_{\varepsilon < 1}$ coverings X. Unless $\{Y_i\}_{i \in I}$ is finite, however, it is *not* an admissible (quasi-affinoid) covering of X. And if it is finite, then X itself must be affinoid by [**6**, Proposition 5.3.8].

Using the rigid G-topology of the last subsection, we now define the category of quasi-affinoid varieties. Let $\varphi : X \to Y$ be a quasi-affinoid morphism (see Definition 2.3.8, below). It follows from the definition of R-subdomain that $\varphi^{-1}(U)$ is an R-subdomain of X for any R-subdomain U of Y. To check that φ is continuous, it remains to show that if $\{U_0, \ldots, U_p\}$ is a quasi-affinoid covering of Y then $\{\varphi^{-1}(U_0), \ldots, \varphi^{-1}(U_p)\}$ is a quasi-affinoid covering of X. Let Z be an affinoid variety and let $\psi : Z \to X$ be a quasi-affinoid map. The fact that the covering $\{\psi^{-1}(\varphi^{-1}(U_i))\}$ of Z has a finite refinement by rational domains then follows from the facts that $\psi^{-1}(\varphi^{-1}(U_i)) = (\varphi \circ \psi)^{-1}(U_i)$, and $\{U_i\}$ is a quasi-affinoid covering of Y. Note, moreover, that the induced maps $\varphi_x^* : \mathcal{O}_{Y,\varphi(x)} \to \mathcal{O}_{X,x}$ of stalks are local homomorphisms for each $x \in X$.

Definition 2.3.8. — Let A be a quasi-affinoid algebra and let $X := \operatorname{Max} A$. The *quasi-affinoid variety* $\operatorname{Sp} A$ is the locally G-ringed space $(X, \mathcal{O}_X)$, where X carries the rigid G-topology. (The Acyclicity Theorem, Theorem 3.2.4, guarantees that $\mathcal{O}_X$ is a sheaf on X for its rigid G-topology.) A *morphism* $(X, \mathcal{O}_X) \to (Y, \mathcal{O}_Y)$ is a pair (φ, φ^*) such that $\varphi^* : \mathcal{O}_Y(Y) \to \mathcal{O}_X(X)$ is a K-algebra homomorphism and φ is the map from $X = \operatorname{Max} \mathcal{O}_X(X)$ to $Y = \operatorname{Max} \mathcal{O}_Y(Y)$ induced by the Nullstellensatz ([**6**, Theorem 4.1.1]).

Fiber products and direct sums exist in this category.

Proposition 2.3.9. — *The category of quasi-affinoid varieties admits fiber products; i.e., if $\varphi_1 : X_1 \to Z$ and $\varphi_2 : X_2 \to Z$ are quasi-affinoid morphisms, then there is a quasi-affinoid variety $X_1 \times_Z X_2$ and quasi-affinoid morphisms $\pi_i : X_1 \times_Z X_2 \to X_i$ such that, given any quasi-affinoid variety Y and morphisms ψ_i and α as shown, there is a unique morphism β that makes*

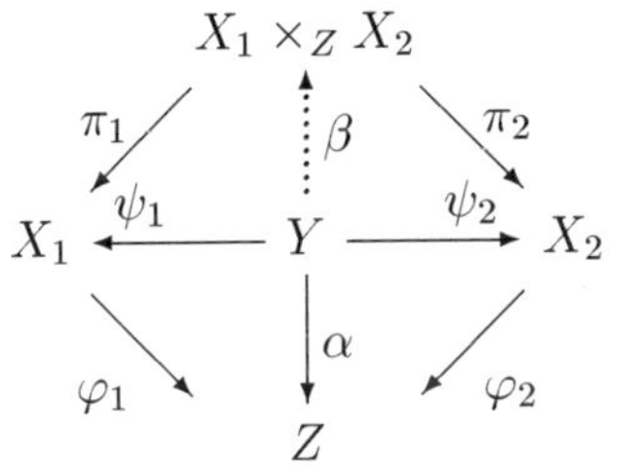

commute.

Proof. — This is just the dual diagram obtained from the diagram of [**6**, Proposition 5.4.3]. Thus,

$$X_1 \times_Z X_2 = \operatorname{Sp}(\mathcal{O}_{X_1}(X_1) \otimes^s_{\mathcal{O}_Z(Z)} \mathcal{O}_{X_2}(X_2)),$$

and the morphisms π_i are dual to the corresponding K-algebra homomorphisms of [**6**, Proposition 5.4.3]. $\square$

Proposition 2.3.10. — *The category of quasi-affinoid varieties admits disjoint unions; i.e., if X_1 and X_2 are quasi-affinoid varieties, then there is a quasi-affinoid variety $X_1 \amalg X_2$ and morphisms $\varphi_1 : X_i \to X_1 \amalg X_2$ such that for any quasi-affinoid variety Y and morphisms $\psi_i : X_i \to Y$, there exists a unique morphism α that makes*

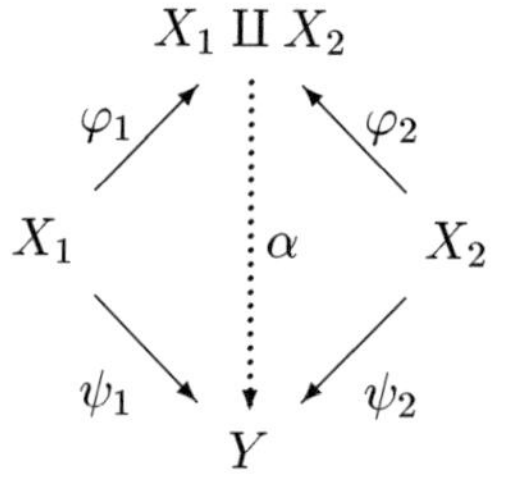

commute.

Proof. — This is the dual of the diagram one obtains for direct sums of quasi-affinoid algebras (see [**6**, Lemma 5.4.1]). Thus

$$X_1 \amalg X_2 = \mathrm{Sp}(\mathcal{O}_{X_1}(X_1) \oplus \mathcal{O}_{X_2}(X_2)).$$

□

For completeness, we include the following.

Corollary 2.3.11. — *Let $\varphi : X \to Y$ be a quasi-affinoid morphism, and let U, V be quasi-affinoid subdomains of Y. Then $U \cap V$ is a quasi-affinoid subdomain of Y and $\varphi^{-1}(U)$ is a quasi-affinoid subdomain of X.*

Proof. — It suffices to note that $U \cap V = U \times_Y V$ and $\varphi^{-1}(U) = U \times_Y X$. That the Universal Mapping Property for quasi-affinoid domains (see [**6**, Section 5.3]) is satisfied is a consequence of Proposition 2.3.9. □

Unlike the situation for affinoid subdomains (see [**2**, Proposition 7.2.2.9]), the disjoint union of two quasi-affinoid subdomains may fail to be a quasi-affinoid subdomain. For example, take $X := \mathrm{Sp}\, S_{1,0}$, $U := \mathrm{Sp}\, S_{1,0}[\![\xi]\!]_s$, $V = \mathrm{Sp}\, S_{1,0}\langle \xi^{-1} \rangle$. Then the diagram

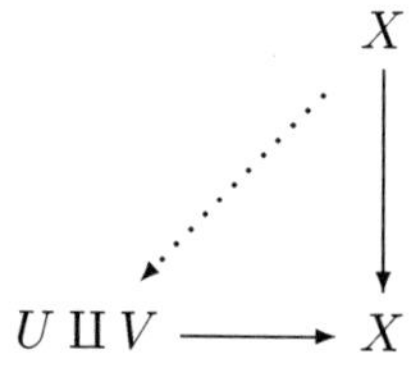

cannot be completed as required; i.e., the closed unit disc is the *set-theoretic* disjoint union of the open unit disc and an annulus, but not as quasi-affinoid subdomains.

3. Coverings and Acyclicity

In Subsection 3.2 we prove our main theorem, that quasi-affinoid coverings are $\mathcal{O}_X$-acyclic (which has the consequence that $\mathcal{O}_X$ is a sheaf for the rigid G-topology on X). The proof follows the general outline given in [**2**, Chapter 8] for the affinoid case. To make it work in our context requires the characterization of quasi-affinoid covers given in Subsection 3.1. This relies on the quantifier elimination of [**7**].

3.1. Refinements by closed R-subdomains. — We define a special class of quasi-affinoid subdomains, the closed R-subdomains, that facilitate our computations and are general enough for our purposes. In Theorems 3.1.4 and 3.1.5, we give the more intrinsic characterization of the quasi-affinoid coverings as those that have a finite refinement by closed R-subdomains.

Definition 3.1.1. — Let $X = \operatorname{Sp} A$ be a quasi-affinoid variety. The class of *closed R-subdomains of X of level $\leq \ell$* is defined inductively as follows. If $f_1, \dots, f_n, g \in A$ generate the unit ideal of A, then

$$X\left(\frac{f}{g}\right) := \operatorname{Max} A\left\langle \frac{f_1}{g}, \dots, \frac{f_n}{g}\right\rangle$$

is a closed R-subdomain of X of level ≤ 1. If $U \subset X$ is a closed R-subdomain of level $\leq \ell$, and V is a closed R-subdomain of U of level ≤ 1, then V is a closed R-subdomain of X of level $\leq \ell + 1$. (Unlike the affinoid case, there may exist closed R-subdomains of X of level > 1; see [**6**, Example 5.3.7].)

Remark 3.1.2. — Note that a closed R-subdomain U of X is relatively affinoid in the sense that $X_\varepsilon \cap U$ is an affinoid rational subdomain of the affinoid variety X_ε (defined in Definition 2.3.4). Thus by Lemma 2.3.5, any finite covering of X by closed R-subdomains is a quasi-affinoid (admissible) covering of X.

Our next goal is to show that a quasi-affinoid covering has a refinement by finitely many closed R-subdomains. The first step is to prove a shrinking lemma for R-subdomains that contain an affinoid. We recall here the definition made in [**6**, Section 5.3]. Write the quasi-affinoid algebra $A = S_{m,n}/I$, and suppose $f_1, \dots, f_r$, $g_1, \dots, g_s$, $h \in A$ generate the unit ideal. Put $X := \operatorname{Max} A$. Then

$$U := \{x \in X : |f_i(x)| \leq |h(x)| \text{ and } |g_j(x)| < |h(x)|,\ 1 \leq i \leq r,\ 1 \leq j \leq s\}$$

is an R-subdomain of X of level ≤ 1, and

$$\mathcal{O}_X(U) = A\left\langle \frac{f_1}{h}, \dots, \frac{f_r}{h}\right\rangle \left[\left[\frac{g_1}{h}, \dots, \frac{g_s}{h}\right]\right]_s = S_{m+r,n+s}/J,$$

where

$$J := I + \sum_{i=1}^{r}(h\xi_{m+i} - f_i) + \sum_{j=1}^{s}(h\rho_{n+j} - g_j).$$

Let $\delta \in \sqrt{|K \setminus \{0\}|}$, say $\delta^\ell = |e|$ for some $e \in K^{\circ\circ}$. We can "shrink" the R-subdomain U to a smaller closed R-subdomain $U(\delta)$ by replacing the strict inequalities $|g_j(x)| < |h(x)|$ with the more restrictive weak inequalities $|g_j(x)| \leq \delta |h(x)|$; i.e., $|g_j^\ell(x)| \leq |eh^\ell(x)|$. We have

$$\mathcal{O}_X(U(\delta)) = (S_{m+r,n+s}/J)\left\langle \frac{\rho_{n+1}^\ell}{e}, \dots, \frac{\rho_{n+s}^\ell}{e} \right\rangle.$$

The point here is to emphasize that $U(\delta)$ is, in fact, a closed R-subdomain with $U(\delta) \subset U$.

This construction can be carried out for an R-subdomain U of any level. Write

$$\mathcal{O}_X(U) = S_{m+r,n+s}/J,$$

where $J \supset I$ is given exactly as in [**6**, Definition 5.3.3]. Then

$$U(\delta) := \mathrm{Max}(S_{m+r,n+s}/J)\left\langle \frac{\rho_{n+1}^\ell}{e}, \dots, \frac{\rho_{n+s}^\ell}{e} \right\rangle$$

is a closed R-subdomain with $U(\delta) \subset U$. Note that the closed R-subdomain $U(\delta)$ may depend on the presentation of U.

Lemma 3.1.3. — *(In the above notation.) Let U be an R-subdomain of*

$$X = \mathrm{Max}\, S_{m,n}/I.$$

Suppose $\varphi : Y \to X$ is a quasi-affinoid morphism with Y affinoid and $\varphi(Y) \subset U$. Then for some $\delta \in \sqrt{|K \setminus \{0\}|}$, $\delta < 1$, $\varphi(Y) \subset U(\delta)$.

Proof. — Write

$$\mathcal{O}_X(U) = S_{m+r,n+s}/J,$$

as above, let $\overline{\rho}_j$ be the image of ρ_j in $\mathcal{O}_X(U)$, $1 \leq j \leq n+s$, and let $\varphi^* : \mathcal{O}_X(U) \to \mathcal{O}_Y(Y)$ be the K-algebra homomorphism corresponding to φ. Put

$$\delta := \max_{1 \leq j \leq s} \|\varphi^*(\overline{\rho}_{n+j})\|_{\sup}.$$

By the Nullstellensatz and the Maximum Modulus Principle, $\delta \in \sqrt{|K \setminus \{0\}|}$ and $\delta < 1$. Then $\varphi(Y) \subset U(\delta)$. □

Theorem 3.1.5 characterizes quasi-affinoid coverings in terms of finite coverings by closed R-subdomains. For the proof of the Acyclicity Theorem of Subsection 3.2, however, we require some precise information about the complexity of the resulting refinements by closed R-subdomains. This is contained in Theorem 3.1.4.

Theorem 3.1.4. — *A covering $\mathfrak{A} = \{U_0, \dots, U_p\}$ of X by finitely many R-subdomains of level ≤ 1 is a quasi-affinoid covering if, and only if, it has a refinement by finitely many closed R-subdomains of X of level ≤ 1.*

Proof

($\Leftarrow$) Immediate by Remark 3.1.2 and Lemma 2.3.5.

($\Rightarrow$) Assume each U_i is of level ≤ 1. Let $X := \operatorname{Sp} A$ and let $A = S_{m,n}/I$ be a representation of A as quotient of a ring of separated power series.

Let $\varepsilon \in \sqrt{|K \setminus \{0\}|}$, $\varepsilon < 1$, and consider the covering $\{X_\varepsilon \cap U_i\}_{0 \leq i \leq p}$ of the affinoid variety X_ε. By assumption, this covering has a refinement by finitely many rational domains, hence by Lemma 3.1.3, for some $\delta \in \sqrt{|K \setminus \{0\}|}$ with $\delta < 1$, $\{X_\varepsilon \cap U_i(\delta)\}_{0 \leq i \leq p}$ is a covering of X_ε. We may therefore define the function $\delta(\varepsilon)$ by

$$\delta(\varepsilon) := \inf\{\delta \in \sqrt{|K \setminus \{0\}|} : X_\varepsilon \cap U_0(\delta), \ldots, X_\varepsilon \cap U_p(\delta) \text{ covers } X_\varepsilon\}.$$

The function $\delta(\varepsilon)$ is definable in the sense of [**7**, Definition 2.7]. Therefore, by the Quantifier Elimination Theorem [**7**, Theorem 4.2], there are c, $\varepsilon_0 \in \sqrt{|K \setminus \{0\}|}$, $\varepsilon_0 < 1$, and $\alpha \in \mathbb{Q}$ such that for $1 > \varepsilon \geq \varepsilon_0$,

$$\delta(\varepsilon) = c\varepsilon^\alpha.$$

Let $e \in K^\circ$ satisfy $|e| = \varepsilon_0^\ell$. Since $\delta(\varepsilon) < 1$, we have two possibilities.

***Case* (A).** — $\lim_{\varepsilon \to 1} \delta(\varepsilon) < 1$.

Choose $\delta \in \sqrt{|K \setminus \{0\}|}$, $\delta < 1$, with $\lim_{\varepsilon \to 1} \delta(\varepsilon) < \delta$. Then $\{U_0(\delta), \ldots, U_p(\delta)\}$ is the desired refinement of $\mathfrak{A}$ by closed R-subdomains of level ≤ 1.

***Case* (B).** — $\lim_{\varepsilon \to 1} \delta(\varepsilon) = 1$.

In this case, $c = 1$ and $\alpha > 0$. Write $\alpha = a/b$, $a, b \in \mathbb{N}$. Since each U_i is of level ≤ 1, we may write

$$\mathcal{O}_X(U_i) = A\left\langle \frac{f_{i1}}{h_i}, \ldots, \frac{f_{ir_i}}{h_i} \right\rangle \left[\left[\frac{g_{i1}}{h_i}, \ldots, \frac{g_{is_i}}{h_i} \right]\right]_s,$$

where $A = S_{m,n}/I$, as above, and

$$J_i := (f_{i1}, \ldots, f_{ir_i}, g_{i1}, \ldots, g_{is_i}, h_i)$$

is the unit ideal for $0 \leq i \leq p$.

Let $\overline{\rho}_i$ be the image of ρ_i in $\mathcal{O}_X(X)$. Define

$$X_j := \{x \in X : |\overline{\rho}_j(x)| = \max_{1 \leq i \leq n} |\overline{\rho}_i(x)| \text{ and } |\overline{\rho}_j(x)| \geq \varepsilon_0\}.$$

Note that X is covered by X_{ε_0} and the X_j. For $x \in X_j$, we have

$$\delta(|\overline{\rho}_j(x)|) = |\overline{\rho}_j(x)|^{a/b} < |\overline{\rho}_j(x)|^{a/2b} < 1. \tag{3.1.1}$$

Put

$$U'_{ij} := \operatorname{Max} A \left\langle \frac{f_{i1}}{h_i}, \ldots, \frac{f_{ir_i}}{h_i}, \frac{g_{i1}^{2b}}{\rho_j^a h_i^{2b}}, \ldots, \frac{g_{is_i}^{2b}}{\rho_j^a h_i^{2b}}, \frac{e}{\rho_j^\ell}, \frac{\rho_1}{\rho_j}, \ldots, \frac{\rho_n}{\rho_j} \right\rangle.$$

By (3.1.1),

$$\{U'_{ij}\}_{\substack{0\le i\le p\\1\le j\le n}} \cup \{X_{\varepsilon_0}\cap U_i\}_{0\le i\le p}$$

is a refinement of $\mathfrak{A}$ that covers X because $\{U'_{ij}\}_{0\le i\le p}$ covers X_j. Since X_{ε_0} is affinoid and $\{U_i\}_{0\le i\le p}$ is a quasi-affinoid covering, there are finitely many rational subdomains V_j of X_{ε_0} such that $\{V_j\}_{0\le j\le q}$ is a covering of X_{ε_0} that refines $\{X_{\varepsilon_0}\cap U_i\}_{0\le i\le p}$. By [**2**, Theorem 7.2.4.2], each V_j is of level ≤ 1 (in fact defined by polynomial inequalities). Moreover, each U'_{ij} is of level ≤ 1. To see this, observe first that in the definition of U'_{ij} we may assume that $\ell = a$ and hence that U'_{ij} is defined by the inequalities

$$\begin{aligned}
|f_{ik}| &\le |h_i| && k=1,\dots,r_i,\\
|g_{ik}^{2b}| &\le |\rho_j^a h_i^{2b}| && k=1,\dots,s_i,\\
|e| &\le |\rho_j^a| && \\
|\rho_k| &\le |\rho_j| && k=1,\dots,n.
\end{aligned}$$

These inequalities are equivalent to

$$\begin{aligned}
|\rho_j^a f_{ik} h_i^{2b-1}| &\le |\rho_j^a h_i^{2b}| && k=1,\dots,r_i,\\
|e f_{ik}^{2b}| &\le |\rho_j^a h_i^{2b}| && k=1,\dots,r_i,\\
|g_{ik}^{2b}| &\le |\rho_j^a h_i^{2b}| && k=1,\dots,s_i,\\
|e h_i^{2b}| &\le |\rho_j^a h_i^{2b}| && \\
|\rho_k \rho_j^{a-1} h_i^{2b}| &\le |\rho_j^a h_i^{2b}| && k=1,\dots,n.
\end{aligned}$$

This is immediate from the fact that J_i is the unit ideal and the Nullstellensatz ([**6**, Theorem 4.1.1]). The functions occurring in the second set of inequalities generate the unit ideal and thus these inequalities define U'_{ij} as a closed R-subdomain of X of level ≤ 1. Therefore

$$\{U'_{ij}\}_{0\le i\le p} \cup \{V_j\}_{0\le j\le q}$$

is the desired refinement of $\mathfrak{A}$. □

In fact, the generalization of Theorem 3.1.4 to level $\le \ell$, $\ell > 1$, is true, as can be seen by a careful examination of the proof of Theorem 3.1.5, but since we do not need this extra information, we do not keep track of it in the proof. Though we don't use it, we include the following theorem which gives a complete characterization of quasi-affinoid coverings.

Theorem 3.1.5. — *A covering is quasi-affinoid if, and only if, it has a refinement by finitely many closed R-subdomains.*

Proof

($\Leftarrow$) Immediate, by Remark 3.1.2 and Lemma 2.3.5.

($\Rightarrow$) Let $X = \operatorname{Max} S_{m,n}/I$ and suppose $U_0,\dots,U_p$ is a quasi-affinoid covering of X. Suppose $X_0,\dots,X_n$ is a covering of X by closed R-subdomains. It suffices to show that each quasi-affinoid covering $\{X_j \cap U_i\}_{0\le i\le p}$ of X_j, $0 \le j \le n$, has a refinement by finitely many closed R-subdomains.

Fix $e \in K^{\circ\circ}\setminus\{0\}$, and consider the following covering of X by closed R-subdomains $X_0, \dots, X_n$:

$$X_0 := X\left(\frac{\rho_1}{e}, \dots, \frac{\rho_n}{e}\right),$$

$$X_j := X\left(\frac{e}{\rho_j}, \frac{\rho_i}{\rho_j}\right)_{1\le i\le n}, \qquad 1 \le j \le n.$$

Since X_0 is affinoid and $\{U_i\}_{0\le i\le p}$ is a quasi-affinoid covering of X, $\{X_0 \cap U_i\}_{0\le i\le p}$ has a refinement by finitely many rational domains.

Observe that

$$\mathcal{O}_X(X_j) = S_{m+n,n}\Big/\Big(I + (\xi_{m+j}\rho_j - e) + \sum_{i\ne j}(\xi_{m+i}\rho_j - \rho_i)\Big),$$

$1 \le j \le n$. Making the substitutions $\rho_i = \xi_{m+i}\rho_j$, $i \ne j$, we may write

$$\mathcal{O}_X(X_j) = S_{m+n,1}/I_j,$$

for the corresponding ideal I_j. Thus, we have reduced the theorem to the case $n = 1$; i.e.,

$$X = \operatorname{Max} S_{m,1}/I.$$

Let $\varepsilon \in \sqrt{|K\setminus\{0\}|}$, and consider the covering $\{X_\varepsilon \cap U_i\}_{0\le i\le p}$ of the affinoid variety X_ε. By assumption, this covering has a finite refinement by rational domains, hence by Lemma 3.1.3, for some $\delta \in \sqrt{|K\setminus\{0\}|}$, $\delta < 1$, $\{X_\varepsilon \cap U_i(\delta)\}$ is a covering of X_ε. We may therefore define the function $\delta(\varepsilon)$ by

$$\delta(\varepsilon) := \inf\{\delta \in \sqrt{|K\setminus\{0\}|} : X_\varepsilon \cap U_0(\delta), \dots, X_\varepsilon \cap U_p(\delta) \text{ covers } X_\varepsilon\}.$$

The function $\delta(\varepsilon)$ is definable in the sense of [**7**, Definition 2.7]. Therefore, by the Quantifier Elimination Theorem [**7**, Theorem 4.2], there are c, $\varepsilon_0 \in \sqrt{|K\setminus\{0\}|}$, $\varepsilon_0 < 1$, and $\alpha \in \mathbb{Q}$ such that for $\varepsilon \ge \varepsilon_0$,

$$\delta(\varepsilon) = c\varepsilon^\alpha.$$

Since $\delta(\varepsilon) < 1$, we have two possibilities.

***Case* (A).** — $\lim_{\varepsilon\to 1}\delta(\varepsilon) < 1$.

Choose $\delta \in \sqrt{|K\setminus\{0\}|}$, $\delta < 1$, with $\lim_{\varepsilon\to 1}\delta(\varepsilon) < \delta$. Then $\{U_0(\delta), \dots, U_p(\delta)\}$ is the desired refinement of $\{U_i\}$.

***Case* (B).** — $\lim_{\varepsilon\to 1}\delta(\varepsilon) = 1$.

In this case $c = 1$ and $\alpha > 0$. Write $\alpha = a/b$, $a, b \in \mathbb{N}$. Let $\overline{\rho}_1$ be the image of ρ_1 in $\mathcal{O}_X(X)$. When $|\overline{\rho}_1(x)| \geq \varepsilon_0$, we have

$$\delta(|\overline{\rho}_1(x)|) = |\overline{\rho}_1(x)|^{a/b} < |\overline{\rho}_1(x)|^{a/2b} < 1.$$

Write

$$\mathcal{O}_X(U_i) = S_{m+r_i,1+s_i}/J_i,$$

where J_i is determined according to [**6**, Definition 5.3.3]. Put

$$U_i' := \operatorname{Max} S_{m+r_i+1+s_i,1+s_i}/J_i',$$

where

$$J_i' = J + (\rho_1\xi_{m+r_i+1} - \varepsilon_0) + \sum_{j=1}^{s_i}(\rho_1^a\xi_{m+r_i+1+j} - \rho_{1+j}^{2b}).$$

Put

$$J_i'' := S_{m+r_i+1+s_i,1} \cap J_i'.$$

By inspection,

$$U_i' = \operatorname{Max} S_{m+r_i+1+s_i,1}/J_i''$$

is exactly the closed R-subdomain obtained from U_i by replacing each strict inequality $|f| < |g|$ that occurred in its definition by the weak inequality $|f| \leq |\rho_1|^{a/2b}|g|$. Now, $\{U_i'\}_{0\leq i\leq p} \cup \{X_{\varepsilon_0} \cap U_i\}_{0\leq i\leq p}$ is a refinement of $\{U_i\}_{0\leq i\leq p}$. As above, we find a refinement of the covering $\{X_{\varepsilon_0} \cap U_i\}_{0\leq i\leq p}$ of the affinoid variety X_{ε_0} by rational domains $\{V_j\}_{0\leq j\leq q}$. Finally $\{U_i'\}_{0\leq i\leq p} \cup \{V_j\}_{0\leq j\leq q}$ is the desired refinement of $\{U_i\}_{0\leq i\leq p}$ by closed R-subdomains of X. □

Theorem 3.1.4, together with the following lemmas, provide the successively simpler refinements of a quasi-affinoid covering that are required to prove the Acyclicity Theorem of the next section.

Definition 3.1.6. — Let A be quasi-affinoid, $X := \operatorname{Max} A$. A *rational covering* of X is a covering of the form

$$\left\{X\left(\frac{f_1}{f_i}, \dots, \frac{f_n}{f_i}\right)\right\}_{1\leq i\leq n},$$

where $f_1, \dots, f_n \in A$ generate the unit ideal. Clearly, any rational covering is quasi-affinoid.

Lemma 3.1.7. — *Any finite covering of X by closed R-domains of level ≤ 1 has a refinement which is a rational covering.*

Proof. — Exactly as in [**2**, Lemma 8.2.2.2]. □

Definition 3.1.8. — Let A be quasi-affinoid, $X := \operatorname{Max} A$. Let $f_1, \ldots, f_n \in A$. A *Laurent covering* of X is a covering of the form

$$\{X(f_1^{\alpha_1}, \ldots, f_n^{\alpha_n})\}_{(\alpha_1, \ldots, \alpha_n) \in \{1,-1\}^n}.$$

Any Laurent covering is quasi-affinoid.

Lemma 3.1.9. — *Let $\mathfrak{A}$ be a rational covering of X. Then there is a Laurent covering $\mathfrak{B}$ of X such that for each $V \in \mathfrak{B}$, the covering $\mathfrak{A}|_V$ is a rational covering of V generated by units $f_1, \ldots, f_n$ of $\mathcal{O}(V)$ such that there are $F_1, \ldots, F_n \in \mathcal{O}_X(X)$ with $f_i = F_i|_V$, $1 \leq i \leq n$.*

Proof. — As in [**2**, Lemma 8.2.2.3]. □

Lemma 3.1.10. — *Let $\mathfrak{A}$ be a rational covering of X generated by units of $\mathcal{O}_X(X)$. Then there is a Laurent covering $\mathfrak{B}$ which is a refinement of $\mathfrak{A}$.*

Proof. — As in [**2**, Lemma 8.2.2.4]. □

3.2. The Quasi-Affinoid Acyclicity Theorem. — The Quasi-affinoid Acyclicity Theorem, Theorem 3.2.4, is the main result of this paper. It follows immediately that the quasi-affinoid structure presheaf $\mathcal{O}_X$ is a sheaf for the rigid G-topology of the quasi-affinoid variety X.

Lemma 3.2.1 (cf. [9]). — *Let $X = \operatorname{Max} A$ be quasi-affinoid and let $f \in A$. Then the covering $\mathfrak{A} := \{X(f), X(f^{-1})\}$ of X is $\mathcal{O}_X$-acyclic.*

Proof. — We follow [**2**, Section 8.2.3], which treats the affinoid case. Since there are only two open sets in $\mathfrak{A}$, the alternating Čech cohomology modules $C_a^q(\mathfrak{A}, \mathcal{O}_X) = (0)$ if $q \neq 0, 1$. Thus, by Proposition 1.1.1, it suffices to prove that the sequence

$$0 \longrightarrow \mathcal{O}_X(X) \xrightarrow{\varepsilon} C_a^0(\mathfrak{A}, \mathcal{O}_X) \xrightarrow{d^0} C_a^1(\mathfrak{A}, \mathcal{O}_X) \longrightarrow 0$$

is exact, where the augmentation homomorphism ε is defined by

$$\varepsilon(g) := (g|_{X(f)}, g|_{X(f^{-1})}).$$

Since $A = \mathcal{O}_X(X)$, the above sequence may be written

$$0 \longrightarrow A \xrightarrow{\varepsilon} A\langle f\rangle \times A\langle f^{-1}\rangle \xrightarrow{d^0} A\langle f, f^{-1}\rangle \longrightarrow 0,$$

where ε is induced by the canonical inclusions of A in $A\langle f\rangle$ and $A\langle f^{-1}\rangle$, and

$$d^0(g_0, g_1) := g_1 - g_0.$$

Let η and ζ be indeterminates. It is sufficient to establish the exactness of the following commutative diagram.

$$\begin{array}{ccccccccc}
 & & & & 0 & & 0 & & \\
 & & & & \downarrow & & \downarrow & & \\
 & & & & (\zeta - f)A\langle\zeta\rangle \times (1 - f\eta)A\langle\eta\rangle & \xrightarrow{\lambda'} & (\zeta - f)A\langle\zeta, \zeta^{-1}\rangle & \longrightarrow & 0 \\
 & & & & \cap\downarrow & & \cap\downarrow & & \\
0 & \longrightarrow & A & \xrightarrow{\iota} & A\langle\zeta\rangle \times A\langle\eta\rangle & \xrightarrow{\lambda} & A\langle\zeta, \zeta^{-1}\rangle & \longrightarrow & 0 \\
 & & \| & & \downarrow & & \downarrow & & \\
0 & \longrightarrow & A & \xrightarrow{\varepsilon} & A\langle f\rangle \times A\langle f^{-1}\rangle & \xrightarrow{d^0} & A\langle f, f^{-1}\rangle & \longrightarrow & 0 \\
 & & & & \downarrow & & \downarrow & & \\
 & & & & 0 & & 0 & &
\end{array}$$

The map $\iota : A \to A\langle\zeta\rangle \times A\langle\eta\rangle$ is the canonical injection, λ is determined by

$$\lambda : A\langle\zeta\rangle \times A\langle\eta\rangle \longrightarrow A\langle\zeta, \zeta^{-1}\rangle : (h_0(\zeta), h_1(\eta)) \longmapsto h_1(\zeta^{-1}) - h_0(\zeta),$$

and λ' is induced by λ.

The columns are exact because

$$A\langle f\rangle = A\langle\zeta\rangle/(\zeta - f), \qquad A\langle f^{-1}\rangle = A\langle\eta\rangle/(1 - f\eta),$$
$$A\langle f, f^{-1}\rangle = A\langle\zeta, \zeta^{-1}\rangle/(\zeta - f).$$

To check the exactness of the first two rows, we require the direct sum decomposition

$$A\langle\zeta\rangle \oplus \zeta^{-1}A\langle\zeta^{-1}\rangle = A\langle\zeta, \zeta^{-1}\rangle = A\langle\zeta, \eta\rangle/(\zeta\eta - 1). \tag{3.2.1}$$

This follows from the fact that for any complete quasi-Noetherian B-ring $B \subset K^\circ$, we have the direct sum decomposition of $B\langle\xi_1, \ldots, \xi_m\rangle[\![\rho_1, \ldots, \rho_n]\!]$-modules

$$B\langle\xi_1, \ldots, \xi_{m+2}\rangle[\![\rho_1, \ldots, \rho_n]\!] = M \oplus N,$$

where

$$M := \left\{ \sum_\nu \rho^\nu \left(\sum_{\mu_{m+2} \geq \mu_{m+1}} a_{\mu\nu}\xi^\mu \right) \right\}$$
$$N := \left\{ \sum_\nu \rho^\nu \left(\sum_{\mu_{m+2} < \mu_{m+1}} a_{\mu\nu}\xi^\mu \right) \right\}.$$

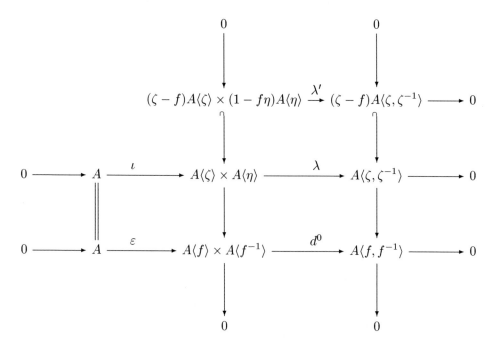

This decomposition induces the corresponding decomposition on $S_{m+2,n}$, which, in turn, induces the decomposition (3.2.1). From (3.2.1), we obtain

$$(\zeta - f)A\langle\zeta,\zeta^{-1}\rangle = (\zeta - f)A\langle\zeta\rangle \oplus (1 - f\zeta^{-1})A\langle\zeta^{-1}\rangle.$$

This yields the surjectivity of λ' and (3.2.1) yields the surjectivity of λ. In particular, the first row is exact. To check the exactness of the second row, note that

$$\lambda\left(\sum_{i\geq 0} a_i\zeta^i, \sum_{i\geq 0} b_i\eta^i\right) = \sum_{i\geq 0} b_i\zeta^{-i} - \sum_{i\geq 0} a_i\zeta^i = 0$$

if, and only if, $a_i = b_i = 0$ for $i > 0$ and $a_0 = b_0$ (see the discussion following [**6**, Definition 5.2.7]).

To see that ε is injective, let $g \in A$, $g \neq 0$. Then, since being 0 is a local property, there is some maximal ideal $\mathfrak{m}$ of A such that the image of g in the localization $A_{\mathfrak{m}}$ is not zero. Thus, by the Krull Intersection Theorem [**8**, Theorem 8.10], the image of g in the completion $\widehat{A}_{\mathfrak{m}}$ is not zero. Since $\{X(f), X(f^{-1})\}$ covers X, the conclusion follows from [**6**, Proposition 5.3.6 (ii)]. Now, by some diagram-chasing, the third row is exact. □

Corollary 3.2.2. — *Let $X = \operatorname{Max} A$ be quasi-affinoid, then any Laurent covering (see Definition 3.1.8) of X is $\mathcal{O}_X$-acyclic.*

Proof. — Use Lemma 3.2.1 and apply Proposition 1.1.5 inductively. □

In fact, the rest of the proof of the $\mathcal{O}_X$-acyclicity of quasi-affinoid coverings holds in greater generality.

Proposition 3.2.3. — *Let $\mathcal{F}$ be a presheaf on the quasi-affinoid variety X. Assume that Laurent coverings are universally $\mathcal{F}$-acyclic on X; i.e., that for each R-subdomain $X' \subset X$, all Laurent coverings of X' are $\mathcal{F}$-acyclic. Then all quasi-affinoid coverings of X are $\mathcal{F}$-acyclic.*

Proof. — The proposition is proved by induction on the complexity of the quasi-affinoid covering, after successive simplifications.

***Claim* (A)**. — *Rational coverings (see Definition 3.1.6) generated by invertible functions are universally $\mathcal{F}$-acyclic.*

By Lemma 3.1.10, such a covering is refined by a Laurent covering. Apply Proposition 1.1.4.

***Claim* (B)**. — *Rational coverings are universally $\mathcal{F}$-acyclic.*

Let $\mathfrak{A}$ be a rational covering. By Lemma 3.1.9, there is a Laurent covering $\mathfrak{B}$ such that for each $V \in \mathfrak{B}$, the covering $\mathfrak{A}|_V$ is a rational covering of V generated by units of $\mathcal{O}_X(V)$, hence is $\mathcal{F}$-acyclic by Claim A. For $U \in \mathfrak{A}$, $\mathfrak{B}|_U$ is a Laurent covering, hence by assumption is $\mathcal{F}$-acyclic. Since $\mathfrak{B}$ is $\mathcal{F}$-acyclic by assumption, the claim follows from Proposition 1.1.3.

***Claim* (C).** — *Coverings by closed R-domains of level* ≤ 1 *are universally* $\mathcal{F}$*-acyclic.*

Let $\mathfrak{A}$ be such a covering. By Lemma 3.1.7, $\mathfrak{A}$ has a rational refinement, $\mathfrak{B}$. Now Claim C follows from Claim B and Proposition 1.1.4.

***Claim* (D).** — *Quasi-affinoid coverings by R-domains of level* ≤ 1 *are universally* $\mathcal{F}$*-acyclic.*

Let $\mathfrak{A} = \{U_0, \ldots, U_p\}$ be such a covering. By Theorem 3.1.4, $\mathfrak{A}$ has a refinement $\mathfrak{B}$ by finitely many closed R-subdomains of level ≤ 1. For each $U_{i_0 \ldots i_r}$, and each r, $\mathfrak{B}|_{U_{i_0 \ldots i_r}}$ is a covering of $U_{i_0 \ldots i_r}$ by finitely many closed R-subdomains, which, as subdomains of $U_{i_0 \ldots i_r}$ have level ≤ 1. Therefore Claim D follows from Claim C and Proposition 1.1.4.

We now conclude the proof of the theorem.

Let $\mathfrak{A} = \{U_0, \ldots, U_p\}$ be a quasi-affinoid covering of X. We say that $\mathfrak{A}$ is of *type* $\leq (\ell, j)$ iff $U_0, \ldots, U_j$ are of level $\leq \ell + 1$ and $U_{j+1}, \ldots, U_p$ are of level $\leq \ell$.

Order the types lexicographically. We prove the claim by induction on (ℓ, j). When $\ell = 1$, $j = -1$, this is Claim D. Suppose the claim holds for quasi-affinoid coverings of type $\leq (\ell, j)$, and let

$$\mathfrak{B} = \{U_0, \ldots, U_j, U'_{j+1}, U_{j+2}, \ldots, U_p\}$$

be a quasi-affinoid covering of type $\leq (\ell, j+1)$. Now, since U'_{j+1} is of level $\leq \ell + 1$, there is an R-subdomain U_{j+1} of level $\leq \ell$ such that $U'_{j+1} \subset U_{j+1}$ and U'_{j+1} is of level ≤ 1 in U_{j+1}. Consider the covering

$$\mathfrak{A} := \{U_0, \ldots, U_{j+1}, \ldots, U_p\},$$

which is a quasi-affinoid covering of type $\leq (\ell, j)$, hence by the inductive hypothesis is $\mathcal{F}$-acyclic.

To apply Proposition 1.1.4, we consider the coverings $\mathfrak{B}|_{U_{i_0 \cdots i_r}}$. If some index $i_s \neq j+1$, then $U_{i_0 \ldots i_r} \subset U_{i_s}$, and $\mathfrak{B}|_{U_{i_0 \cdots i_r}}$ is refined by the trivial covering $\{U_{i_0 \ldots i_r}\} \cap U_{i_s}$. In this case, $\mathfrak{B}|_{U_{i_0 \cdots i_r}}$ is $\mathcal{F}$-acyclic by Proposition 1.1.2 since the trivial covering is $\mathcal{F}$-acyclic. It remains to consider the covering

$$\mathfrak{B}|_{U_{j+1}} = \{U_{j+1} \cap U_0, \ldots, U_{j+1} \cap U_j, U'_{j+1}, U_{j+1} \cap U_{j+2}, \ldots, U_{j+1} \cap U_p\}.$$

This is a covering of U_{j+1} of type $\leq (\ell, j)$, which is $\mathcal{F}$-acyclic by the inductive hypothesis. Now, since $\mathfrak{A}$ is $\mathcal{F}$-acyclic, $\mathfrak{B}$ must also be $\mathcal{F}$-acyclic by Proposition 1.1.2. To finish the proof, note that any quasi-affinoid covering of type $\leq (\ell + 1, -1)$ is of type $\leq (\ell, p)$ for some p. □

***Theorem 3.2.4* (Quasi-Affinoid Acyclicity Theorem).** — *Let* X *be a quasi-affinoid variety. Any quasi-affinoid covering of* X *is* $\mathcal{O}_X$*-acyclic.*

Proof. — This is an immediate consequence of Corollary 3.2.2 and Proposition 3.2.3. □

Corollary 3.2.5. — *Let X be a quasi-affinoid variety. Then $\mathcal{O}_X$ is a sheaf with respect to the rigid G-topology on X.*

References

[1] V. Berkovich. — *Spectral Theory and Analytic Geometry Over Non-Archimedean Fields.* Math. Surveys and Monographs, Vol. 33, A.M.S., Providence, 1990.

[2] S. Bosch, U. Güntzer and R. Remmert. — *Non-Archimedean Analysis.* Springer-Verlag, 1984.

[3] R. Hartshorne. — *Algebraic Geometry.* Springer-Verlag, 1977.

[4] R. Huber —*Continuous Valuations.* Math Zeit., 212 (1993), 455–477.

[5] L. Lipshitz. — *Rigid subanalytic sets.* Amer. J. Math., 115 (1993) 77-108.

[6] L. Lipshitz and Z. Robinson. — *Rings of separated power series.* This volume.

[7] L. Lipshitz and Z. Robinson. — *Model completeness and subanalytic sets.* This volume.

[8] H. Matsumura. — *Commutative Ring Theory.* Cambridge University Press, 1989.

[9] J. Tate. — *Rigid analytic spaces.* Invent. Math., 12, (1971) 257-289.

A RIGID ANALYTIC APPROXIMATION THEOREM

Zachary Robinson

1. Introduction

The main result of this paper is Theorem 5.1, which gives a global Artin Approximation Theorem between a "Henselization" $H_{m,n}$ of a ring T_{m+n} of strictly convergent power series and its "completion" $S_{m,n}$. These rings will be defined precisely in Section 2

A normed ring (A, v) is a ring A together with a function $v : A \to \mathbb{R}_+$ such that $v(a) = 0$ if, and only if, $a = 0$; $v(1) = 1$; $v(ab) \le v(a)v(b)$ and $v(a+b) \le v(a) + v(b)$. For example, when K is a complete, non-Archimedean valued field, the ring

$$K\langle \xi_1, \ldots, \xi_m \rangle := \left\{ \sum a_\mu \xi^\mu : |a_\mu| \to 0 \text{ as } |\mu| = \mu_1 + \ldots \mu_m \to \infty \right\}$$

of strictly convergent power series endowed with the Gauss norm

$$\left\| \sum a_\mu \xi^\mu \right\| := \max_\mu |a_\mu|$$

(see **[6]** or Section 2, below) is a complete normed ring. Another example may be obtained by endowing a Noetherian integral domain A with the I-adic norm induced by a proper ideal I of A.

An extension $A \subset \widehat{A}$ of normed rings is said to have the Approximation Property iff the following condition is satisfied:

Let $f_1, \ldots, f_r \in A[X_1, \ldots, X_s]$ be polynomials. For any $\hat{x}_1, \ldots, \hat{x}_s \in \widehat{A}$ such that $f(\hat{x}) = 0$ and for any $\varepsilon > 0$, there exist $x_1, \ldots, x_s \in A$ such that $f(x) = 0$ and $\max_{1 \le i \le s} v(\hat{x}_i - x_i) < \varepsilon$.

Let $\mathbb{C}[\![\xi]\!]$ be the ring of formal power series and $\mathbb{C}\{\xi\}$ the ring of convergent power series in several variables ξ, with complex coefficients. The prototype of the result proved in this paper is the theorem of Artin **[1]** that the extension $\mathbb{C}\{\xi\} \subset \mathbb{C}[[\xi]]$ has the Approximation Property with respect to the (ξ)-adic norm, which answered a conjecture of Lang **[9]**.

In [**4**], Bosch showed that the extension $K\langle\langle\xi\rangle\rangle \subset K\langle\xi\rangle$ has the Approximation Property with respect to the Gauss norm, where $K\langle\langle\xi\rangle\rangle$ denotes the ring of overconvergent power series

$$K\langle\langle\xi\rangle\rangle := \left\{\sum a_\mu \xi^\mu \in K[[\xi_1, \ldots, \xi_m]] : \text{for some } \varepsilon > 1, \lim_{|\mu|\to\infty} |a_\mu|\,\varepsilon^{|\mu|} = 0\right\},$$

and $K\langle\xi\rangle$ is the ring of strictly convergent power series defined above. (In fact, Bosch's result is much stronger.) From this result, he recovered the result of [**5**] that $K\langle\langle\xi\rangle\rangle$ is algebraically closed in $K\langle\xi\rangle$, which generalized [**15**].

In this paper we prove another approximation property possessed by the rings of strictly convergent power series. Namely, the extension $H_{m,n} \subset S_{m,n}$ (for definitions, see Section 2, below) has the Approximation Property with respect to the (ρ)-adic norm (Theorem 5.1, below). From Theorem 5.1 it follows that $H_{m,n}$, defined as a "Henselization" of the ring $T_{m+n} = K\langle\xi_1, \ldots, \xi_m; \rho_1, \ldots, \rho_n\rangle$, is in fact the algebraic closure of T_{m+n} in the ring $S_{m,n} = K\langle\xi\rangle[[\rho]]_s$ of separated power series (see [**11**, Definition 2.1.1]). Moreover, from Theorem 5.1 and the fact that the $S_{m,n}$ are UFDs, it follows that the $H_{m,n}$ are also UFDs.

The following is a summary of the contents of this paper.

In Section 2, we define the rings $H_{m,n}$ of Henselian power series. We also summarize (from [**11**]) the definition and some of the properties of the rings $S_{m,n}$ of separated power series.

In Section 3, we use a flatness property of the inclusion of a Tate ring T_{m+n} into a ring $S_{m,n}$, together with work of Raynaud [**13**], to deduce a Nullstellensatz for $H_{m,n}$.

In Section 4, we show that $H_{m,n}$ is excellent and that the inclusion $H_{m,n} \to S_{m,n}$ is a regular map of Noetherian rings. We define auxiliary rings $H_{m,n}(B,\varepsilon)$ and $S_{m,n}(B,\varepsilon)$ that in their (ρ)-adic topologies are, respectively, Henselian and complete. The inclusion $H_{m,n}(B,\varepsilon) \to S_{m,n}(B,\varepsilon)$ is a regular map of Noetherian rings. These auxiliary rings play a key role in the proof of the Approximation Theorem.

Section 5 contains the proof that the pair $H_{m,n} \subset S_{m,n}$ has the (ρ)-adic Approximation Property. The proof uses Artin smoothing (see [**14**]) and the fact that the rings $H_{m,n}(B,\varepsilon) \subset S_{m,n}(B,\varepsilon)$ have the (ρ)-adic Approximation Property.

I am happy to thank Leonard Lipshitz, who posed the question of an Approximation Property of the sort proved in this paper, and Mark Spivakovsky for helpful discussions.

2. The Rings of Henselian Power Series

Throughout this paper, K denotes a field of any characteristic, complete with respect to the non-trivial ultrametric absolute value $|\cdot| : K \to \mathbb{R}_+$. By K°, we denote the valuation ring of K, by $K^{\circ\circ}$ its maximal ideal, and by $\widetilde{K}$ the residue field. For integers $m, n \in \mathbb{N}$, we fix variables $\xi = (\xi_1, \ldots, \xi_m)$ and $\rho = (\rho_1, \ldots, \rho_n)$, thought (usually) to range, respectively, over K° and $K^{\circ\circ}$.

Let E be an ultrametric normed ring, let $E[[\xi]]$ denote the formal power series ring in m variables over E, and by $E\langle\xi\rangle$ denote the subring

$$E\langle\xi\rangle := \left\{ f = \sum_{\mu \in \mathbb{N}^m} a_\mu \xi^\mu \in E[[\xi]] : \lim_{|\mu| \to \infty} a_\mu = 0 \right\}.$$

The ring $K\langle\xi\rangle$ is called the ring of *strictly convergent power series* over K, which we often denote by T_m. The rings T_m are Noetherian ([**6**, Theorem 5.2.6.1]) and excellent ([**3**, Satz 3.3.3] and [**8**, Satz 3.3]). Moreover, they possess the following Nullstellensatz ([**6**, Proposition 7.1.1.3] and [**6**, Theorem 7.1.2.3]): For every $\mathfrak{M} \in \operatorname{Max} T_m$, the field $T_m/\mathfrak{M}$ is a finite algebraic extension of the field K. Let $|\cdot|$ denote the unique extension of the absolute value on the complete field K to one on a finite algebraic extension of K, and by $\bar{\cdot}$ denote the canonical map of a ring into a quotient ring. Then the maximal ideals of T_m are in bijective correspondence with those maximal ideals $\mathfrak{m}$ of the polynomial ring $K[\xi]$ that satisfy $|\bar{\xi}_i| \le 1$ in $K[\xi]/\mathfrak{m}$, $1 \le i \le m$, via $\mathfrak{m} \mapsto \mathfrak{m} \cdot T_m$. Moreover, any prime ideal $\mathfrak{p} \in \operatorname{Spec} T_m$ is an intersection of maximal ideals of T_m.

There is a natural K-algebra norm on T_m, called the *Gauss norm*, given by

$$\Big\| \sum_{\mu \in \mathbb{N}^m} a_\mu \xi^\mu \Big\| := \max_{\mu \in \mathbb{N}^m} |a_\mu| .$$

Put

$$\begin{aligned} T_m^\circ &:= \{f \in T_m : \|f\| \le 1\}, \\ T_m^{\circ\circ} &:= \{f \in T_m : \|f\| < 1\}, \\ \widetilde{T}_m &:= T_m^\circ / T_m^{\circ\circ} = \widetilde{K}[\xi] . \end{aligned}$$

The rings T_m are the rings of power series over K which converge on the "closed" unit polydisc $(K^\circ)^m$.

The rings $S_{m,n}$ of *separated power series* (see [**10**], [**11**] and [**2**]) are rings of power series which represent certain bounded analytic functions on the polydisc $(K^\circ)^m \times (K^{\circ\circ})^n$. When the ground field is a perfect field K of mixed characteristic, there is a complete, discretely valued subring $E \subset K^\circ$ whose residue field $\widetilde{E} = \widetilde{K}$. Then an example of a ring of separated power series is given by

$$S_{m,n} := K \widehat{\otimes}_E E\langle\xi\rangle[[\rho]],$$

where $\widehat{\otimes}_E$ is the complete tensor product of normed E-modules (see [**6**, Section 2.1.7]). Clearly $T_{m+n} \subset S_{m,n}$. In this paper $S_{m,n}$ plays the role of a kind of completion of T_{m+n}.

In general the rings of separated power series are defined by

$$\begin{aligned} S_{m,n} &:= K \otimes_{K^\circ} S^\circ_{m,n} \subset K[[\xi, \rho]], \\ S^\circ_{m,n} &:= \varinjlim_{B \in \mathfrak{B}} B\langle\xi\rangle[[\rho]], \end{aligned}$$

where $\mathfrak{B}$ is a certain directed system (under inclusion) of complete, quasi-Noetherian rings $B \subset K^\circ$. (For the definition and basic properties of *quasi-Noetherian* rings, see [**6**, Section 1.8].) The elements $B \in \mathfrak{B}$ are obtained as follows. Let E be a complete, quasi-Noetherian subring of K°, which we assume to be fixed throughout. When $\operatorname{Char} K \neq 0$, we take E to be a complete DVR. (If, for example, K is a perfect field of mixed characteristic, we may take E to be the ring of Witt vectors over $\widetilde{K}$.) Then a subring $B \subset K^\circ$ belongs to $\mathfrak{B}$ iff there is a zero sequence $\{a_i\}_{i\in\mathbb{N}} \subset K^\circ$ such that B is the completion in $|\cdot|$ of the local ring

$$E[a_i : i \in \mathbb{N}]_{\{b \in E[a_i : i\in\mathbb{N}] : |b|=1\}}.$$

It follows from the results of [**6**, Section 1.8], that each $B \in \mathfrak{B}$ is quasi-Noetherian; in particular, the value semigroup $|B \setminus \{0\}| \subset \mathbb{R}_+ \setminus \{0\}$ is discrete. It is easy to see that $\mathfrak{B}$ forms a direct system under inclusion and that $\varinjlim_{B\in\mathfrak{B}} B = K^\circ$. Furthermore, for a fixed $\varepsilon \in K^\circ \setminus \{0\}$ and for any $B \in \mathfrak{B}$, there is some $B' \in \mathfrak{B}$ such that $K^\circ \cap \varepsilon^{-1} \cdot B \subset B'$; indeed, this is an immediate consequence of the fact that the ideal $\{b \in B : |b| \leq |\varepsilon|\} \subset B$ is quasi-finitely generated. It follows that $T_{m+n} \subset S_{m,n}$, and $S_{m,0} = T_m$.

By $\widetilde{B}$ denote the residue field of the local ring B. If $\widetilde{E} = \widetilde{K}$, then $\widetilde{B} = \widetilde{K}$ for all $B \in \mathfrak{B}$. In any case, $\{\widetilde{B}\}_{B\in\mathfrak{B}}$ forms a direct system under inclusion and $\varinjlim_{B\in\mathfrak{B}} \widetilde{B} = \widetilde{K}$. We will need certain residue modules obtained from an element $B \in \mathfrak{B}$. Since the value semigroup of B is discrete, there is a sequence $\{b_p\}_{p\in\mathbb{N}} \subset B \setminus \{0\}$ with $|B \setminus \{0\}| = \{|b_p|\}_{p\in\mathbb{N}}$ and $1 = |b_0| > |b_1| > \cdots$. The sequence of ideals

$$B_p := \{a \in B : |a| \leq |b_p|\},\ p \in \mathbb{N},$$

is called the *natural filtration* of B. For $p \in \mathbb{N}$, put $\widetilde{B}_p := B_p/B_{p+1}$; then $\widetilde{B} = \widetilde{B}_0 \subset \widetilde{K}$. By $\sim: K^\circ \to \widetilde{K}$ denote the canonical residue epimorphism. Then for $p \in \mathbb{N}$, we may identify the $\widetilde{B}$-vector space $\widetilde{B}_p$ with the $\widetilde{B}$-vector subspace $(b_p^{-1}B_p)^\sim$ of $\widetilde{K}$ via the map $(a + B_{p+1}) \mapsto (b_p^{-1}a)^\sim$. This yields a residue map

$$\pi_p : B_p \longrightarrow \widetilde{B}_p \subset \widetilde{K} : a \mapsto (b_p^{-1}a)^\sim.$$

When $p > 0$, the above identification of $\widetilde{B}_p$ with a $\widetilde{B}$-vector subspace of $\widetilde{K}$ is useful, though not canonical.

There is a natural K-algebra norm on $S_{m,n}$, also called the *Gauss norm*, given by

$$\Big\| \sum_{\substack{\mu\in\mathbb{N}^m \\ \nu\in\mathbb{N}^n}} a_{\mu\nu}\xi^\mu\rho^\nu \Big\| := \max_{\mu,\nu} |a_{\mu,\nu}|.$$

We have $S^\circ_{m,n} = \{f \in S_{m,n} : \|f\| \leq 1\}$, and, unless K is discretely valued, this ring is not Noetherian. Put

$$\begin{aligned} S^{\circ\circ}_{m,n} &:= \{f \in S_{m,n} : |f| < 1\}, \text{ and} \\ \widetilde{S}_{m,n} &:= S^\circ_{m,n}/S^{\circ\circ}_{m,n} = \varinjlim_{B\in\mathfrak{B}} \widetilde{B}[\xi][\![\rho]\!]\,. \end{aligned}$$

Note that if $\widetilde{E} = \widetilde{K}$ then $\widetilde{S}_{m,n} = \widetilde{K}[\xi][\![\rho]\!]$. In any case, by [**11**, Lemma 2.2.1], $\widetilde{S}_{m,n}$ is Noetherian, $(\rho)\cdot\widetilde{S}_{m,n} \subset \operatorname{rad}\widetilde{S}_{m,n}$ and $\widetilde{K}[\xi][\![\rho]\!]$, the (ρ)-adic completion of $\widetilde{S}_{m,n}$, is faithfully flat over $\widetilde{S}_{m,n}$. It follows by descent that $\widetilde{S}_{m,n}$ is a flat $\widetilde{T}_{m,n}$-algebra.

We recall here some basic facts about the rings $S_{m,n}$. The rings $S_{m,n}$ are Noetherian ([**11**, Corollary 2.2.4]). Moreover, let $M \subset (S_{m,n})^r$ be an $S_{m,n}$-submodule, and put

$$M^\circ := (S^\circ_{m,n})^r \cap M, \quad M^{\circ\circ} := (S^{\circ\circ}_{m,n})^r \cap M, \quad \widetilde{M} := M^\circ/M^{\circ\circ} \subset (\widetilde{S}_{m,n})^r.$$

Lift a set $\widetilde{g}_1,\dots,\widetilde{g}_s$ of generators of $\widetilde{M}$ to elements $g_1,\dots,g_s$ of M°. Then for every $f \in M$, there are $h_1,\dots,h_s \in S_{m,n}$ such that

$$f = \sum_{i=1}^{s} h_i g_i \quad \text{and} \quad \max_{1\leq i\leq s} \|h_i\| = \|f\|\,;$$

in particular, $g_1,\dots,g_s$ generate the $S^\circ_{m,n}$-module M° ([**11**, Lemma 3.1.4]). Note that the above holds also in $T_m = S_{m,0}$.

The rings $S_{m,n}$ satisfy the following Nullstellensatz ([**11**, Theorem 4.1.1]): For every $\mathfrak{M} \subset \operatorname{Max} S_{m,n}$, the field $S_{m,n}/\mathfrak{M}$ is a finite algebraic extension of K. The maximal ideals of $S_{m,n}$ are in bijective correspondence with those maximal ideals $\mathfrak{m}$ of $K[\xi,\rho]$ that satisfy $|\overline{\xi}_i| \leq 1$, $|\overline{\rho}_j| < 1$ in $K[\xi,\rho]/\mathfrak{m}$, $1 \leq i \leq m$, $1 \leq j \leq n$, via $\mathfrak{m} \mapsto \mathfrak{m}\cdot S_{m,n}$. Moreover, any prime ideal of $S_{m,n}$ is an intersection of maximal ideals. It follows that $T_{m+n} \cap \mathfrak{M} \in \operatorname{Max} T_{m+n}$ for any $\mathfrak{M} \in \operatorname{Max} S_{m,n}$. Finally, for any $\mathfrak{M} \in \operatorname{Max} S_{m,n}$, the natural inclusion $T_{m+n} \to S_{m,n}$ induces an isomorphism

$$(T_{m+n})^{\widehat{}}_{\mathfrak{m}} \xrightarrow{\sim} (S_{m,n})^{\widehat{}}_{\mathfrak{M}},$$

where $\mathfrak{m} := T_{m+n} \cap \mathfrak{M}$ and $\widehat{\ }$ denotes completion of a local ring in its maximal-adic topology ([**11**, Proposition 4.2.1]). Since $S_{m,n}$ is Noetherian, it follows from [**12**, Theorem 8.8] by faithfully flat descent that $S_{m,n}$ is a flat T_{m+n}-algebra.

Definition 2.1. — The ring $A_{m,n}$ $(n \geq 1)$ is given by

$$A_{m,n} := K \otimes_{K^\circ} A^\circ_{m,n} \subset S_{m,n}, \quad A^\circ_{m,n} := \left(T^\circ_{m+n}\right)_{1+(\rho)} \subset S^\circ_{m,n}.$$

We have $A^\circ_{m,n} = \{f \in A_{m,n} : \|f\| \leq 1\}$. Put

$$A^{\circ\circ}_{m,n} := \{f \in A_{m,n} : \|f\| < 1\}, \quad \widetilde{A}_{m,n} := A^\circ_{m,n}/A^{\circ\circ}_{m,n} = \left(\widetilde{T}_{m+n}\right)_{1+(\rho)}.$$

Note that $(\rho)\cdot A^\circ_{m,n} \subset \operatorname{rad} A^\circ_{m,n}$. By [**13**, Chapitre XI], there is a Henselization $(H^\circ_{m,n},(\rho))$ of the pair $(A^\circ_{m,n},(\rho))$, but unless K is discretely valued, $H^\circ_{m,n}$ is not

Noetherian. Finally, the ring $H_{m,n}$ of *Henselian power series* is defined by

$$H_{m,n} := K \otimes_{K^\circ} H^\circ_{m,n}.$$

3. Flatness

In this section, we show that $H_{m,n}$ is a regular ring of dimension $m+n$ and that $H_{m,n}$ satisfies a Nullstellantz similar to that for $S_{m,n}$. The main result is Theorem 3.3: the canonical $A_{m,n}$-morphism $H_{m,n} \to S_{m,n}$ is faithfully flat.

The next lemma will allow us to effectively apply the results of [**13**].

Lemma 3.1. — *The following natural inclusions are flat.*

(i) $T^\circ_{m+n} \longrightarrow S^\circ_{m,n}$.

(ii) $A^\circ_{m,n} \longrightarrow S^\circ_{m,n}$.

(iii) $A_{m,n} \longrightarrow S_{m,n}$.

Moreover, the maps in (ii) *and* (iii) *are even faithfully flat.*

Proof. — Suppose we knew that $T^\circ_{m+n} \hookrightarrow S^\circ_{m,n}$ were flat; then since $(\rho)\cdot S^\circ_{m,n} \subset \operatorname{rad} S^\circ_{m,n}$, also $A^\circ_{m,n} \hookrightarrow S^\circ_{m,n}$ would be flat by [**12**, Theorem 7.1]. The induced map

$$K^\circ\langle\xi\rangle = A^\circ_{m,n}/(\rho) \longrightarrow S^\circ_{m,n}/(\rho) = K^\circ\langle\xi\rangle$$

is an isomorphism. Since $(\rho)\cdot A^\circ_{m,n} \subset \operatorname{rad} A^\circ_{m,n}$, it follows that no maximal ideal of $A^\circ_{m,n}$ can generate the unit ideal of $S^\circ_{m,n}$; hence $A^\circ_{m,n} \hookrightarrow S^\circ_{m,n}$ is faithfully flat by [**12**, Theorem 7.2]. This proves (ii).

By faithfully flat base-change

$$A_{m,n} = K \otimes_{K^\circ} A^\circ_{m,n} \longrightarrow \left(K \otimes_{K^\circ} A^\circ_{m,n}\right) \otimes_{A^\circ_{m,n}} S^\circ_{m,n} = S_{m,n}$$

is faithfully flat. This proves (iii).

It remains to show that $T^\circ_{m+n} \hookrightarrow S^\circ_{m,n}$ is flat.

***Claim* (A)**. — *Let $M \subset (T_m)^r$ be a T_m-module, and put*

$$M^\circ := (T^\circ_m)^r \cap M, \quad M^{\circ\circ} := (T^{\circ\circ}_m)^r \cap M, \quad \widetilde{M} := M^\circ/M^{\circ\circ} \subset (\widetilde{T}_m)^r.$$

Suppose $\widetilde{g}_1,\ldots,\widetilde{g}_s \in \widetilde{M}$ generate the $\widetilde{T}_m$-module $\widetilde{M}$, and find $g_1,\ldots,g_s \in M^\circ$ that lift the $\widetilde{g}_i$. Put

$$N := \left\{(f_1,\ldots,f_s) \in (T_m)^s : \sum_{i=1}^s f_i g_i = 0\right\},$$

$$N' := \left\{(\widetilde{f}_1,\ldots,\widetilde{f}_s) \in (\widetilde{T}_m)^s : \sum_{i=1}^s \widetilde{f}_i \widetilde{g}_i = 0\right\}.$$

Then $N' = \widetilde{N}$.

Clearly, $\widetilde{N} \subset N'$. Let $\widetilde{f} = (\widetilde{f}_1, \dots, \widetilde{f}_s) \in N'$ and find $h = (h_1, \dots, h_s) \in (T_m^\circ)^s$ that lifts $\widetilde{f}$. Since $\|\sum_{i=1}^{s} h_i g_i\| < 1$, and since the $\widetilde{g}_i$ generate $\widetilde{M}$, by [**11**, Lemma 3.1.4], there is some $h' = (h'_1, \dots, h'_s) \in (T_m^{\circ\circ})^s$ such that

$$\sum_{i=1}^{s} h'_i g_i = \sum_{i=1}^{s} h_i g_i.$$

Put $f := h - h'$; then $f \in N^\circ$ and f lifts $\widetilde{f}$. This proves the claim.

***Claim* (B)**. — *Let $M \subset (T_{m+n})^r$ be a T_{m+n}-module and put $L := M \cdot S_{m,n} \subset (S_{m,n})^r$. Then $L^\circ = M^\circ \cdot S_{m,n}^\circ$.*

Find generators $\widetilde{g}_1, \dots, \widetilde{g}_s$ of $\widetilde{M}$ and, using [**11**, Lemma 3.1.4], lift them to generators $g_1, \dots, g_s$ of the T_{m+n}°-module M°. Let N and $N' = \widetilde{N}$ be the corresponding modules, as in Claim A. (It follows from [**11**, Lemma 3.1.4], that N° is a finitely generated T_{m+n}°-module.) Suppose $f_1, \dots, f_s \in S_{m,n}^\circ$; by [**11**, Lemma 3.1.4], we must find elements $h_1, \dots, h_s$ of $S_{m,n}^\circ$ such that

$$\sum_{i=1}^{s} f_i g_i = \sum_{i=1}^{s} h_i g_i \quad \text{and} \quad \max_{1 \le i \le s} \|h_i\| \le \Big\|\sum_{i=1}^{s} f_i g_i\Big\|.$$

For this, we may assume that

$$\max_{1 \le i \le s} \|f_i\| > \Big\|\sum_{i=1}^{s} f_i g_i\Big\| > 0. \tag{3.1}$$

Let $B \in \mathfrak{B}$ (see Section 2 for the definition of $\mathfrak{B}$) be chosen so that $f_1, \dots, f_s \in B\langle\xi\rangle[\![\rho]\!]$, $g_1, \dots, g_s \in (B\langle\xi, \rho\rangle)^r$, and $(B\langle\xi, \rho\rangle)^s$ contains generators of the T_{m+n}°-module N° (hence by Claim A, $(\widetilde{B}[\xi, \rho])^s$ contains generators of N'). Since the value semigroup $|B \setminus \{0\}| \subset \mathbb{R}_+ \setminus \{0\}$ is discrete, it suffices to show that there are $h_1, \dots, h_s \in B\langle\xi\rangle[\![\rho]\!]$ with

$$\sum_{i=1}^{s} f_i g_i = \sum_{i=1}^{s} h_i g_i \quad \text{and} \quad \max_{1 \le i \le s} \|h_i\| < \max_{1 \le i \le s} \|f_i\|. \tag{3.2}$$

Let $B = B_0 \supset B_1 \supset \cdots$ be the natural filtration of B and find $p \in \mathbb{N}$ so that

$$(f_1, \dots, f_s) \in (B_p\langle\xi\rangle[\![\rho]\!])^s \setminus (B_{p+1}\langle\xi\rangle[\![\rho]\!])^s.$$

By $\pi_p : B_p \to \widetilde{B}_p \subset \widetilde{K}$ denote the B-module residue epimorphism $a \mapsto (b_p^{-1}a)^\sim$ and write $\widetilde{K} = \widetilde{B}_p \oplus V$ for some $\widetilde{B}$-vector space V. By (3.1), $\sum_{i=1}^{s} \pi_p(f_i)\widetilde{g}_i = 0$. Since $\widetilde{K}[\xi, \rho] \hookrightarrow \widetilde{S}_{m,n}$ is flat (see Section 2), by [**12**, Theorem 7.4(i)],

$$(\pi_p(f_1), \dots, \pi_p(f_s)) \in N' \cdot \widetilde{S}_{m,n}.$$

Since

$$\widetilde{K}[\xi][\![\rho]\!] = \widetilde{B}_p[\xi][\![\rho]\!] \oplus V[\xi][\![\rho]\!]$$

as $\widetilde{B}[\xi][\![\rho]\!]$-modules, and since $(\widetilde{B}[\xi,\rho])^s$ contains generators of N', we must have

$$(\pi_p(f_1),\dots,\pi_p(f_s)) \in \left(\left(\widetilde{B}[\xi,\rho]\right)^s \cap N'\right) \cdot \widetilde{B}_p[\xi][\![\rho]\!] .$$

Thus by Claim A, there is some $(f'_1,\dots,f'_s) \in (B_p\langle\xi\rangle[\![\rho]\!])^s$ such that

$$\sum_{i=1}^{s} f'_i g_i = 0 \quad \text{and} \quad f_i - f'_i \in B_{p+1}\langle\xi\rangle[\![\rho]\!] ,\ 1 \le i \le s.$$

Putting $h_i := f_i - f'_i$, $1 \le i \le s$, satisfies (3.2). This proves the claim.

Now let $g_1,\dots,g_r \in T^\circ_{m+n}$ and put

$$M := \{(f_1,\dots,f_r) \in (T_{m+n})^r : \sum_{i=1}^{r} f_i g_i = 0\},$$

$$N := \{(f_1,\dots,f_r) \in (S_{m,n})^r : \sum_{i=1}^{r} f_i g_i = 0\}.$$

By [**12**, Theorem 7.6], to show that $T^\circ_{m+n} \hookrightarrow S^\circ_{m,n}$ is flat, we must show that $N^\circ = M^\circ \cdot S^\circ_{m,n}$. But since $T_{m+n} \hookrightarrow S_{m,n}$ is flat (see Section 2,) this is an immediate consequence of Claim B. □

By [**13**, Exemple XI.2.2], the pairs $(B\langle\xi\rangle[\![\rho]\!], (\rho))$ are Henselian. Since the pair $(S^\circ_{m,n}, (\rho))$ is the direct limit of the Henselian pairs $(B\langle\xi\rangle[\![\rho]\!], (\rho))$, $B \in \mathfrak{B}$, it follows [**13**, Proposition XI.2.2] that $(S^\circ_{m,n}, (\rho))$ is Henselian. By the Universal Mapping Property of Henselizations ([**13**, Definition XI.2.4]), it follows that there is a canonical $A^\circ_{m,n}$-algebra morphism $H^\circ_{m,n} \to S^\circ_{m,n}$. We wish to show that this morphism is faithfully flat. It then follows from [**12**, Theorem 7.5], that, in particular, we may regard $H^\circ_{m,n}$ as a subring of $S^\circ_{m,n}$.

Lemma 3.2 **(*cf.*** [**13**, Proposition VII.3.3]). — *Let (A, I) be a pair with $I \subset \operatorname{rad} A$. Then the following are equivalent:*

(i) *(A, I) is Henselian.*

(ii) *If (E, J) is a local-étale neighborhood of (A, I), then $A \to E$ is an isomorphism.*

Proof

(ii)⇒(i). Let (A', I') be an étale neighborhood of (A, I). By [**13**, Proposition XI.2.1], we must show that there is an A-morphism $A' \to A$. Put $E := A'_{1+I'}$, $J := I' \cdot E$; then (E, J) is a local-étale neighborhood of (A, I). Hence the map $\varphi : A \to E$ is an isomorphism, and the composition

$$A' \to A'_{1+I'} = E \xrightarrow{\varphi^{-1}} A$$

is an A-morphism, as required.

(i)⇒(ii). Let (E, J) be a local-étale neighborhood of (A, I); then there is an étale neighborhood (A', I') of (A, I) such that $E = A'_{1+I'}$, $J = I' \cdot E$. By [**13**, Proposition XI.2.1], there is an A-morphism $\varphi : A' \to A$. Since $\varphi(I') = I \subset \operatorname{rad} A$, φ extends to an A-morphism $\psi : E \to A$, and we must show that $\operatorname{Ker}\psi = (0)$. For this, it suffices to show that the image of $\operatorname{Ker}\psi$ in $E_{\mathfrak{n}}$ is (0) for every maximal ideal $\mathfrak{n}$ of E.

Let $\mathfrak{n} \in \operatorname{Max} E$; then there is some $\mathfrak{m} \in \operatorname{Max} A$ such that $\mathfrak{n} = \psi^{-1}(\mathfrak{m})$. (Indeed, since $J \subset \psi^{-1}(I)$, ψ induces an A-morphism

$$A/I \cong A'/I' \cong E/J \longrightarrow A/I,$$

which must be an isomorphism; but $J \subset \operatorname{rad} E$ and $I \subset \operatorname{rad} A$.) It therefore suffices to show for each $\mathfrak{m} \in \operatorname{Max} A$ that the map

$$A'_{\mathfrak{m}'} \longrightarrow A_{\mathfrak{m}}$$

induced by φ is an isomorphism, where $\mathfrak{m}' := \varphi^{-1}(\mathfrak{m})$.

We now apply the Jacobian Criterion ([**13**, Théorème V.2.5]). Write

$$A' = A[Y_1, \ldots, Y_N]/\mathfrak{a}$$

for some finitely generated ideal $\mathfrak{a}$ of $A[Y]$, and by $\mathfrak{b}$ denote the inverse image of $\operatorname{Ker}\varphi$ in $A[Y]$. Then $\mathfrak{a} \subset \mathfrak{b}$. Let $\mathfrak{m} \in \operatorname{Max} A$, put $\mathfrak{m}' := \varphi^{-1}(\mathfrak{m})$ and let $\mathfrak{M}$ be the inverse image of $\mathfrak{m}'$ in $A[Y]$. We conclude the proof by showing that $\mathfrak{a} \cdot A[Y]_{\mathfrak{m}} = \mathfrak{b} \cdot A[Y]_{\mathfrak{M}}$. Since A' is étale over A, there are $f_1, \ldots, f_N \in \mathfrak{a}$ such that the images of $f_1, \ldots, f_N$ in $A[Y]_{\mathfrak{M}}$ generate $\mathfrak{a} \cdot A[Y]_{\mathfrak{M}}$ and $\det(\partial f_i/\partial Y_j) \notin \mathfrak{M}$. Then since $f_1, \ldots, f_N \in \mathfrak{b}$ and since $A[Y]/\mathfrak{b} = A$ is étale over A, the images of $f_1, \ldots, f_N$ in $A[Y]_{\mathfrak{M}}$ also generate $\mathfrak{b} \cdot A[Y]_{\mathfrak{M}}$; i.e., $\mathfrak{a} \cdot A[Y]_{\mathfrak{M}} = \mathfrak{b} \cdot A[Y]_{\mathfrak{M}}$. □

Theorem 3.3. — *The canonical $A^\circ_{m,n}$-morphism $H^\circ_{m,n} \to S^\circ_{m,n}$ is faithfully flat; it follows by faithfully flat base-change that $H_{m,n} \to S_{m,n}$ is also faithfully flat.*

Proof. — It suffices to prove that $S^\circ_{m,n}$ is flat over $H^\circ_{m,n}$. Indeed, since $(\rho) \cdot H^\circ_{m,n} \subset \operatorname{rad} H^\circ_{m,n}$, and since the induced map

$$K^\circ\langle\xi\rangle = H^\circ_{m,n}/(\rho) \longrightarrow S^\circ_{m,n}/(\rho) = K^\circ\langle\xi\rangle$$

is an isomorphism, this is a consequence of [**12**, Theorem 7.2].

Now, $H^\circ_{m,n}$ is a direct limit of local-étale neighborhoods (E, I) of $(A^\circ_{m,n}, (\rho))$ by [**13**, Théorème XI.2.2]. Therefore, it suffices to show that the induced map $E \to S^\circ_{m,n}$ is flat.

Since by Lemma 3.1 $S^\circ_{m,n}$ is a flat $A^\circ_{m,n}$-algebra, the map

$$E \longrightarrow (S^\circ_{m,n} \otimes_{A^\circ_{m,n}} E)_{1+(\rho)}$$

induced by $1 \otimes \mathrm{id}$ is flat. It therefore suffices to show that the map

$$\mu : (S^\circ_{m,n} \otimes_{A^\circ_{m,n}} E)_{1+(\rho)} \longrightarrow S^\circ_{m,n}$$

induced by $\sum f_i \otimes g_i \mapsto \sum f_i g_i$ is an isomorphism.

Now, since $(S^\circ_{m,n}, (\rho))$ is a Henselian pair, by Lemma 3.2, it suffices to show that $((S^\circ_{m,n} \otimes_{A^\circ_{m,n}} E)_{1+(\rho)}, J)$ is a local-étale neighborhood of $(S^\circ_{m,n}, (\rho))$, where $J :=$

$(\rho) \cdot (S^\circ_{m,n} \otimes_{A^\circ_{m,n}} E)_{1+(\rho)}$. For some étale neighborhood (E', I') of $(A^\circ_{m,n}, (\rho))$, we have

$$(E, I) = (E'_{1+I'}, I' \cdot E'_{1+I'}),$$

where $I' = (\rho) \cdot E'$. Since localization commutes with tensor product, it suffices to show that

$$(S^\circ_{m,n} \otimes_{A^\circ_{m,n}} E', (\rho) \cdot (S^\circ_{m,n} \otimes_{A^\circ_{m,n}} E'))$$

is an étale neighborhood of $(S^\circ_{m,n}, (\rho))$. But this is immediate from [**13**, Proposition II.2]. □

From now on, we regard $H_{m,n}$ as a subring of $S_{m,n}$. In particular, the Gauss norm $\|\cdot\|$ is defined on $H_{m,n}$.

Corollary 3.4. — $H^\circ_{m,n} = \{f \in H_{m,n} : \|f\| \leq 1\}$.

Proof. — We must show that $H^\circ_{m,n} = S^\circ_{m,n} \cap H_{m,n}$. Clearly, $H^\circ_{m,n} \subset S^\circ_{m,n} \cap H_{m,n}$; we prove $\supset$. Let $f \in S^\circ_{m,n} \cap H_{m,n}$; then for some $\varepsilon \in K^\circ \setminus \{0\}$, $\varepsilon f \in H^\circ_{m,n}$. But by [**12**, Theorem 7.5], $\varepsilon H^\circ_{m,n} = H^\circ_{m,n} \cap \varepsilon S^\circ_{m,n}$. It follows that $f \in H^\circ_{m,n}$. □

Since $S_{m,n}$ is a faithfully flat $H_{m,n}$-algebra, any strictly increasing chain of ideals of $H_{m,n}$ extends to a strictly increasing chain of ideals of $S_{m,n}$. Since $S_{m,n}$ is Noetherian, we obtain the following.

Corollary 3.5. — *$H_{m,n}$ is a Noetherian ring.*

Theorem 3.3 on the faithful flatness of $H^\circ_{m,n} \to S^\circ_{m,n}$ allows us to pull back to $H_{m,n}$ information from $S_{m,n}$ on the structure of maximal ideals and completions with respect to maximal-adic topologies.

***Corollary 3.6* (Nullstellensatz for $H_{m,n}$).** — *For every $\mathfrak{m} \in \operatorname{Max} H_{m,n}$, the field $H_{m,n}/\mathfrak{m}$ is a finite algebraic extension of K. The maximal ideals of $H_{m,n}$ are in bijective correspondence with those maximal ideals $\mathfrak{n}$ of $K[\xi, \rho]$ that satisfy*

$$|\overline{\xi}_i| \leq 1, \ |\overline{\rho}_j| < 1, \quad 1 \leq i \leq m, \ 1 \leq j \leq n \tag{3.3}$$

in $K[\xi,\rho]/\mathfrak{n}$ via the map $\mathfrak{n} \mapsto \mathfrak{n} \cdot H_{m,n}$. Moreover, each prime ideal of $H_{m,n}$ is an intersection of maximal ideals.

Proof. — Let $\mathfrak{n} \in \operatorname{Max} K[\xi, \rho]$ satisfy (3.3), and put $\mathfrak{m} := \mathfrak{n} \cdot H_{m,n}$, $\mathfrak{M} := \mathfrak{n} \cdot S_{m,n}$. Since $H_{m,n} \to S_{m,n}$ is faithfully flat, $\mathfrak{m} = H_{m,n} \cap \mathfrak{M}$; hence $H_{m,n}/\mathfrak{m} \to S_{m,n}/\mathfrak{M}$ is injective. Since $K \subset H_{m,n}$ and $S_{m,n}/\mathfrak{M}$ is a finite algebraic extension of K, by [**12**, Theorem 9.3], $\mathfrak{m} \in \operatorname{Max} H_{m,n}$. Moreover, $H_{m,n}/\mathfrak{m}$ is a finite algebraic extension of K.

Let $\mathfrak{m} \in \operatorname{Max} H_{m,n}$ be arbitrary. Since $H_{m,n} \to S_{m,n}$ is faithfully flat, there is some $\mathfrak{M} \in \operatorname{Max} S_{m,n}$ with $\mathfrak{M} \supset \mathfrak{m} \cdot S_{m,n}$ and $\mathfrak{m} = H_{m,n} \cap \mathfrak{M}$. By the Nullstellensatz for $S_{m,n}$, $\mathfrak{M} = \mathfrak{n} \cdot S_{m,n}$ for some $\mathfrak{n} \in \operatorname{Max} K[\xi, \rho]$ satisfying (3.3). Since $\mathfrak{n} \subset \mathfrak{m}$, it follows that $\mathfrak{m} = \mathfrak{n} \cdot H_{m,n}$, as desired.

Now let $\mathfrak{p} \in \operatorname{Spec} H_{m,n}$ and put

$$\mathfrak{q} := \bigcap_{\substack{\mathfrak{m} \in \operatorname{Max} H_{m,n} \\ \mathfrak{m} \supset \mathfrak{p}}} \mathfrak{m}, \qquad \mathfrak{Q} := \bigcap_{\substack{\mathfrak{M} \in \operatorname{Max} S_{m,n} \\ \mathfrak{M} \supset \mathfrak{p} \cdot S_{m,n}}} \mathfrak{M};$$

we must show that $\mathfrak{p} \supset \mathfrak{q}$. Let $f \in \mathfrak{q} \subset \mathfrak{q}$. By the Nullstellensatz for $S_{m,n}$, $f^\ell \in \mathfrak{p} \cdot S_{m,n}$ for some $\ell \in \mathbb{N}$. Since $H_{m,n} \to S_{m,n}$ is faithfully flat, $f^\ell \in \mathfrak{p}$, and since $\mathfrak{p}$ is prime, $f \in \mathfrak{p}$. □

Corollary 3.7. — *Let $\mathfrak{M} \in \operatorname{Max} S_{m,n}$ and consider the maximal ideals put $\mathfrak{m} := H_{m,n} \cap \mathfrak{M}$, $\mathfrak{n} := A_{m,n} \cap \mathfrak{M}$ and $\mathfrak{p} := K[\xi, \rho] \cap \mathfrak{M}$. Then the inclusions $K[\xi, \rho] \hookrightarrow A_{m,n} \hookrightarrow H_{m,n} \hookrightarrow S_{m,n}$ induce isomorphisms*

$$K[\xi, \rho]_{\mathfrak{p}}\widehat{\ } \cong (A_{m,n})_{\mathfrak{n}}\widehat{\ } \cong (H_{m,n})_{\mathfrak{m}}\widehat{\ } \cong (S_{m,n})_{\mathfrak{M}}\widehat{\ },$$

where $\widehat{\ }$ denotes the maximal-adic completion of a local ring. Moreover $H_{m,n}$ is a regular ring of Krull dimension $m + n$.

Proof. — It follows by descent, from Lemma 3.1 and Theorem 3.3, that each of the inclusions $A_{m,n} \to H_{m,n} \to S_{m,n}$ is faithfully flat. Let $\ell \in \mathbb{N}$. Since by [**11**, Theorem 4.1.1] $\mathfrak{M} = \mathfrak{p} S_{m,n}$, each of $\mathfrak{p}^\ell$, $\mathfrak{n}^\ell$, $\mathfrak{m}^\ell$ and $\mathfrak{M}^\ell$ is generated by the monomials of degree ℓ in the generators of $\mathfrak{p}$, it follows that the natural maps

$$(A_{m,n})_{\mathfrak{n}}\widehat{\ } \longrightarrow (H_{m,n})_{\mathfrak{m}}\widehat{\ } \longrightarrow (S_{m,n})_{\mathfrak{M}}\widehat{\ }$$

are injective. But by [**11**, Proposition 4.2.1], $(A_{m,n})_{\mathfrak{n}}\widehat{\ } \to (S_{m,n})_{\mathfrak{M}}\widehat{\ } \cong K[\xi, \rho]_{\mathfrak{p}}\widehat{\ }$ is surjective; thus also $(H_{m,n})_{\mathfrak{m}}\widehat{\ } \to (S_{m,n})_{\mathfrak{M}}\widehat{\ } \cong K[\xi, \rho]_{\mathfrak{p}}\widehat{\ }$ is surjective. By Hilbert's Nullstellensatz $\mathfrak{p}$ can be generated by $m + n$ elements, and $\dim K[\xi, \rho]_{\mathfrak{p}} = m + n$. In particular $K[\xi, \rho]_{\mathfrak{p}}\widehat{\ }$ is a regular local ring of dimension $m + n$. Since $\mathfrak{m} = \mathfrak{p} H_{m,n}$ and $(H_{m,n})_{\mathfrak{m}}\widehat{\ } = K[\xi, \rho]_{\mathfrak{p}}\widehat{\ }$, it follows that $(H_{m,n})_{\mathfrak{m}}$ is a regular local ring of dimension $m+n$. Moreover by [**12**, Theorem 19.3], $H_{m,n}$ is a regular ring. □

4. Regularity

To obtain our Approximation Theorem, we will apply [**14**, Theorem 1.1]. For that, we need to know that certain maps are regular maps of Noetherian rings.

Proposition 4.1. — *$H_{m,n}$ is excellent; in particular it is a G-ring.*

Proof. — By [**12**, Theorem 32.4], to show that $H_{m,n}$ is a G-ring, it suffices to show that the map

$$(H_{m,n})_{\mathfrak{m}} \longrightarrow (H_{m,n})_{\mathfrak{m}}\widehat{\ }$$

is regular for each $\mathfrak{m} \in \operatorname{Max} H_{m,n}$. Fix $\mathfrak{m} \in \operatorname{Max} H_{m,n}$, and $\mathfrak{q} \in \operatorname{Spec}(H_{m,n})_{\mathfrak{m}}$; we must show that

$$\widehat{H}(\mathfrak{q}) := (H_{m,n})\widehat{_{\mathfrak{m}}} \otimes_{(H_{m,n})_{\mathfrak{m}}} \kappa(\mathfrak{q})$$

is geometrically regular over $\kappa(\mathfrak{q})$, the field of fractions of $(H_{m,n})_{\mathfrak{m}}/\mathfrak{q}$.

Since $A_{m,n}$ is a localization of the excellent ring $T_{m,n}$, it is a G-ring. In particular, by Corollary 3.7,

$$\widehat{H}(\mathfrak{p}) := (H_{m,n})\widehat{_{\mathfrak{m}}} \otimes_{(A_{m,n})_{\mathfrak{n}}} \kappa(\mathfrak{p}) = (A_{m,n})\widehat{_{\mathfrak{n}}} \otimes_{(A_{m,n})_{\mathfrak{n}}} \kappa(\mathfrak{p})$$

is geometrically regular over $\kappa(\mathfrak{p})$, where $\mathfrak{n} := A_{m,n} \cap \mathfrak{m}$ and $\mathfrak{p} := (A_{m,n})_{\mathfrak{n}} \cap \mathfrak{q} \in \operatorname{Spec}(A_{m,n})_{\mathfrak{n}}$. Suppose we knew: (i) that $\widehat{H}(\mathfrak{q})$ were a localization of $\widehat{H}(\mathfrak{p})$, and (ii) that $\kappa(\mathfrak{q})$ were separably algebraic over $\kappa(\mathfrak{p})$. Then by (i), we would have (i′) $\widehat{H}(\mathfrak{q})$ is geometrically regular over $\kappa(\mathfrak{p})$, and by (ii), we would have (ii′) $\Omega_{\kappa(\mathfrak{q})/\kappa(\mathfrak{p})} = (0)$ by [**12**, Theorem 25.3], (where $\Omega_{\kappa(\mathfrak{q})/\kappa(\mathfrak{p})}$ is the module of differentials of $\kappa(\mathfrak{q})$ over $\kappa(\mathfrak{p})$).

Let $\mathfrak{a}$ be a maximal ideal of $\widehat{H}(\mathfrak{q})$; then by (i′), $\widehat{H}(\mathfrak{q})_{\mathfrak{a}}$ is geometrically regular over $\kappa(\mathfrak{p})$. By [**12**, Theorem 28.7], $\widehat{H}(\mathfrak{q})_{\mathfrak{a}}$ must be $\mathfrak{a}$-smooth over $\kappa(\mathfrak{p})$. Hence by (ii′) and [**12**, Theorem 28.6], $\widehat{H}(q)_{\mathfrak{a}}$ is $\mathfrak{a}$-smooth over $\kappa(\mathfrak{q})$. By [**12**, Theorem 28.7], this implies that $\widehat{H}(\mathfrak{q})_{\mathfrak{a}}$ is geometrically regular over $\kappa(\mathfrak{q})$. Since this holds for every maximal ideal $\mathfrak{a}$ of $\widehat{H}(\mathfrak{q})$, $\widehat{H}(\mathfrak{q})$ must be geometrically regular over $\kappa(\mathfrak{q})$. The proposition follows.

It remains to prove (i) and (ii). By [**13**, Théorème XI.2.2], $(H^{\circ}_{m,n}, (\rho))$ is a direct limit of local-étale neighborhoods (E, I) of $(A^{\circ}_{m,n}, (\rho))$; thus $(H_{m,n})_{\mathfrak{m}}$ is a local-ind-étale $(A_{m,n})_{\mathfrak{n}}$-algebra. By [**13**, Théorème VIII.4.3],

$$H(\mathfrak{p}) := (H_{m,n})_{\mathfrak{m}} \otimes_{(A_{m,n})_{\mathfrak{n}}} \kappa(\mathfrak{p}) = \left((H_{m,n})_{\mathfrak{m}}/\mathfrak{p} \cdot (H_{m,n})_{\mathfrak{m}}\right)_{\mathfrak{p}}$$

is a finite product of separable algebraic extensions of $\kappa(\mathfrak{p})$. It follows that $\kappa(\mathfrak{q})$ is the localization of $H(\mathfrak{p})$ at the maximal ideal $\mathfrak{q} \cdot H(\mathfrak{p})$, and that $\kappa(\mathfrak{q})$ is a separable algebraic extension of $\kappa(\mathfrak{p})$. This proves (ii). Note that

$$\widehat{H}(\mathfrak{q}) = (H_{m,n})\widehat{_{\mathfrak{m}}} \otimes_{(H_{m,n})_{\mathfrak{m}}} H(\mathfrak{p})_{\mathfrak{q}\cdot H(\mathfrak{p})},$$

which is a localization of

$$\widehat{H}(\mathfrak{p}) = (H_{m,n})\widehat{_{\mathfrak{m}}} \otimes_{(A_{m,n})_{\mathfrak{n}}} \kappa(\mathfrak{p}) = (H_{m,n})\widehat{_{\mathfrak{m}}} \otimes_{(H_{m,n})_{\mathfrak{m}}} H(\mathfrak{p}),$$

proving (i). □

Theorem 4.2. — *The inclusion $H_{m,n} \to S_{m,n}$ is a regular map of Noetherian rings.*

Proof. — Let $\mathfrak{M} \in \operatorname{Max} S_{m,n}$ and put $\mathfrak{m} := H_{m,n} \cap \mathfrak{M}$; we remark that

$$(H_{m,n})_{\mathfrak{m}} \longrightarrow (S_{m,n})_{\mathfrak{M}} \tag{4.1}$$

is regular. Indeed, since $(S_{m,n})_{\mathfrak{M}} \to (S_{m,n})\widehat{_{\mathfrak{M}}}$ is faithfully flat, [**12**, Theorem 8.8], by [**12**, Theorem 32.1], it suffices to show that $(H_{m,n})_{\mathfrak{m}} \to (S_{m,n})\widehat{_{\mathfrak{M}}}$ is regular. But by Corollary 3.7 $(H_{m,n})\widehat{_{\mathfrak{m}}} = (S_{m,n})\widehat{_{\mathfrak{M}}}$, hence this follows from Proposition 4.1.

Let $\mathfrak{p} \in \operatorname{Spec} H_{m,n}$. Since $S_{m,n}$ is flat over $H_{m,n}$ (Theorem 3.3), to show that $H_{m,n} \to S_{m,n}$ is regular, we must show that $S(\mathfrak{p}) := S_{m,n} \otimes_{H_{m,n}} \kappa(\mathfrak{p})$ is geometrically regular over $\kappa(\mathfrak{p})$. Let $\mathfrak{q} \in \operatorname{Spec} S(\mathfrak{p})$; it suffices to show that $S(\mathfrak{p})_{\mathfrak{q}}$ is geometrically regular over $\kappa(\mathfrak{p})$. Put $\mathfrak{P} := S_{m,n} \cap \mathfrak{q}$ and let $\mathfrak{M} \in \operatorname{Max} S_{m,n}$ be a maximal ideal containing $\mathfrak{P}$. Put $\mathfrak{m} := H_{m,n} \cap \mathfrak{M}$ and

$$S_{\mathfrak{M}}(\mathfrak{p}) := (S_{m,n})_{\mathfrak{M}} \otimes_{(H_{m,n})_{\mathfrak{m}}} \kappa(\mathfrak{p} \cdot (H_{m,n})_{\mathfrak{m}}).$$

Note that $S_{\mathfrak{M}}(\mathfrak{p}) = (S(\mathfrak{p}))_{\mathfrak{M}}$ and that $\mathfrak{q} = \mathfrak{P} \cdot S(\mathfrak{p})$. Since $\mathfrak{M} \supset \mathfrak{P}$, it follows that $S(\mathfrak{p})_{\mathfrak{q}}$ is a localization of $S_{\mathfrak{M}}(\mathfrak{p})$, which, by the regularity of (4.1) is geometrically regular over $\kappa(\mathfrak{p} \cdot (H_{m,n})_{\mathfrak{m}}) = \kappa(\mathfrak{p})$. Therefore, $S(\mathfrak{p})_{\mathfrak{q}}$ is geometrically regular over $\kappa(\mathfrak{p})$, as desired. □

Let $B \in \mathfrak{B}$, let $\varepsilon \in K^{\circ\circ} \setminus \{0\}$ and let $I(B,\varepsilon)$ be the ideal

$$I(B,\varepsilon) := \{b \in B : |b| \le |\varepsilon|\} \subset B.$$

It follows from the definition of quasi-Noetherian rings (see Section 2 and [**6**, Section 1.8]) that $B/I(B,\varepsilon)$ is Noetherian. Put

$$T_{m+n}(B) := B\langle \xi, \rho \rangle\,, \quad A_{m,n}(B) := T_{m+n}(B)_{1+(\rho)} \text{ and } S_{m,n}(B) := B\langle \xi \rangle[\![\rho]\!].$$

Note that

$$T_{m+n}(B,\varepsilon) := \big(B/I(B,\varepsilon)\big)\,[\xi,\rho]$$

is Noetherian, and

$$A_{m,n}(B,\varepsilon) := T_{m+n}(B,\varepsilon)_{1+(\rho)},$$

being a localization of a Noetherian ring, is Noetherian as well. Moreover, $(\rho) \cdot A_{m,n}(B,\varepsilon) \subset \operatorname{rad} A_{m,n}(B,\varepsilon)$. Let $(H_{m,n}(B,\varepsilon),(\rho))$ be a Henselization of the pair $(A_{m,n}(B,\varepsilon),(\rho))$.

The (ρ)-adic completion of $A_{m,n}(B,\varepsilon)$ is

$$S_{m,n}(B,\varepsilon) := \big(B/I(B,\varepsilon)\big)\,[\xi][\![\rho]\!],$$

which must coincide with the (ρ)-adic completion of $H_{m,n}(B,\varepsilon)$.

(Indeed, $(A_{m,n}(B,\varepsilon)/(\rho)^{\ell},(\rho))$ being (ρ)-adically complete, is a Henselian pair by [**13**, Exemple XI.2.2]. If (E,I) is a local-étale neighborhood of $(A_{m,n}(B,\varepsilon),(\rho))$, then by [**13**, Proposition II.2], $(E/(\rho)^{\ell}, I \cdot E/(\rho)^{\ell})$ is a local-étale neighborhood of $(A_{m,n}(B,\varepsilon)/(\rho)^{\ell},(\rho))$. By Lemma 3.2, $E/(\rho)^{\ell}$ is isomorphic to $A_{m,n}(B,\varepsilon)/(\rho)^{\ell}$. Since $H_{m,n}(B,\varepsilon)$ is a direct limit of local-étale neighborhoods of $A_{m,n}(B,\varepsilon)/(\rho)$, the (ρ)-adic completions of $H_{m,n}(B,\varepsilon)$ and $A_{m,n}(B,\varepsilon)$ coincide.)

Since the rings $A_{m,n}(B,\varepsilon)$ and $H_{m,n}(B,\varepsilon)$ are both Noetherian, $S_{m,n}(B,\varepsilon)$ is faithfully flat over both $A_{m,n}(B,\varepsilon)$ and $H_{m,n}(B,\varepsilon)$ by [**12**, Theorem 8.14]. Therefore, by [**12**, Theorem 7.5], we may regard $H_{m,n}(B,\varepsilon)$ as a subring of $S_{m,n}(B,\varepsilon)$.

Proposition 4.3. — *Fix $B \in \mathfrak{B}$ and $\varepsilon \in K^{\circ\circ} \setminus \{0\}$. The inclusion $H_{m,n}(B,\varepsilon) \to S_{m,n}(B,\varepsilon)$ is a regular map of Noetherian rings.*

Proof. — Find $\varepsilon' \in K^{\circ\circ}\setminus\{0\}$ such that $|\varepsilon'| = \max\{|b| : b \in B \cap K^{\circ\circ}\}$. For convenience of notation, put

$$\begin{aligned} A &:= A_{m,n}(B,\varepsilon), & H &:= H_{m,n}(B,\varepsilon), & S &:= S_{m,n}(B,\varepsilon)\\ \widetilde{A} &:= A_{m,n}(B,\varepsilon'), & \widetilde{H} &:= H_{m,n}(B,\varepsilon'), & \widetilde{S} &:= S_{m,n}(B,\varepsilon'). \end{aligned}$$

Note that

$$\widetilde{A} = \widetilde{B}[\xi,\rho]_{1+(\rho)} \quad \text{and} \quad \widetilde{S} = \widetilde{B}[\xi][\![\rho]\!],$$

where $\widetilde{B}$ is the residue field of the local ring B. Furthermore, by the Krull intersection theorem [**12**, Theorem 8.10], ideals of A, H and S are closed in their radical-adic topologies. It follows that

$$\widetilde{A} = A/I(B,\varepsilon')\cdot A, \quad \widetilde{H} = H/I(B,\varepsilon')\cdot H, \quad \widetilde{S} = S/I(B,\varepsilon')\cdot S.$$

Let $\mathfrak{p} \in \operatorname{Spec} H$; we must show that $S \otimes_H \kappa(\mathfrak{p})$ is geometrically regular over $\kappa(\mathfrak{p})$. Each element of $I(B,\varepsilon')\cdot H$ is nilpotent; hence $I(B,\varepsilon')\cdot H \subset \mathfrak{p}$. Let $\widetilde{\mathfrak{p}} \in \operatorname{Spec}\widetilde{H}$ denote the image of $\mathfrak{p}$ in $\widetilde{H}$. Then

$$S \otimes_H \kappa(\mathfrak{p}) = \widetilde{S} \otimes_{\widetilde{H}} \kappa(\widetilde{\mathfrak{p}}),$$

and it suffices to show that $\widetilde{S} \otimes_{\widetilde{H}} \kappa(\widetilde{\mathfrak{p}})$ is geometrically regular over $\kappa(\widetilde{\mathfrak{p}})$.

We note the following facts. (i) The maps $\widetilde{\mathfrak{M}} \mapsto \widetilde{\mathfrak{M}}\cdot\widetilde{A} + (\rho)$, $\widetilde{\mathfrak{M}} \mapsto \widetilde{\mathfrak{M}}\cdot\widetilde{H} + (\rho)$, $\widetilde{\mathfrak{M}} \mapsto \widetilde{\mathfrak{M}}\cdot\widetilde{S} + (\rho)$ are bijections between the elements of $\operatorname{Max}\widetilde{B}[\xi]$ and the elements, respectively, of $\operatorname{Max}\widetilde{A}$, $\operatorname{Max}\widetilde{H}$ and $\operatorname{Max}\widetilde{S}$. (ii) Let $\widetilde{\mathfrak{M}} \in \operatorname{Max}\widetilde{S}$, $\widetilde{\mathfrak{M}} := \widetilde{H} \cap \widetilde{\mathfrak{M}} \in \operatorname{Max}\widetilde{H}$ and $\widetilde{\mathfrak{n}} := \widetilde{A} \cap \widetilde{\mathfrak{M}} \in \operatorname{Max}\widetilde{A}$; then $\widetilde{A} \to \widetilde{H} \to \widetilde{S}$ induces isomorphisms

$$\widehat{\widetilde{A}_{\widetilde{\mathfrak{n}}}} \cong \widehat{\widetilde{H}_{\widetilde{\mathfrak{M}}}} \cong \widehat{\widetilde{S}_{\widetilde{\mathfrak{M}}}}$$

(iii) The ring $\widetilde{A}$, being a localization of the excellent ring $\widetilde{B}[\xi,\rho]$ is excellent, and in particular, a G-ring.

Arguing just as in the proof of Proposition 4.1, we show that $\widetilde{H}$ is a G-ring. Then we argue as in Theorem 4.2 to show that $\widetilde{S} \otimes_{\widetilde{H}} \kappa(\widetilde{\mathfrak{p}})$ is geometrically regular over $\kappa(\widetilde{\mathfrak{p}})$. □

5. Approximation

***Theorem 5.1* (Approximation Theorem).** — *For a given system of polynomial equations with coefficients in $H_{m,n}$, any solution over $S_{m,n}$ can be approximated by a solution over $H_{m,n}$ arbitrarily closely in the (ρ)-adic topology.*

Proof. — Let $Y = (Y_1, \ldots, Y_N)$ be variables, let J be an ideal of $H_{m,n}[Y]$, and consider the finitely generated $H_{m,n}$-algebra $C := H_{m,n}[Y]/J$. Suppose we have a homomorphism $\widehat{\varphi} : C \to S_{m,n}$; then $\widehat{\varphi}(Y)$ is a solution over $S_{m,n}$ of the system of polynomial equations with coefficients in $H_{m,n}$ given by generators of the ideal J. Fix

$\ell \in \mathbb{N}$. We wish to demonstrate the existence of a homomorphism $\varphi : C \to H_{m,n}$ such that each $\varphi(Y_i) - \widehat{\varphi}(Y_i) \in (\rho)^\ell \cdot S_{m,n}$.

Since $H_{m,n} \to S_{m,n}$ is a regular map of Noetherian rings, by [**14**, Theorem 1.1], we may assume that C is smooth over $H_{m,n}$. Let E be the symmetric algebra of the C-module J/J^2. By Elkik's Lemma ([**7**, Lemme 3]), $\operatorname{Spec} E$ is smooth over $\operatorname{Spec} H_{m,n}$ of constant relative dimension N, there is a surjection

$$H_{m,n}[Y_1, \dots, Y_{2N+r}] \to E$$

for some $r \in \mathbb{N}$, and there are elements $g_1, \dots, g_{N+r}, h \in H_{m,n}[Y]$ such that

$$\left(H_{m,n}[Y]/I\right)_h \cong E,$$

where $I := (g_1, \dots, g_{N+r})$, and

$$(1) = h \cdot H_{m,n}[Y] + I.$$

Since $\operatorname{Spec} E$ is smooth of relative dimension N over $\operatorname{Spec} H_{m,n}$, $\Omega_{E/H_{m,n}}$ is locally free of rank N. It follows that

$$h^d \in \mathfrak{M} + I$$

for some $d \in \mathbb{N}$, where $\mathfrak{M}$ is the ideal in $H_{m,n}[Y]$ generated by all $(N+r) \times (N+r)$ minors of the matrix

$$M(Y) := \left(\frac{\partial g_i}{\partial Y_j}\right)_{\substack{1 \le i \le N+r \\ 1 \le j \le 2N+r}}.$$

We may extend $\widehat{\varphi}$ to E; in particular, $g(\widehat{\varphi}(Y)) = 0$. Replacing Y by $\alpha^{-1}Y$ for a suitably small scalar $\alpha \in K^\circ \setminus \{0\}$ and normalizing by another scalar, we may assume $g_1, \dots, g_{N+r}, h \in H^\circ_{m,n}[Y]$, $\widehat{\varphi}(Y) \in (S^\circ_{m,n})^{2N+r}$, and

$$\varepsilon \in h \cdot H^\circ_{m,n}[Y] + \sum_{i=1}^{N+r} g_i H^\circ_{m,n}[Y] \tag{5.1}$$

$$\varepsilon h^d \in \mathfrak{M}^\circ + \sum_{i=1}^{N+r} g_i H^\circ_{m,n}[Y]. \tag{5.2}$$

for a suitably small $\varepsilon \in K^{\circ\circ} \setminus \{0\}$, where $\mathfrak{M}^\circ$ is the ideal in $H^\circ_{m,n}[Y]$ generated by all $(N+r) \times (N+r)$ minors of the matrix M, above.

For each $B \in \mathfrak{B}$, let $(H_{m,n}(B), (\rho))$ be a Henselization of the pair $(A_{m,n}(B), (\rho))$. Since $A^\circ_{m,n} = \varinjlim A_{m,n}(B)$, we have a canonical isomorphism $\varinjlim H_{m,n}(B) \cong H^\circ_{m,n}$. Find $B \in \mathfrak{B}$ such that

$$\widehat{\varphi}(Y_1), \dots, \widehat{\varphi}(Y_{2N+r}) \in S_{m,n}(B) := B\langle\xi\rangle[\![\rho]\!],$$

and such that $g_1, \dots, g_{N+r} \in H_{m,n}(B)[Y]$. Consider the commutative diagram

$$\begin{array}{ccccc} A_{m,n}(B) & \longrightarrow & H_{m,n}(B) & \longrightarrow & S_{m,n}(B) \\ \downarrow & & \downarrow & & \downarrow \\ A_{m,n}(B,\varepsilon^{2d+2}) & \longrightarrow & H_{m,n}(B,\varepsilon^{2d+2}) & \longrightarrow & S_{m,n}(B,\varepsilon^{2d+2}), \end{array}$$

where the two outer vertical arrows represent reduction modulo $I(B,\varepsilon^{2d+2})$ and the other arrows represent the canonical morphisms. It follows from the Universal Mapping Property for Henselizations that all the vertical arrows must be surjective. Thus by Proposition 4.3 and [**14**, Theorem 11.3], there are $\eta_1,\dots,\eta_{2N+r} \in H^\circ_{m,n}$ such that $\eta_i - \widehat{\varphi}(Y_i) \in (\rho)^{2\ell+1}\cdot S^\circ_{m,n}$, $1 \le i \le 2N+r$, and $\|g_i(\eta)\| \le |\varepsilon^{2d+2}|$, $1 \le i \le N+r$.

Replacing Y by η in (5.1), we find $g', h' \in H^\circ_{m,n}$ such that $h(\eta)h' = \varepsilon(1-\varepsilon^{2d+1}g')$. It follows that there is some $\delta \in K^\circ \setminus \{0\}$ with $|\delta| \ge |\varepsilon|$ and some unit h'' of $H^\circ_{m,n}$ such that $h(\eta) = \delta h''$. Replacing Y by η in (5.2), we find some $g'' \in H^\circ_{m,n}$ such that $\varepsilon^{d+1}((h'')^d - \varepsilon^{d+1}g'') \in \mathfrak{M}^\circ(\eta)$, where $\mathfrak{M}^\circ(\eta)$ is the ideal of $H^\circ_{m,n}$ generated by all $(N+r)\times(N+r)$ minors of the matrix $M(\eta)$. Since h'' is a unit of $H^\circ_{m,n}$, it follows that

$$\varepsilon^{d+1} \in \mathfrak{M}^\circ(\eta).$$

We follow the proof of Tougeron's Lemma given in [**7**] to obtain $y_1,\dots,y_{2N+r} \in H^\circ_{m,n}$ such that $y_i - \eta_i \in (\rho)^\ell \cdot H^\circ_{m,n}$, $1 \le i \le 2N+r$, and $g_1(\eta) = \dots = g_{N+r}(\eta) = 0$.

Let $\mu_1,\dots,\mu_s$ denote the monomials in ρ of degree ℓ. Since the ideal generated by the $(N+r)\times(N+r)$ minors of $M(\eta)$ contains the $\varepsilon^{d+1}\mu_i$, there are $(2N+r)\times(N+r)$ matrices $N_1,\dots,N_s$ such that

$$M(\eta)N_i = \varepsilon^{d+1}\mu_i \mathrm{Id}_{N+r},$$

where Id_{N+r} is the $(N+r)\times(N+r)$ identity matrix. We will find elements $u_i = (u_{i,1},\dots,u_{i,2N+r}) \in ((\rho)\cdot H^\circ_{m,n})^{2N+r}$, $1 \le i \le s$, such that

$$g_j(\eta + \sum_{i=1}^s \varepsilon^{d+1}\mu_i u_i) = 0, \qquad 1 \le j \le N+r.$$

We have the Taylor expansion

$$\begin{bmatrix} g_1(\eta + \sum_{i=1}^s \varepsilon^{d+1}\mu_i u_i) \\ \vdots \\ g_{N+r}(\eta + \sum_{i=1}^s \varepsilon^{d+1}\mu_i u_i) \end{bmatrix} = \begin{bmatrix} g_1(\eta) \\ \vdots \\ g_{N+r}(\eta) \end{bmatrix} + \sum_{i=1}^s \varepsilon^{d+1}\mu_i M(\eta) \begin{bmatrix} u_{i,1} \\ \vdots \\ u_{i,2N+r} \end{bmatrix} +$$

$$+ \sum_{i,j} \varepsilon^{2d+2}\mu_i\mu_j P_{ij},$$

where each P_{ij} is a column vector whose components are polynomials in the u_i of order at least 2. We must solve

$$(5.3)\qquad 0=\begin{bmatrix} g_1(\eta)\\ \vdots \\ g_{N+r}(\eta)\end{bmatrix}+\sum_{i=1}^{s}\varepsilon^{d+1}\mu_i M(\eta)\begin{bmatrix} u_{i,1}\\ \vdots \\ u_{i,2N+r}\end{bmatrix}+\sum_{i,j}\varepsilon^{2d+2}\mu_i\mu_j P_{ij}.$$

Since $\|g_i(\eta)\|\leq\left|\varepsilon^{2d+2}\right|$ and $g_i(\eta)\in(\rho)^{2\ell+1}\cdot H^{\circ}_{m,n}$, we have

$$\begin{bmatrix} g_1(\eta)\\ \vdots \\ g_{N+r}(\eta)\end{bmatrix}=\sum_{i,j}(\varepsilon^{d+1}\mu_i)(\varepsilon^{d+1}\mu_j)\begin{bmatrix} f_{ij1}\\ \vdots \\ f_{ijN+r}\end{bmatrix},$$

where the $f_{ijk}\in(\rho)\cdot H^{\circ}_{m,n}$. Thus (5.3) becomes

$$\begin{aligned}0=\sum_{i=1}^{s}\varepsilon^{d+1}\mu_i M(\eta)\left(\sum_{j=1}^{s}N_j\begin{bmatrix} f_{ij1}\\ \vdots \\ f_{ijN+r}\end{bmatrix}\right)\ &+\ \sum_{i=1}^{s}\varepsilon^{d+1}\mu_i M(\eta)\begin{bmatrix} u_{i,1}\\ \vdots \\ u_{i,2N+r}\end{bmatrix}+\\ &+\ \sum_{i=1}^{s}\varepsilon^{d+1}\mu_i M(\eta)\left(\sum_{j=1}^{s}N_jP_{ij}\right),\end{aligned}$$

and it suffices to solve

$$(5.4)\qquad 0=\begin{bmatrix} u_{i,1}\\ \vdots \\ u_{i,2N+r}\end{bmatrix}+\sum_{j=1}^{s}N_j\left(P_{ij}+\begin{bmatrix} f_{ij1}\\ \vdots \\ f_{ijN+r}\end{bmatrix}\right),\qquad 1\leq i\leq s.$$

Since 0 is a solution of this system modulo (ρ), and since its Jacobian at 0 is 1, the system (5.4) represents an étale neighborhood of $(H^{\circ}_{m,n},(\rho))$, hence has a true solution (u_{ij}). Putting

$$(y_i):=(\eta_i)+\sum_{j=1}^{s}\varepsilon^{d+1}\mu_j u_j,$$

we obtain a solution in $H^{\circ}_{m,n}$ of the system $g=0$ which agrees with $\widehat{\varphi}(Y)$ up to order ℓ in ρ. □

Corollary 5.2. — *$H_{m,n}$ is a UFD.*

Proof. — Let $f\in H_{m,n}$ be irreducible. We must show that $f\cdot H_{m,n}$ is a prime ideal. Since $S_{m,n}$ is a faithfully flat $H_{m,n}$-algebra (Theorem 3.3), and since $S_{m,n}$ is a UFD ([**11**, Theorem 4.2.7]), it suffices to show that f is an irreducible element of $S_{m,n}$. That is a consequence of Theorem 5.1. □

References

[1] M. Artin. — *On the solutions of analytic equations.* Invent. Math., 5 (1968), 277–291.

[2] W. Bartenwerfer. — *Die Beschränktheit der Stückzahl der Fasern K-analytischer Abbildungen.* J. reine angew. Math., 416 (1991), 49-70.

[3] R. Berger, R. Kiehl, E. Kunz and H-J. Nastold. — *Differential Rechnung in der Analytischen Geometrie.* Springer Lecture Notes in Math, 38, 1967.

[4] S. Bosch. — *A rigid analytic version of M. Artin's theorem on analytic equations.* Math. Ann., 255 (1981), 395–404.

[5] S. Bosch, B. Dwork and P. Robba. — *Un théorème de prolongement pour des fonctions analytiques.* Math. Ann., 252 (1980), 165–173.

[6] S. Bosch, U. Güntzer and R. Remmert. — *Non-Archimedean Analysis.* Springer-Verlag, 1984.

[7] R. Elkik. — *Solutions d'équations a coefficients dans un anneau Hensélien.* Ann. Scient. Éc. Norm. Sup., 4e série, 6 (1973) 553–604.

[8] R. Kiehl. — *Ausgezeichnete Ringe in der nicht-Archimedischen analytischen Geometrie.* J. Reine Angew. Math., 234 (1969), 89–98.

[9] S. Lang. — *On quasi-algebraic closure.* Ann. Math., 55 (1952), 373–390.

[10] L. Lipshitz. — *Isolated points on fibers of affinoid varieties.* J. reine angew. Math., 384 (1988), 208-220.

[11] L. Lipshitz and Z. Robinson. — *Rings of separated power series.* This volume.

[12] H. Matsumura. — *Commutative Ring Theory.* Cambridge University Press, 1989.

[13] M. Raynaud. — *Anneaux Locaux Henséliens.* Springer Lecture Notes in Mathematics, 169, 1970.

[14] M. Spivakovsky. — *A new proof of D. Popescu's theorem on smoothing of ring homomorphisms.* J. Amer. Math. Soc., 12 (1999), 381-444.

[15] L. van den Dries. — *A specialization theorem for p-adic power series converging on the closed unit disc.* J. Algebra, 73 (1981), 613-623.

INDEX

ASTÉRISQUE

2000

265. O. BIQUARD – *Métriques d'Einstein asymptotiquement symétriques*
264. L. LIPSHITZ, Z. ROBINSON – *Rings of Separated Power Series and Quasi-Affinoid Geometry*
263. C. SABBAH – *Équations différentielles à points singuliers irréguliers et phénomène de Stokes en dimension 2*
262. A. VASY – *Propagation of singularities in three-body scattering*
261. Géométrie complexe et systèmes dynamiques, colloque en l'honneur d'Adrien Douady, Orsay 1995, M. FLEXOR, P. SENTENAC et J.-C. YOCCOZ, éditeurs

1999

260. S. D. CUTKOSKY – *Local monomialization and factorization of morphisms*
259. R. KRIKORIAN – *Réductibilité des systèmes produits-croisés à valeurs dans des groupes compacts*
258. Structure Theory of Set Addition, J.-M. DESHOUILLERS, B. LANDREAU and A.A. YUDIN, editors
257. J.-P. LABESSE – *Cohomologie, stabilisation et changement de base (avec la collaboration de L. BREEN et L. CLOZEL)*
256. F. MOREL – *Théorie homotopique des schémas*
255. R.E. KOTTWITZ, D. SHELSTAD – *Foundations of twisted endoscopy*
254. C.J. BUSHNELL, G. HENNIART – *Local tame lifting for* $\mathrm{GL}(n)$ *II : wildly ramified supercuspidals*
253. B. MAGNERON – *Involutions complexes et vecteurs sphériques associés pour les groupes de Lie nilpotents réels*

1998

252. SÉMINAIRE BOURBAKI, volume 1997/1998, exposés 835-849
251. Nombre et répartition de points de hauteur bornée, E. PEYRE, éditeur
250. C. BONATTI, R. LANGEVIN – *Difféomorphismes de Smale des surfaces (avec la collaboration de E. JEANDENANS)*
249. P. AUSCHER, P. TCHAMITCHIAN – *Square root problem for divergence operators and related topics*
248. P. COLMEZ – *Intégration sur les variétés* p*-adiques*
247. G. PISIER – *Non-commutative vector valued* L_p*-spaces and completely* p*-summing maps*

1997

246. V. TARASOV, A. VARCHENKO – *Geometry of* q*-hypergeometric functions, quantum affine algebras and elliptic quantum groups*
245. SÉMINAIRE BOURBAKI, volume 1996/1997, exposés 820-834
244. J.-M. BISMUT – *Holomorphic families of immersions and higher analytic torsion forms*
243. L. LAFFORGUE – *Chtoucas de Drinfeld et conjecture de Ramanujan-Petersson*
242. N. BURQ – *Pôles de diffusion engendrés par un coin*
241. SÉMINAIRE BOURBAKI, volume 1995/1996, exposés 805-819

1996

240. A. SÀ BARETTO, R. B. MELROSE, M. ZWORSKI – *Semilinear diffraction of conormal waves*
239. J.-L. VERDIER – *Des catégories dérivées des catégories abéliennes*
238. A. BROISE, F. DAL'BO, M. PEIGNÉ – *Méthodes des opérateurs de transfert : transformations dilatantes de l'intervalle et dénombrement de géodésiques fermées*
237. SÉMINAIRE BOURBAKI, volume 1994/1995, exposés 790-804
236. Hommage à P. A. MEYER et J. NEVEU
235. J.-P. OTAL – *Le théorème d'hyperbolisation pour les variétés fibrées de dimension 3*
234. A. GENESTIER – *Espaces symétriques de Drinfeld*

1995

233. I. KRIZ, J.P. MAY – *Operads, algebras modules and motives*
232. Recent advances in operator algebras (Orléans, 1992)
231. J.-C. YOCCOZ – *Petits diviseurs en dimension 1*
230. J.-Y. CHEMIN – *Fluides parfaits incompressibles*
229. B. PERRIN-RIOU – *Fonctions L p-adiques des représentations p-adiques*
228. Columbia University number theory seminar (New-York, 1992)
227. SÉMINAIRE BOURBAKI, volume 1993/1994, exposés 775-789

1994

226. K-theory (Strasbourg, 1992)
225. L. BREEN – *On the classification of 2-gerbes and 2-stacks*
224. P. SCHAPIRA, J.-P. SCHNEIDERS – *Index theorem for elliptic pairs*
223. Périodes p-adiques (séminaire de Bures, 1988)
222. Complex analytic methods in dynamical systems (IMPA, janvier 1992)
221. A. OGUS – *F-Crystals, Griffiths transversality, and the Hodge decomposition*
220. H.H. ANDERSEN, J.C. JANTZEN, W. SOERGEL – *Représentations of quantum groups at a p-th root of unity and of semisimple groups in characteristic p : independence of p*
219. H. RUBENTHALER – *Les paires duales dans les algèbres de Lie réductives*

1993

218. Journées de géométrie algébrique d'Orsay (juillet 1992)
217. Colloque d'analyse complexe et géométrie (Marseille, janvier 1992)
216. SÉMINAIRE BOURBAKI, volume 1992/1993, exposés 760-774
215. M. DUFLO, S. KUMAR, M. VERGNE – *Sur la cohomologie équivariante des variétés différentiables*
214. J. LE POTIER – *Systèmes cohérents et structures de niveau*
213. R. HARVEY, B. LAWSON – *A theory of characteristic currents associated with a singular connection*
212. M. BROUÉ, G. MALLE, J. MICHEL – *Représentations unipotentes génériques et blocs des groupes réductifs finis (avec un appendice de G. LUSZTIG)*

1992

211. J. KOLLAR – *Flips and abundance for algebraic threefolds. A summer seminar at the University of Utah (Salt Lake City, 1991)*
210. Méthodes semi-classiques, Vol. II (Colloque international, Nantes, juin 1991)
209. Journées Arithmétiques de Genève (1991), D. CORAY, Y.F.S. PETERMANN, éditeurs
208. A. YEKUTIELI – *An explicit construction of the Grothendieck residue complex*
207. Méthodes semi-classiques, Vol. I (École d'été, Nantes, juin 1991)
206. SÉMINAIRE BOURBAKI, volume 1991/1992, exposés 745-759
205. J.-M. BISMUT, W. ZHANG – *An extension of a theorem by Cheeger and Müller. (With an appendix by F. LAUDENBACH)*

1991

204. P. LE CALVEZ – *Propriétés dynamiques des difféomorphismes de l'anneau et du tore*

201-202-203. SÉMINAIRE BOURBAKI, volume 1990/1991, exposés 730-744

198-199-200. Journées Arithmétiques de Luminy (1989)

196-197. Courbes modulaires et courbes de Shimura

194-195. G. MALTSINIOTIS – *Privilège numérique uniforme*

193. G. DAVID, S. SEMMES – *Singular integrals and rectifiable sets in $\mathbb{R}^n$. Au-delà des graphes lipschitziens*

Contents

CNRS EDITIONS

SAVOIRS ACTUELS

Collection dirigée par *Michèle Leduc*

Responsable des mathématiques : ***Claude Sabbah***

Coéditée par *CNRS ÉDITIONS* *et* *EDP Sciences*

Les ouvrages de la collection Savoirs Actuels, écrits par des chercheurs, reflètent des enseignements dispensés dans le cadre de la formation à la recherche. Ils s'adressent donc aux étudiants avancés, aux chercheurs désireux de perfectionner leurs connaissances ainsi qu'à tout lecteur passionné par la science contemporaine, que ce soit dans le domaine de l'astrophysique, de la chimie, des mathématiques ou de la physique.

En mathématiques, ouvrages toujours disponibles:

Géométrie algébrique.
Une introduction
Daniel Perrin
1995 - 16 x 23 - 316 pages
2-271-05271-8 - broché : 240 FF

Opérateurs pseudo-différentiels
et théorème de Nash-Moser
Serge Alinhac, Patrick Gérard
1991 - 16 x 23 - 192 pages
2-222-04534-7 - broché : 230 FF

Groupe quantiques.
Introduction au point de vue formel
Alain Guichardet
1995 - 16 x 23 -164 pages
2-271-05272-6 - broché : 160 FF

Théorie des fonctions holomorphes
de plusieurs variables
Christine Laurent-Thiébaut
1997 - 16 x 23 - 248 pages
2-271-05501-6 - broché : 280 FF

B O N D E C O M M A N D E

à remettre à : **CNRS EDITIONS 15, rue Malebranche 75005 Paris**

NOM .... PRENOM ....

ADRESSE ....

CODE POSTAL .... VILLE ....

PAYS ....

ISBN	TITRE	Qté	P.U	Total
05271-8	Géométrie algébrique. Une introduction	....	240 FF	....
05272-6	Groupes quantique. Introduction au point de vue formel	....	160 FF	....
04534-7	Opérateurs pseudo-différentiels et théorème de Nash-Moser	....	230 FF	....
05501-6	Théorie des fonctions holomorphes de plusieurs variables	....	280 FF	....

Port par ouvrage : France 30FF - Etranger 35FF

Ci-joint mon règlement de ....FF ☐ Chèque bancaire ☐ C.C.P.

à l'ordre de CNRS EDITIONS

Date.............................. SIGNATURE :

Frais de Port ....

TOTAL ....

Imprimé en France. - JOUVE, 18, rue Saint-Denis, 75001 Paris
N° 275902T - Dépôt légal : Avril 2000